THE WREN

THE NEW NATURALIST

The aim of THE NEW NATURALIST series is to interest the general reader in the wild life of Britain by recapturing the inquiring spirit of the old naturalists. The Editors believe that the natural pride of the British public in their native fauna and flora, to which must be added concern for their conservation, is best fostered by maintaining a high standard of accuracy combined with clarity of exposition in presenting the results of modern scientific research. The volumes in the main series deal with large groups of animals and plants, with the natural history of particular areas or habitats in Britain, and with certain special subjects. THE NEW NATURALIST SPECIAL VOLUMES, on the other hand, cover, in greater detail, a single species or group of species. In both the main series and special volumes the animals and plants are described in relation to their homes and habitats.

EDITORS:

JAMES FISHER M.A.
JOHN GILMOUR M.A.
JULIAN HUXLEY M.A., D.Sc., F.R.S.
L. DUDLEY STAMP C.B.E., B.A., D.Sc.

PHOTOGRAPHIC EDITOR:
ERIC HOSKING F.R.P.S.

THE NEW NATURALIST

THE WREN

by

EDWARD A. ARMSTRONG

With 20 Black and White Photographs
41 Drawings and Diagrams

COLLINS
ST JAMES'S PLACE, LONDON
1955

To the
Memory of my Father

Other Works by the
Same Author

★

BIRDS OF THE GREY WIND
(*3rd edition 1946*)

SHAKESPEARE'S IMAGINATION
(*Revised edition 1946*)

BIRD DISPLAY AND BEHAVIOUR
(*2nd edition 1947*)

THE WAY BIRDS LIVE
(*4th impression 1947*)

BIRD LIFE
(*1949*)

Printed in Great Britain
Collins Clear-Type Press: London and Glasgow

CONTENTS

LIST OF PLATES

EDITORS' PREFACE

IN BRITAIN the Church has long had a beneficent influence on the study of natural history and particularly of ornithology. Legends about Saint Columba and poetry attributed to him, show that this influence was almost contemporaneous with the introduction of Christianity. It continued in the delightful Irish nature poetry of the ninth and tenth centuries. In the twelfth century we find Giraldus Cambrensis showing an interest in natural history, and from William Turner in the sixteenth century, with notable successors such as John Ray and Gilbert White, the tradition of parson ornithologists, to which the author of this volume belongs, has continued to the present day.

E. A. Armstrong describes his early interest in natural history in *Birds of the Grey Wind*, a book which was awarded the Burroughs Medal in 1942 in the United States as the most notable natural history book of the year. Since then he has written many other bird books, one of them a standard work on bird behaviour, and has contributed many papers on ornithological and anthropological topics to scientific journals. Cambridge University recently conferred on him the honorary degree of M.A. in recognition of his contributions to psychology and biology.

Knowledge of individual species is a necessary foundation for the generalisations about behaviour and evolution which are the objectives of scientific research. Readers of *The Wren* will find interesting descriptions not only of the behaviour of the bird with which they are familiar in woods and gardens but also of the characteristics of other races. As far as we are aware there has been no other comparative study so extensive of any other British bird, nor, indeed, perhaps, of any bird. The author's travels in many parts of the Old World have given him remarkable opportunities to explore the habitats and observe the behaviour of many subspecies, and during extensive journeys in North, Central and South America he became acquainted with wrens of a number of other species.

The Editors of the New Naturalist are very glad that the first abundant and resident British bird species to be included in our series is the wren and that it has so excellent and sympathetic a monographer. To this book the author has brought not only his vast general knowledge of bird behaviour, but the results of many years of intensive, critical, and careful field studies of a fascinating bird.

AUTHOR'S PREFACE

IN ORDER to reduce the number of bracketed references in the text the names of a few frequently-quoted authorities are omitted where the context makes it plain to whom I owe the data. Thus where allusion is made to the house wren the work referred to is Dr. S. C. Kendeigh's paper published in 1941. Similarly, unreferenced mention of the prairie marsh wren quotes from the late Dr. W. A. Welter's paper. Mention of Dr. Kluijver or " the Dutch observers " calls attention to observations made at Stein and recorded in the paper by Kluijver and his colleagues which appeared in 1940, or, in a few contexts, to data obtained from the MS. notebooks of these observers. In my papers on the Iceland, Shetland, Hebridean and St. Kilda wrens, to which lists of references are appended, will be found more information on these, and some other, races than could be included here. In some instances matters dealt with summarily will be found discussed in more detail in *Bird Display and Behaviour*. The requirements of this series have necessitated drastic abbreviation and condensation. Small numbers in the text refer to information available since the book was written, inserted in the addenda (p. 285).

To avoid confusion with other forms I have called *Troglodytes t. troglodytes* " the European wren." Other European subspecies are distinguished by their scientific or vernacular names. Where it is essential to make a distinction between *T. troglodytes* in all its races and other species of wren it may be called the " Holarctic wren." I trust that in ordinary usage the bird will continue to be styled " the wren." " Common wren " should not be used now that " wren " is no longer employed by ornithologists in connection with such birds as the willow warbler and goldcrest. It is unfortunate that various Asian and Australian species, unrelated to the Troglodytidae are called " wrens."

The scientific names and distribution of subspecies of *Troglodytes troglodytes* are listed in the Appendix. Other species mentioned in the text appear in the Index. The nomenclature adopted for New World forms is that of Hellmayr (1934) with a few modifications from the A.O.U. check-list and other sources. I have occasionally employed the term " neotropical house wren " when referring to *T. musculus* without distinguishing any particular race, and I have used alternative vernacular names suggested by Dr. A. F. Skutch where these seemed preferable to Hellmayr's.

Cambridge, October 1951   E. A. A.

CHAPTER I

STUDYING THE WREN

The wren inhabits shrubberies and holes and cannot easily be caught. Now it is shy and of a feeble habit, but endowed with great ability of getting food and knowledge of its craft.

ARISTOTLE. *H.A.* ix, 615a, 17.

DARKNESS WAS FALLING on a November evening in 1943 and the bombers were roaring off into the gloom when, happening to look out of my study window, I saw a small bird alight on the trellis outside and then fly up into the ivy on the wall. A couple of evenings later the wren was there again. Evidently he came regularly to these sleeping quarters. My interest was again captured by a bird which had fascinated me as a boy. Here was a species about which I should like to know more. I had recently come to live in Cambridge after years spent in the centre of a great industrial area where there had been few opportunities to watch birds, but now, in war-time, if any observations I might make were to be other than superficial I must accept severe limitations on their scope. War constrains some to be excessively peripatetic, others it limits to a very restricted orbit. I was in the latter category. Perhaps I could make the best use of my meagre opportunities if I were to concentrate on studying the " life and conversation," as Gilbert White would have put it, of a single species. Comparatively little was known about the wren, although folklore testified to the interest the bird had aroused for many centuries, and that little had its mysteries. It was common and, moreover, resident throughout the year—a great advantage—for to study a migratory bird involves reconciling oneself to personal acquaintance with no more than a cross-section of its life history.

TECHNIQUE

However great the rewards of studying such a species the difficulties are considerable. He who is interested in a migratory bird need not be afield more than about five months of the year and intensive observation may be concentrated into a few weeks. Resident birds

demand study throughout the whole year and, as I soon discovered,
none requires more unflagging, persistent observation than the wren,
for nest-building is prolonged over some five months and to miss the
construction of a single nest may involve serious gaps in one's records.
Daily observation during this period is essential. Nor can vigilance
be relaxed during the other months as territorial changes may take
place at any time; in spring courtship behaviour invites attention; in
autumn and winter the roosting procedure has to be studied, and
opportunities must be sought to trap and ring the birds. It would
have been impossible for me to carry out my project but for the
fortunate dispensation by which birds are most active and, therefore,
most interesting, in the early morning, so that folk with little leisure
may do their bird-watching before the day's duties begin. But only
those can realise the pleasures of such early rising who have borne
its pains.

No matter how great his diligence, the amateur is immensely
handicapped as compared with the professional ornithologist who is
in a position to plan his time and deploy his energies entirely to suit
his field work, and is able daily, over a prolonged period, to follow a
bird's activities. In a few weeks or months he may learn what the
amateur with other claims on his time has to piece together from clues
obtained during several seasons. However, the reward of years of
interest in a bird is an intuitive understanding not to be explained in
words but which is, perhaps, the bird-lover's supreme pleasure.

The only study of the wren prior to my own, apart from desultory
observations, was carried out by Dutch clergy in the garden of their
missionary seminary at Stein. Working in relays under the guidance
of Dr. H. N. Kluijver they maintained regular observations for five
years until the Nazi invasion. The admirable paper describing their
observations, prepared by Dr. Kluijver after his collaborators had
become dispersed, reached me in the form of microfilms from the
United States after I had independently worked out the main outlines
and many of the details of the wren's life-history. I was thus able to
compare results at a phase in the investigations when to do so was
very valuable for my subsequent study. It was a great pleasure, after
the war, to show Dr. Kluijver the scene of my observations and discuss
the behaviour of wrens with him.

OBSERVATION AREAS

My main centre of observation lies in the western suburbs of
Cambridge, nearly a mile from my home, a wood of just over four
acres, of which one and two-thirds acres are occupied by a shallow

reed-grown pond. It is maintained as a sanctuary for wild life by the Cambridge Sanctuary Club, and I refer to it in these pages as Wren Wood. In 1894 skating enthusiasts excavated the pond, planting trees around it, so that eventually tall, crowded greenery arose in the midst of an area of flat pasture-land. In recent years villas have been built adjoining the rectangular, fenced wood. The tall willows, massive yew trees and unkempt vegetation contrast strongly with the neighbouring meadows and ordered primness of lawns and rose-beds. An area of some 15 acres around the wood, delimited by roads on three sides and fields on the fourth, was kept under observation, but the Sanctuary wrens conveniently restricted their activities mainly to it.

The wood consists of trees bordering the pond, in which is an island. The varied vegetation includes Scots pines and other conifers, white poplars, walnuts annually robbed of their nuts by rooks, and unpruned apple and pear trees. Large hawthorns grow parallel with the fence on three sides and there are thickets of privet and briar. Guelder roses and elders brighten the banks of the pond with their flowers, and later their berries. Deadly nightshade maintains itself amid the nettles which crowd the clearings, and the tree-stumps are adorned with ivy and bryony. In their season drifts of snowdrops and daffodils fringe the paths, ground-ivy carpets dells grazed by rabbits and, in a sunny space, scarlet pimpernel peeps out here and there amid a blue foam of forget-me-not blossoms.

On rare occasions a heron flies up hungry from pools where no fish swim or frogs spawn, and kingfishers sometimes optimistically haunt the willows for a few days. The pond, in which grass snakes are sometimes seen, usually dries up in summer and is consequently but meagrely populated with micro-organisms or any other form of animal life, apart from mosquito larvae. Year by year broods of ducklings and fluffy black waterhen chicks appear, and in the bushes the lesser whitethroat, bullfinch and long-tailed tit rear their young. The great spotted woodpecker's tattoo and the green woodpecker's laughter resound in the tall willows, and in winter the water rail leaves large, precise footprints in the snow. Now and then there are other interesting visitors—a pied flycatcher on migration, a wandering hawfinch, a snipe, or a woodcock awaiting nightfall to seek more spacious woods.

From the ornithologist's point of view Wren Wood has the great advantage of being private. I have grown familiar with it in all weathers and at almost all hours of the day and night. Often I have seen the sunrise there, and it has meant much to me as a tranquil place where the sensation of intruding on Nature's arcana has been so intense that to do more than mention such experiences would be to risk brushing the bloom from my memory of them.

Although Wren Wood's isolation from other woods enabled me to locate the wrens and map their domains with comparative ease, I was disappointed to find that, after 1944, it was not until 1949 that there were three males in occupation of breeding territories. Perhaps I gained more than I lost by concentrating on a few individuals, but time might have been used more economically had it been unnecessary so frequently to supplement my observations elsewhere.

A secondary "control" observation area was provided by my large garden, with others adjoining it and, across the road, a private bird sanctuary overrun with raspberries and dogwood. Sometimes other wren habitats claimed my attention when I discovered or suspected interesting developments there. Observations in these areas and in various localities elsewhere in the British Isles and abroad, restrained the temptation to generalise unthriftily from conditions in one type of habitat.

FIG. 1. Observation nesting-box. A hide of sacking conceals the observer. A dark cloth attached above and below the removable panel of the nesting-box and placed over the observer's head prevents the bird from noticing his presence.

RECORDS AND EQUIPMENT

The twelve notebooks into which my wren diary has expanded include daily weather and phenological observations, though for more exact data I have made use of the records kept at Cambridge Botanic Gardens, three-quarters of a mile from my home. After my investigation had made some progress, I was given the handsome present of 9×35 bloomed binoculars. Occasionally I used an $8 \times$ monocular as it could be conveniently carried in a pocket. At first, by means of an electrical counter, kindly loaned by the Edward Grey Institute, and later with an instrument devised by Dr. H. L. K. Whitehouse, automatic recordings of activities at nests were obtained. By placing empty cans in niches some wrens were induced to nest in convenient sites. In order to study the feeding of chicks at close range I transferred a nest to an observation nesting-box with a hide attached, so that I could watch the birds with my eyes only a few inches from them.

TRAPPING AND RINGING

We were all day hunting the wren;
We were all day hunting the wren;
The wren so cute and we so cunning.
He stayed in the bush when we were running.

Waterford Wren Song

" Better a wren in the hand than a crane on the wing," says the proverb, but wrens are not easy birds to catch. Their curiosity rather than the attractiveness of any bait leads them to enter Potter traps occasionally, but I could not rely on such chance captures, so my birds were caught at the nest—males, females and fledged young when roosting, males also when building, visiting the nest or feeding young, females when brooding or tending nestlings. I found that there was less risk of disturbing the breeding cycle when birds were released in the open and not replaced in the nests where they were trapped. In order to reduce the chances of desertion incubating wrens were not caught, and frequently when activities were at an interesting stage I judged it better to let events take their course rather than risk the interference that ringing entails. I found catching wrens difficult, time-consuming and exasperating. Each nest presented a special problem. At some which were too high for me to reach from the ground or were otherwise awkwardly placed—and few were not—I arranged a swing-door of wire gauze so that it could be pulled to when the bird entered. I usually carried a small net on a wire frame to clap over a nest entrance when opportunity offered, but wrens are quick to perceive and avoid even the least conspicuous mesh, and I found a glass jam-jar placed quickly over the aperture more effective when the nest was so situated that this was possible. To catch a number of wrens, such as a roosting fledged brood, I used a bee-keeper's veil with wire visor. A spacious cone-shaped compartment could thus be created from which the birds were easily extracted.

Most adults were marked with coloured celluloid rings and several carried an aluminium ring in addition. As I found that celluloid rings sometimes disappeared from the legs of birds I usually equipped adults with two or three. Chicks were particularly prone to lose their rings either before or after they fledged, so, latterly, I marked them with the small numbered aluminium rings used by aviculturists. To obviate the possibility of the parents picking at, and even eating, the nestlings' rings in mistake for faecal sacs, as has been recorded of some species, pale-coloured rings were not placed on them.

Wrens, like most birds, peck at their rings until they get used to them. This may take a day or two, but they are not seriously incommoded. A bird caught while building may be found at work again next day; similarly, a female trapped while brooding the young at night will feed them in the morning. I found it advisable to mark each bird with rings of a single dominant colour to avoid uncertainty when, as so often happens, identification has to be based on a momentary glimpse.

In the following pages ringed wrens are referred to under names embodying some reference to the colour of their rings, e.g. Silverband, Pinkie, Cherry and Cinnabar. Cherry had cerise rings and Cinnabar carried four rings striped alternately yellow and black like the larva of the cinnabar moth (*Tyria jacobaeae*). Thus the name Cinnabar distinguishes him from Stripes and Yellow-and-Black, who were somewhat similarly adorned. One or two unringed wrens important in the narrative are given names, not connoting colour, such as Bunty. The reader will thus know when the bird mentioned was identifiable with certainty. One female was exceptional among unringed wrens as she could be distinguished by an excrescence at the base of her bill. Many ringed and unringed wrens, not individually important in the narrative, are not mentioned by name.

Birds which are easily induced to breed in nesting-boxes, and conspicuous social species, are much more suitable than the wren for large-scale ecological or ethological study, but although I have often felt that I could not have selected a more difficult species, it has never occurred to me that I could have chosen one more fascinating.

CHAPTER 2

DISTRIBUTION AND HABITAT

And when for their abode they seek
An opportune recess,
The hermit has no finer eye
For shadowy quietness.

WORDSWORTH. *A Wren's Nest*

DISTRIBUTION

IN ORIGIN the wren is an American bird, one of the very few species which have successfully invaded the Old World from the New.[1] According to Mayr (1946) the family originated in the southern half of North America. There are 14 genera in Central America, three of which are endemic, and eight in South America, one being endemic. Costa Rica, for example, with an area of 18,000 square miles, one-seventh of the area of the British Isles, possesses 22 species. Chapman and Griscom (1924) pointed out that not less than 240 of the 289 American species and subspecies of wren are restricted to the tropics.* As recently, apparently, as the Pleistocene (E. Mayr, *in litt.*) the ancestors of our European wrens traversed the land-bridge at Bering Strait to penetrate across Eurasia to the farthest limits of the west, and colonise Iceland and Ireland.

During the Tertiary epoch, when a tropical or subtropical climate prevailed in the southern half of North America, the Old and New Worlds were repeatedly connected in the region of Bering Strait. At times this land-bridge extended considerably south of the present strait. It seems that for some 65 million years the trend of bird emigration has been from Eurasia to North America. Thus some birds, such as the jays, have been established across the Atlantic so long that they have had time to evolve into new genera, while others, including the wheatear and the yellow wagtail, have arrived in America so recently that they have not changed in appearance or behaviour.

Very few birds of New World origin have succeeded in invading

---

*According to the classification adopted by Hellmayr (1934) there are in the Americas 16 genera divided into 70 species and 297 subspecies, omitting the forms of *Troglodytes troglodytes*.

7

Eurasia. Indeed, the only birds which Mayr definitely places in this
category are the grouse, the buntings and the wren. He thinks that
the dippers and waxwings may also have originated in the Western
Hemisphere. If, as seems probable, the bunting stock originated in
America, it must have preceded the wren by an immense period as it
has diverged into many species ranging from the Arctic to South Africa.

Mayr and Amadon (1951) are cautious as to the origin and
relationship of the dippers. The many similarities in details of
behaviour between them and wrens which appear in the following
pages show, that if these groups are not related interesting con-
vergences between them have occurred. The dippers are distributed
from Tucuman in Northern Argentina to Alaska, as well as in Europe
and Asia.

A number of typical birds of the tundra have a circumpolar
distribution, but bare country and bleak conditions prevent the
diffusion of species unable to maintain themselves in treeless regions.
However, even a slightly milder climate, favouring the growth of
coniferous forest such as the Siberian taiga, would have enabled the
wren and many arboreal species to extend their range, and we know
that birds availed themselves of the opportunities provided by
temperate conditions in the North Pacific (Stegmann 1938).

The austerities which wrens survive in Alaska and Iceland give an
indication of the conditions in which they could have crossed Bering
Strait. Presumably, therefore, much earlier than the Pleistocene
climatic conditions would have permitted colonising wrens to take
advantage of the land-bridge there. That they did not do so suggests
that only about this epoch had the ancestral stock advanced sufficiently
far northward from their presumptive centre of origin. Chapman and

---

FIG. 2 (*opposite*). Breeding distribution of *Troglodytes troglodytes*. Where there is
some uncertainty in regard to the areas occupied by a race boundaries are indicated
by a broken line. Notably in Central Asia the distribution of races cannot be shown
precisely. The continental shelf is delineated to indicate where land-bridges occurred.
The numbers indicate subspecies, as follows :

1. *troglodytes:* 2. *islandicus:* 3. *borealis:* 4. *zetlandicus:* 5. *fridariensis:* 6. *hebridensis:*
7. *hirtensis:* 8. *bergensis:* 9. *koenigi:* 10. *mulleri:* 11. *stresemanni:* 12. *kabylorum:*
13. *juniperi:* 14. *syriacus:* 15. *cypriotes:* 16. *hyrcanus:* 17. *zagrossiensis:* 18. *magrathi:*
19. *subpallidus:* 20. *nipalensis:* 21. *tibetana:* 22. *talifuensis:* 23. *neglectus:* 24. *tian-
schanicus:* 25. *dauricus:* 26. *peninsulae:* 27. *idius:* 28. *szetchuanus:* 29. *suprapallidus:*
30. *fumigatus:* 31. *ogawae:* 32. *utanoi:* 33. *orii:* 34. *mosukei:* 35. *taiwanus:* 36. *kurilensis:*
37. *pallescens:* 38. *hiemalis:* 39. *pullus:* 40. *meligerus:* 41. *kiskensis:* 42. *alascensis:*
43. *tanagensis:* 44. *seguamensis:* 45. *petrophilus:* 46. *semidiensis:* 47. *helleri:* 48. *stevensoni:*
49. *pacificus.* (Cf. p. 303)

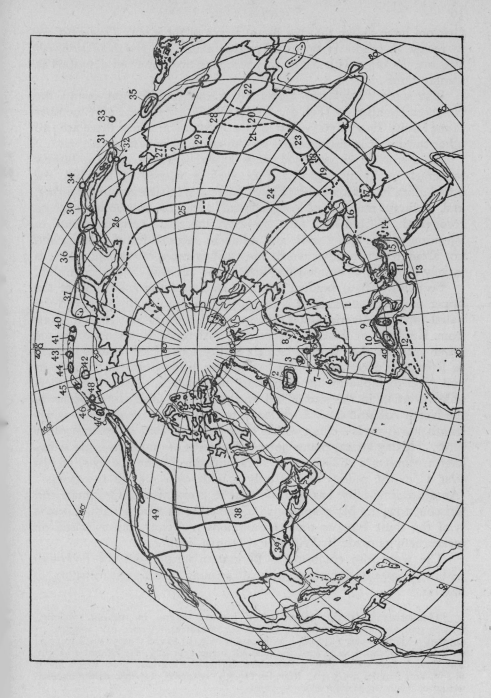

Griscom have shown that the house wrens of the genus *Troglodytes* are so recent in origin as to justify calling them " a group of to-day." Possibly the birds with which we are concerned could be described in similar terms.

The wren (*Troglodytes troglodytes*) is distributed right round the Northern Hemisphere (Fig. 2). In the Old World it is the only member of the family Troglodytidæ, but in North America, where there are two other species, it is distinguished by the name of winter wren.

As might be expected in such a wide-ranging species, largely sedentary in habits and living in such a variety of habitats, the populations in different areas show differences in size and in colouring, and a large number of geographical races or subspecies can be recognised. Within each race, however, there is a certain amount of variation in size and colour, and adjacent races differ in average and not absolutely. In other words the various races intergrade and it is largely a matter of opinion just how many are worthy of recognition.

Seebohm (1890) pointed out that so far as the coloration of the upper parts is concerned it is impossible to draw a line between the palest birds of Algeria and Turkestan, and the darkest tropical forms from Kashmir or Sikkim. A greater difference is apparent in the lower parts for they tend to be pale in European birds and as far east as Russian Turkestan, but the far-eastern birds from the Himalayas and Altai to Japan incline to be dark underneath. There is considerable variation in the size of bill and feet. The insular subspecies of the North Atlantic show a tendency to an increase of bill- and wing-length northwards—clines which have been noticed in various other birds. Huxley (1942) points out: " A change of one per cent in wing-length requires a difference of 2° N. latitude in the redpolls, of just over 1° in the puffins and of only a little over 0.5° in the wrens." (An altitudinal cline has been noticed in house wrens (Chapman and Griscom 1924)). My graph showing the cline in wing-length of wrens is of the same type as that of Salomonsen (1933), but is based on measurements made by Williamson (1951a, *in litt.*).

The wren also conforms to Bergmann's rule that the body-size within a species increases with decreasing mean temperature of habitat.*

*Timmermann (1935) noticed that Iceland wrens in autumn weighed 13.5-20 gm. as compared with 7.5-11 gm. for continental wrens, also weighed in autumn (Niethammer, 1937-38). Williamson (1951b) found that 50 birds trapped on Fair Isle averaged 12.21 gm., the heaviest being 15.1 gm., the lightest 10.1 gm. The Rev. J. Lees writes that in Ross-shire during the autumn males weigh about 11 gm. and females 9-9.5 gm. Marples (1935b) reported 9.27 gm. as the average weight of seven wrens trapped in England.

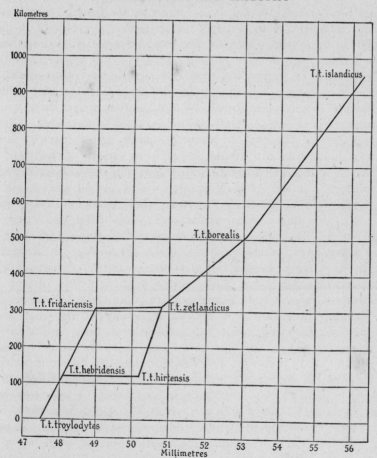

Fig. 3. Graph showing the cline in wing-length of Wrens (♂ and ♀) from Scotland to Iceland. Data supplied by Mr. K. Williamson.

Evolutionary adaptation to the temperature of the habitat may be comparatively rapid. Calhoun (1947) has shown by measuring a large number of house sparrows that there has been a perceptible increase in the average size since the introduction of the species to the United States. The increase has been greatest in those areas of the bird's range where the winters are coldest.

Linnaeus gave the scientific name of *Motacilla troglodytes* to the wren with which he was acquainted in Sweden. The wrens were subsequently removed from the genus *Motacilla* and given the generic name *Troglodytes*, the species becoming known as *Troglodytes troglodytes*. With the recognition of racial forms and the adoption of trinomial nomenclature, the race found in Sweden has to be known as *Troglodytes troglodytes troglodytes* (Linn.). This race breeds as far north as 67° in Norway, occasionally to 69°,* and 64° in Finland and extends south to the Mediterranean, west to Ireland and east to the Urals. Other races are recognised in Iceland, the Faeroe Is., the Shetland Is., St. Kilda and the Hebrides. Williamson (1951a) has provided evidence that the Fair Isle wren has distinctive characteristics.

In Asia various subspecies occur in the Middle East and across the mountain chains from Persia to Turkestan, the Himalayas, Tibet, the mountains of W. and N. China, and as far south as Kashmir and Burma. They occur also in the great mountain areas extending from Turkestan along the northern frontier of Mongolia to Amuria and Kamchatka, and in Korea, Japan and the Kuriles.

In North America races are found in the Aleutian islands and Alaska, and thence breed southward along the Rocky Mountains to central California and northern Colorado; also across Canada and the northern States to Labrador, Newfoundland and New England, down through the Alleghenies to northern Georgia.

Whilst the races found on islands and in some isolated mountainous areas are sedentary, birds from the northern parts of the ranges of the continental races migrate south in winter.

HABITAT

In the British Isles there is no more widely distributed species than the wren. It is at home in English spinneys and on Shetland moors, on lacustrine and marine islands and in extensive woods. More than twenty nests were found on the Little Skellig, a rock-stack off the Kerry coast (Turle 1900), and wrens have bred on the Farne islands (Bolam 1932). I noticed a wren singing near the summit of the 600-foot cliff of Noss in Shetland, and Saxby (1874) records a nest half-way down a cliff of this height. Near the top of the 1220-foot cliff on Foula, Pennie (1948) heard a wren. The wrens of St. Kilda and the Faeroes inhabit precipices, and sometimes nest in puffin colonies. On Lundy wrens are found among nesting kittiwakes (R. Perry, *in litt.*). Individuals are commonly seen on the high fells of the Lake District in winter. Here the wren goes up to 2000 feet or even higher (J. F. Thomas, *in litt.*). It nests as high as 1700 feet (Blezard *et al.*, 1943). In the Grampians and on Skye wrens are found at 1500-2000

*A wren was heard singing 50 miles north of the Arctic circle in Swedish Lapland (D. Snow, *in litt.*) and another was seen in November at 65° 20′ N. (Holm 1950). In 1952 five males were heard singing on the island of Andöya, in the Westeraalen group, at latitude 69° 17′ N. (D. Jenkins, personal communication). These may have been *T. t. bergensis.*

E. A. Armstrong

Plate Ia. Habitat of wren, *Troglodytes t. islandicus*, in Iceland. Hvalfjördur, looking towards Sula.

Ib. Habitat of wren, *Troglodytes t. kabylorum*, in North Middle Atlas cedar forest near Ifrane at 6000 feet.

D. W. Snow

feet (R. Perry, *in litt.*, 1948), and a family party has been seen at 2500 feet in the Welsh mountains (Ingram and Salmon 1934). Shakespeare's words are only too sadly true of the English, Welsh and Irish mountains:

> Wrens make prey where eagles dare not perch.
> *Richard III*. I. iii. 71

In Switzerland, where the wren is found alike in coniferous and deciduous woods (Thorpe 1926), I have noted it in summer at nearly 5000 feet, at which height it breeds. Birds may be observed at well over 6000 feet and some winter at about 4000 feet (Fatio and Studer 1907). In the forest of Galicica on the Albanian frontier the song has been heard in September at this altitude (Thorpe, Cotton and Holmes 1936). On Majorca wrens are found at 4500 feet (Munn 1931). Wrens inhabit the cedar forests of the Middle Atlas in North Africa at 6000 feet (D. Snow, *in litt.*). Trevor-Battye (1913) watched a wren searching for food in the crevices of drifted snow at 7700 feet on Mount Ida in Crete.

In Japan and northern Burma the species is found at 9500 feet (Jahn 1942; Smythies 1949). In Sikkim and Nepal it occurs at 10,000 feet, while in south-eastern Tibet and Kashmir nests have been discovered between 12,500 and 13,000 feet (Ludlow and Kinnear 1944; Bates and Lowther 1952), but the bird goes as high as 15,000 feet (Walton 1905).

Although the wren is very adaptable there are two types of habitat to which it cannot accommodate itself. It is not found breeding where there are areas of open country undiversified by bushy vegetation, irregular ground or water-courses, though in the Hebrides, Shetland, and to a rather less extent in Ireland, wrens nest on the moors, but only where streams, lochs or small declivities break their monotony. Wrens may frequent comparatively bare regions in winter, such as low-lying heaths by the sea (Lack and Venables 1937) or even salt-marshes, but they go elsewhere to nest. They explore extensive reed-beds in the autumn and winter, but only a small proportion remain to breed. The availability of suitable nesting sites has an important bearing on the choice of localities for breeding.

At the other extreme wrens find densely built-up areas uncongenial. During six years in the centre of Leeds and five in the industrialised outskirts I never saw or heard a wren, though an occasional robin appeared, pied wagtails were not infrequent during seasons of passage, willow warblers sometimes sang in autumn in my grimy garden, and from time to time a kestrel drifted over. The wren is now

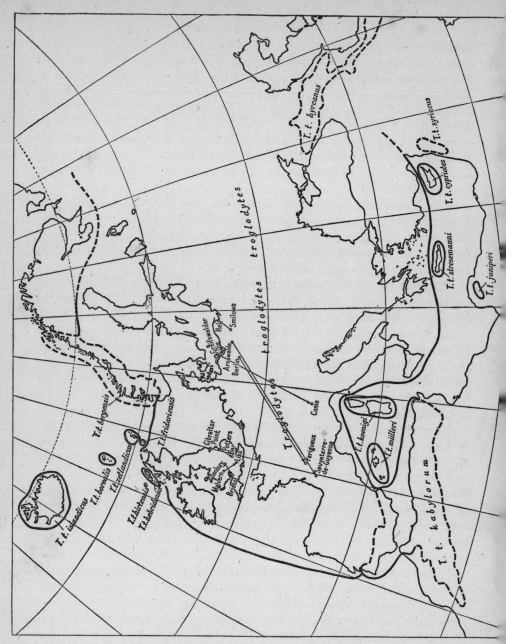

FIG. 4. Breeding distribution of the wren in Europe, North Africa and the Near East, and recoveries of ringed birds. Where there is some uncertainty in regard to the area occupied by race boundaries are shown with a broken line.

hardly more than a visitor to the built-up areas of London (Fitter 1945), though in 1879 Hamilton recorded that it bred regularly in Kensington Gardens and Regent's Park, and had been heard in Portman Square. Fifty years later Macpherson found it a decreasing breeding species in inner London. An unlined nest discovered in Kensington Gardens in 1947 and a building bird seen there in 1948, were sufficiently noteworthy to be commented upon in the *Reports of the Committee on Bird Sanctuaries in the Royal Parks*. Fairly frequently wrens breed, or attempt to breed, in Battersea Park (Cramp and Teagle 1952).

Of course, it is not suggested that the wren cannot be considered a garden bird. It is a welcome resident in very many gardens, but only where bricks and mortar do not predominate over greenery. In populous areas where each house has its pocket-handkerchief garden wrens do not find congenial quarters.

Capable as the European wren may be of adapting itself to varied environments it prefers thick cover, as is apparent when counts of birds in newly-afforested areas are compared. Although it is rather infrequent in the heathland of East Anglia it becomes fairly common in young pines from five to twelve years of age, but decreases when the lower branches are trimmed off (Lack 1939b). However, the adaptability of the wren is indicated by the conclusions reached by Dr. and Mrs. Lack (1951a) that " wrens are much less affected by afforestation than any other bird."

In woodland the wren, like the hedge sparrow, is a denizen of the undergrowth, but the statement that the robin and wren predominate in the " herb layer "—from three inches to four feet from the ground (Colquhoun and Morley 1943)—needs qualification so far as the wren is concerned. It feeds low down in the winter, but tends to seek food at a higher level in spring when the young leaves offer pasture to caterpillars. A still finer distinction may be made, for in spring and summer the male tends to frequent a higher zone than the female, partly because he seeks elevated song-perches. The tendency for male and female to feed in different vertical zones is even more pronounced in one of the forms of Bewick's wren found in California, Vigors's wren (*Thryomanes bewickii spilurus*). In early spring, when these birds form pairs, and only then, the male forages in trees and the female, who is sometimes fed by him, follows at a foot or two above the ground (Miller 1941). The female redstart also feeds lower than the male (Ruiter 1941; Buxton 1950). This differentiation between the feeding zones of the sexes reduces competition for food and enables the resources of a locality to be efficiently exploited. Western winter wrens (*Troglodytes t. pacificus*) do not come into conflict in winter with Nicasio wrens (*Thryomanes bewickii marinensis*), because they feed about a foot from the ground while Nicasio wrens forage higher in the brushwood (Miller 1941).

The most favourable wren habitats are damp, deciduous, mixed woods with much small growth and thick cover, overgrown valleys with streams, untended garden-woodland areas and sheltered, deep, tree-fringed lanes. The presence of water renders a suitable locality particularly congenial. Arid areas are avoided and in many of the drier parts of the wren's range it prefers to nest near brooks and lakes. For this reason the wren tends to be a mountain dweller in southern Europe and in its southerly range in Asia. In North Africa, however, although I found wrens in a typically damp habitat in the gorge of the river Rummel at Constantine, they are not confined to areas near standing or running water, but occur in woods varying from ever-green oak to dry pine (*Pinus halepensis*), and even in open scrub (D. Snow, *in litt.*). So far as my observations go, Corsican wrens in spring keep to the woods and broken ground in the valleys, ravines or mountains, but usually avoid the open maquis. Mouillard (1934) found them only within reach of water. In Spain wrens inhabit arid hills (P. Westall, *in litt.*).

Human activities in the woods, such as making clearings, piling logs and constructing huts, sometimes render a locality more attractive to wrens, though our bird is not quite so responsive to the facilities unintentionally provided by man as the house wren, of which Chapman (1930) remarked: " Build a house almost anywhere from Patagonia to Canada and a house wren appears."

CHAPTER 3

MIGRATION, DISPERSAL AND HOMING

The petty wrens of Tarsus will fly hence
And open this to Pericles.
SHAKESPEARE. *Pericles*, IV. iii. 22

THE WREN is migratory in the most northerly part of its range. In Europe, and probably in Asia, it is apparently unable to endure the winter farther north than about the 20° F. January isotherm. Birds from the north visit the Punjab (Vaurie 1951) and the Shanghai area in winter, though some winter in Korea, and individuals go as far south as Fukien and Kwangtung (Wilkinson 1929; La Touche 1925-30). Wrens of high mountain ranges, such as the western Himalayas, western China and Japan (Hartert 1910; Seebohm 1890), the Alps, as well as our British mountain-dwelling wrens to some extent descend to lower levels in winter. The rock wren and many other passerines also come down the mountains in winter (Jaeger 1950). Most Iceland wrens go to the coast in autumn. The wrens of the Faeroes, Hebrides, St. Kilda, Fair Isle and Shetland, are non-migratory.

We have very little exact knowledge of wren migration owing to the paucity of ringing returns, but birds on passage were regularly recorded in spring and autumn at the European migration research stations at Heligoland and Rossitten, and wrens also pass regularly through our British bird observatories. Apart from these passage movements birds of the year tend to disperse widely and, as we shall see, some of the records indicate that at least a few birds make remarkably long journeys.

Considering more in detail what is known of the migratory movements of the species we may first comment on the evidence from the northernmost regions of its range in Europe, where passage is most in evidence, and then discuss observations made in this country.

Only occasionally are wrens recorded in Finland during winter (Hortling 1929). They go south in September and October and move northwards during the latter half of April (P. Palmgren, *in litt.*). Winter wrens in Labrador have a much shorter season, for they leave,

17

at latest, by the middle of August (Townsend and Allen 1907). Løven-skiold (1947) states that in Norway the majority of wrens are resident, but birds are reported at the lighthouses from mid-April into May and from late September to mid-November with the peak in the first half of October. (Wrens trapped in southern Norway during autumn passage by Cambridge University students were rather dark in colour and may have been *T. t. bergensis*.) According to *Forteckning över Sveriges fåglar* (1949) there is a movement from Sweden at the same period to central and southern Europe and a return movement mainly in April, but apparently most of the wrens of southern Sweden are non-migratory. The birds which occur regularly at Danish light-houses are believed to be Swedish, for the wrens of Denmark are doubtless mainly sedentary (B. Løppenthin, *in litt.*). At Rossitten the spring passage peak is in April (Thienemann 1909), and observations made on Heligoland indicate that the majority of spring migrant wrens pass through from mid-April to the end of the month; there is a return passage in autumn. For some unknown reason the records show a great preponderance of males (Weigold 1926, 1930). As many as fifty wrens have been recorded in the peak month of October.

Continental returns of ringed birds are meagre, but a few of them are extremely interesting (Fig. 4, p. 14). A young bird ringed on 16 May 1930, in Arnswalde, Neumark (53° 3′ N., 15° 57′ E.) was reported dead on 5 January 1931 at Sauveterre-de-Guyenne in Gironde (44° 42′ N., 0° 6′ W.), having travelled 908 miles (1460 km.) to the south-west (Schüz 1931b). Another nestling ringed near Berlin on 29 May 1928, flew into a room in Périgueux, Dordogne (48° 12′ N., 0° 30′ E.) the following December, having covered a distance of some 804 miles (1220 km.) (Drost 1931). There is a Polish record of a wren travelling 127 miles (203 km.) in a north-easterly direction (Rydzewski 1949). A bird which may have come from Sweden, banded at Greifswalder Oie in the Baltic (54° 15′ N., 13° 55′ E.), was reported nearly a year later from Como in northern Italy (Niethammer 1937-38). If, as these records suggest, it is not very unusual for wrens to travel long distances, further migration returns may throw light on the possibility that a tendency towards long-range dispersal contributed to the rapidity of the wren's invasion of Eurasia.

The wren has not succeeded in establishing itself in the Canary Islands or the Azores, although the goldcrest is found in both these groups; and there is only one somewhat doubtful record for Madeira (Harcourt 1851). However, the breeding of a pair of marsh wrens (*Telmatodytes palustris*) in Greenland and the recent establishment of a colony of fieldfares there (Salomonsen 1948, 1951; Winge 1898) indicate that the long-range dispersal of *Troglodytes troglodytes* is not to be considered out of the question.

In extending their breeding range southward the house wren, American robin, song sparrow and blue-headed vireo did so by " hops " of about 100 miles (Odum and Johnston 1951). We may also take note of the lesser redpoll's achievement in colonisation. It was introduced into New Zealand in 1862 and has now reached islands 700 miles to the W.N.W., 500 miles to the S. and 900 miles to the S.W. (Hindwood 1948).

A number of records indicate that, in contrast to those young birds which the returns just quoted show to have been very peripatetic, others winter near where they are reared. Moreover, adults ringed in October may remain in the same neighbourhood. The Dutch recoveries show that one bird stayed where it was ringed until the following January, that a female was recaptured a year after ringing and another two years after ringing, both in the garden at Stein. One of the males ringed in this garden in December, 1934, was noted again in January 1939, having been recaptured several times during these years. A year after a nestling was ringed it was recorded 33 miles (53 km.) E.N.E., and another ringed in May 1930 was found dead nearly two years later 25 miles (40 km.) away. Yet another was discovered breeding a short distance from where it had been ringed thirteen months before. A female mentioned in the notebooks of the observers at Stein as rearing two broods before leaving, was captured some 6.2 miles (10 km.) E.S.E. in November. Spending the breeding season successfully in a favourable locality did not inhibit the impulse to go elsewhere. This agrees with other evidence that there is a stronger bond between male wrens and their territories than between females and their breeding localities.

MIGRATION IN THE BRITISH ISLES

The English and Irish Migration Reports show that passage movements in the British Isles are most noticeable in April and October. They are recorded as early as the third week of March in the Western Isles and Orkneys, but not until the second week of April do migrants, apparently from the continent, appear on the southern coasts of England and Ireland. These movements continue until the first or second week of May (Ticehurst 1938).

As long ago as 1872 Cordeaux noted wrens arriving at Spurn Head in October a few days before the woodcock and their " pilots " the goldcrests. The passage may continue for more than six weeks (Nelson 1907), but data for the last five years supplied by Mr. G. H.

Ainsworth show a tendency for the peak to occur in the last week of October. Wrens may appear with " rushes " of migrants, such as snow buntings, bramblings and redwings on the Northumberland coast (Bolam 1912; R. Perry, *in litt.*). They sometimes alight on ships in the North Sea far from land (Harvie-Brown and Cordeaux 1880). A few are seen at the Scottish lighthouses as early as August, and at Skerryvore a trickle passes through from mid-September. During the winter an occasional wren is noted at the Scottish lighthouses, at Spurn Head, Holy Island and the Irish lighthouses and lightships (Ussher and Warren 1900). Probably these birds are merely making local and weather movements. From the second week of October, and possibly sometimes rather earlier, there is a passage movement from England and Ireland to the continent (Ticehurst 1938). Wrens are seen on rare occasions from ships in the English Channel between September and November (J. A. R. Bickford, *in litt.*), but they may be moving south-west along the French coast rather than travelling from England.

Detailed records of wren passage movements at the Isle of May are available for the years 1934-38 and 1946-49 inclusive. The maximum spring passage occurs from 3 to 21 April. Autumn observations being scanty, the peak period cannot be so closely defined. Few wrens pass through (or are seen at Gibraltar Point) until after 18 September, but there is evidence of passage in October and the first week or two of November. Spring passage is apparently only slightly less than in autumn. Great numbers are not seen. The maximum recorded is ten on 10 April 1937. At peak periods two wrens per day is the average (A. G. S. Bryson, *in litt.*). Mr. H. F. D. Elder, who is familiar with the passage movements on the Isle of May, writes that he is strongly of the opinion that a few of the arrivals are winter visitors from abroad and Mr. K. Williamson tells me that some European wrens occur on Fair Isle. Of course, it cannot be assumed that wrens on islands close to the coast in spring or autumn are on their way from or to distant places. Birds may move from higher ground to winter on the coast and may visit or sojourn on such islands.

The few returns of wrens ringed in Britain furnish little information. In October, at Liss in Hampshire, a cat killed a wren which had been ringed at Malvern on the previous 31 May. This may be regarded as an instance of local dispersal rather than migration. A youngster ringed near Banbury in 1949 was reported from Bristol, 67 miles S.W., in January 1951, and an adult, probably on a migratory journey, ringed at Gibraltar Point in September 1949, was found dead at Potter's Bar, 100 miles south, sixteen months later (Thomson 1951). (Fig. 4, p. 14). A nestling Shetland wren ringed at Mid-Yell on the

Plate IIa. Iceland wren bringing food to nest-lings. (*F. Guðmundsson*)

St. Kilda wren re-
oving faeces.
(*Robert Atkinson*)

c. Shetland wren foraging.
(*E. A. Armstrong*)

island of Yell was found drowned two months later at Baltasound, on the island of Unst, some eighteen miles to the N.N.E. A wren which was trapped on 10 November 1937 on the Isle of May was noted there again on 25 March 1938. Whether it left the island in the interval is unknown, but it seems probable that it remained. An adult ringed on Skokholm on 2 October 1936, was re-trapped there on 12 April 1937, and 10 April 1938. The wren is a winter visitor to this island, the main arrivals and departures being in October and March. The average number remaining on Skokholm in winter is between ten and twenty, but none stay to breed, although wrens nest on the island of Skomer. (On Heligoland, according to Drost (1927) the wren has bred only once.) It would seem that this ringed individual might have remained unobserved on the island, but Mr. R. M. Lockley, who was living there, assures me that it could not have been overlooked. Perhaps the bird moved over from the mainland each year, as two robins noted in three successive years may have done (Lockley 1946) or, less probably, it may have made the island a port of call on migratory journeys in successive years.

HOMING

Wrens captured in my regular observation areas were too valuable to risk upsetting normal conditions by removing them even for a short time, so I tried but one experiment to ascertain whether the species has any homing ability. I found a bird building in a pollard willow by the Granta during July. He had no young to be interested in and may have been without a mate. I trapped, ringed and transported him to Wren Wood, rather more than a mile away, taking care that he could not observe any landmarks *en route*. Next day he was back in his usual place by the river. Thus, although there was only one male in Wren Wood, and he unmated, my captive returned to his territory. It is more probable that orientation was by the sun than by topographical clues.

Other species of wren possess homing ability. Some male house wrens will return from distances up to 22 miles. The homing impulse increases in strength with the progress of the nesting cycle. Probably this is also true of the females. An intruding male Carolina wren (*Thryothorus ludovicianus*), which began building in a box where a pair of birds of the same species were feeding nestlings, jeopardised their lives by piling nesting material on top of them. He was caught and deported 3 miles, but returned. He was again trapped and did not reappear after being taken 18½ miles away (Laskey 1950).

The return of these birds is not surprising in view of experiments with other species, such as house and tree sparrows (Marples 1933; Wojtusiak and Ferens 1947), and the return of birds without mate, eggs or young to the area from which they had been displaced (Gillespie 1930; Stimmelmayr 1930; Alexander 1938).

CHAPTER 4

GENERAL BEHAVIOUR AND FEEDING HABITS

Ah! There's Miss Kitty Wren, with her cocked tail,
Cocked like a cooper's thumb. Miss Kitty goes
In 'neath the bank, and then comes out again
By some queer hole. Thus all day long she plies
Her quest from hedge to bank, scarce ever seen.
Flying above your head in open air.
Unsmitten by the heat where now she is,
She strikes into her song—Miss Kitty's song!
(We never think of male in Kitty's case.)
Short is the song, not varied, yet not dull,
So liquid clear of pipe she opens it,
And, with increasing vigour to the end,
Goes through it quite: Thus all the year she sings,
Except in frost, the spunky little bird.

THOMAS AIRD. *A Summer Day*

AMONG EUROPEAN BIRDS only the goldcrest and firecrest are smaller than the wren, if we regard the long-tailed tit as being disqualified by its disproportionate tail; yet in spite of its diminutive size and sober colouring the wren is familiar, at least by repute, to almost everybody. Moreover, the bird is famous in folklore (Armstrong 1946a; in preparation).

The wren's appearance needs scant description, for the small, brown, stump-tailed bird can hardly be confused with any other European species. Attempts have been made, with meagre justification, to differentiate local subspecies within the British area in addition to the recognised subspecies of St. Kilda, the Outer Hebrides, Shetland

and the apparently distinct Fair Isle wren. From my own experience I can testify that in the field the Iceland, Shetland and St. Kilda wrens are distinguishable from the European wren, not only in appearance but also in song.

To the countryman and town-dwelling bird-lover alike the wren is familiar as a pert, feathered vehemence shrilling his song from a twig or proceeding in fits and starts through the undergrowth or hedge-bottom. Saxby (1874) was informed in Shetland that the wren " was too much like a mouse to lay eggs," and in Iceland and the Faeroes it is called " the mouse's brother." Although the wren, robin and hedge sparrow, share the lowest zone of the woodland, the feeding habits of the three species differ so noticeably that there is nothing surprising about the wren's success as an invader from the New World in occupying an ecological niche so little exploited by other species. We can see at a glance that while the wren's small size, sharp beak and powerful legs and feet are such as to enable it to seek its prey in cramped quarters, to probe into crevices and cling to twigs, the hedge sparrow is adapted to explore the ground and to pick up relatively exposed objects rather than pry into tiny nooks. The robin's technique of watching from a lookout point and flying down to seize small creatures is again different from the methods of the other two species.

The wren can squeeze through small apertures, hop and run, move backwards out of an enclosed space, cling like a tit, hover momentarily like a humming-bird, jerk up a tree-trunk like a tree-creeper and even pose head downwards on a vertical surface, nuthatch fashion. Its rounded, broad wings are of the type adapted to carry it efficiently on its frequent short flights from perch to perch " thridding the bosky wood," yet they have enabled it to reach remote windswept islands. The St. Kilda wren's speed in the air is at least 12 m.p.h. (Harrisson and Buchan 1936), but European and Iceland wrens almost certainly can fly quicker than this.

The wren impresses the observer with its incessant activity and overflowing vitality. It is quite unusual to see a wren, as I once did, perched practically immobile for two to three minutes, though I have known an Iceland wren to behave in this way. Here and there goes the wren, often low along hedge-banks, through thickets and in and out of old walls, lodging on each perch with strong legs flexed and body low. It will creep into a pile of logs to explore the interstices, and in the absence of the owners has been observed investigating a long-tailed tit's nest (Selous 1905). It has none of the abhorrence of enclosed spaces characteristic of many birds. When feeding, it frequently presses urgently forward as if it had an appointment in mind, moving either with little hops or long, wing-aided leaps. Often, when excited, it perks and bobs, or " teeters " like a dipper curtseying on a stone in midstream. The abbreviated tail, after which the bird is nicknamed " Stumpy " in the Pennines, is sometimes held flamboyantly aloft as the bird sings or scolds, but this posture, betokening excitement, is not as general as artists and writers of popular natural history would have us believe.

Food and Feeding Habits

Wrens, like other small active species, such as humming-birds, consume a relatively large amount of food. In captivity, young fledged birds will eat more than their own weight per day (R. Hinde, *in litt.*). Although they are difficult to maintain in an aviary, a pair, fed on mealworms and " ants' eggs ", bred successfully in a small cage (Grunack 1879). During the misguided craze for introducing birds of the homeland to New Zealand 30s. was offered for each pair of wrens reaching that country, but it is not surprising, in view of the difficulty of keeping them alive in captivity, that the reward was never claimed (Thomson 1922).

Although the wren eats some seeds, especially in winter (Collinge 1913), its diet is almost entirely animal matter, mainly insects, including the larvæ and pupæ of butterflies and moths, and occasionally the imagines, also small beetles, daddy-long-legs, mosquitoes, aphides and spiders. The stomach contents of a bird killed in January consisted entirely of small beetles (Thompson 1849). Fatio and Studer (1907) record millepedes or centipedes (mille-pieds), earwigs and woodlice, as well as ants and the eggs of many insects. On account of the bird's diet, and not for sentimental reasons, Andrew Boorde in his *Dyetary* (1562) advised his readers not to eat wrens, " the whiche doth eate spyders and poyson." Collinge's record of leather jackets may be erroneous. Rarely small worms are brought to the nestlings (p. 207). I have seen a female pick up a small slug (*Arion hortensis*), carry it a few feet, peck it tentatively, then drop it and wipe her bill, apparently repelled by the slime. On St. Kilda wrens may eat sandhoppers and small mollusca. They feed the nestlings mainly on arthropods. In autumn Clarke (1915) found remains of beetles, flies and spiders, as well as a few seeds in the birds' stomachs. Shetland wrens will spend minutes worrying a mollusc on the sea-shore. The wrens in Iceland feed on molluscs and other marine organisms during the winter when they frequent the coast (Timmermann 1935), but in summer, according to my observations, they forage in the birch scrub even when the shore is not far away.

Wrens sometimes paddle and forage in shallow streams, and individuals have been seen taking caddis fly larvæ (Rope 1889), tadpoles (Hyde-Parker 1938), minnows (Scholey 1933) and trout fry (Huxley 1949). Winter wrens occasionally immerse their heads while securing prey (Forbush 1929), and a European wren was seen to " walk over head into the water by the shallow margin of a brook, as in search of insect food " (Haslam 1844). Such forms of behaviour have been held to support the suspected relationship between the wrens and the dippers, but it would be easy to attach too much importance to them, though they show the way the dipper type could have evolved. Several other passerines, including the blackbird (Jourdain 1938a), robin (Lack 1948b) and pied wagtail (Brown 1948a), have been observed either catching fish or giving them to their young.

In England, as in the inclement Aleutians, wrens remain active during a snow-storm (Sutton and Wilson 1946) and, when a white coverlet conceals the herbage, they creep beneath laden tufts, and may spend a minute or longer foraging in the dark and frosty labyrinths. Winter is the season when wrens feed most frequently on or quite near the ground. As the year advances and the leaves of deciduous trees open they tend to feed higher, but, as has been remarked, this is more characteristic of the males than of the secretive females. Where there are hawthorn trees of some size wrens move here and there amid the fresh foliage, twisting their elongated necks like leaf warblers as they stretch up to pick larvæ from the underside of the leaves. In autumn and winter some European wrens feed along the shore on marine organisms.

The remarkable feeding adaptation of the northern cactus wrens (*Campylorhynchus brunneicapillus couesi*) in California is worthy of comment. These birds have been seen overturning stones weighing more than themselves in search of insects (Jaeger 1947, 1950). In Europe only the turnstone feeds in this way.

" TAMENESS "

A wren has been known habitually to explore a bedroom, staying as long as half an hour looking for spiders and flies, paying no attention to the occupant of the bed (Whitaker 1945). Another was seen to enter by a window open only a few inches; after examining the picture rail and the panes of three windows, it dragged a small tortoise-shell butterfly (*Aglais urticae*) from the fold of a curtain, retreated

T.W.   C through the opening and broke up its prey on the window sill (Truman 1947). Yet another roosted in an attic to which it penetrated by a small hole. During my boyhood I was lying awake in bed one morning when a wren hopped in through the window, which was two or three inches ajar. To my delight, it proceeded to make a tour of the room and then departed neatly through the same small aperture. As wrens are liable to escape when being ringed, I usually took the precaution of attaching the rings indoors. Sometimes a captive eluded me and fluttered before a window, but even in its bewilderment it never collided violently with the pane. I placed a sheet of glass over the hole by which a wren entered a shed to its nest, but when it perceived the obstruction as it flew to the aperture it hovered in front. Probably the relatively high development of the pecten of the wren's eye facilitates its perception of minute specks on glass and enables the bird to avoid contact (Menner 1938). This adaptation must be of great value to wrens when exploring thick undergrowth.

Although wrens are so adept in finding their way out of an enclosed space they are sometimes caught in wicker eel-traps stored away to dry (Tomes 1901).

In severe weather wrens rarely visit bird-tables or seek scraps strewn by the kindhearted. They seldom or never make the first step towards true tameness—associating a person with the food he provides. Grey (1927) stated that his wife " once tamed even a wren to come into the house and take food from her fingers," but he does not suggest that the bird persisted in this behaviour for any length of time nor that it showed any real attachment for Viscountess Grey. He contrasts the wren's wary, zigzag approach with the bold demeanour of a tame robin which " brisk alights on the warm hearth." The wren goes his own independent way and seldom seeks charity. Wordsworth aptly styled him " self-contented." Indeed, there are few birds so unsociable. This is probably true of all the subspecies of *Troglodytes troglodytes*. The apparent sociability of some New World wrens, such as cactus wrens, appears to be based on a family bond rather than true gregariousness. Adult European wrens never " flock " in the ordinary sense of the word and practically never associate with their own kind except when breeding, and in wintry weather when stringent conditions force them to take refuge in a common dormitory. They do not accompany flocks of tits and other small birds in the winter woods. When two wrens are seen in company in autumn, as is not very unusual, their association is due to unseasonable sexuality, or sometimes, to a temporary bond prior to roosting together. Timmermann (1935) was informed of a score or more Iceland wrens being

seen in November along a short stretch of road, and Dall (1873) refers
to the Unalaska wren (*T. t. petrophilus*) as " to some extent gregarious."
The most probable explanation of such observations is, that con-
centrations of birds occurred when food was locally abundant.

The European wren is not so much timid as circumspect in regard
to the proximity of human beings. The Shetland wren is more tolerant.
Hebridean wrens seem shyer than Shetland birds and, when alarmed,
are apt to squat in cover. In Iceland the wrens are secretive rather
than timid. They readily dive into the birch scrub when they see a
human observer close at hand, but they usually do so spontaneously
after venturing for a short time to any exposed perch. In winter they
enter farmhouses and pick at the joints of meat. Faeroe wrens also
enter buildings where meat is stored and, no doubt, St. Kilda wrens
crept into the " cleits " when they were used for storing bird carcasses.
Munn (1931) refers to the wrens of the Balearic Islands as being
" extremely shy." Comparison of wren subspecies suggests that
" alarm distance " is a genetically determined character, although
modifiable through experience (Leopold 1944).

Wrens which appropriate man-made niches for their nests make
use of them without acquiring " tameness " in the sense of social
feeling towards man, though they may adopt a nonchalant attitude
to him. A wren built within eight inches of a circular saw, driven by
a noisy engine a few feet away, although the saw was in use for eight
hours a day. In spite of the apparatus being moved forty feet when
there were eggs in the nest, the young were reared (Tutt 1947). Another fed her brood for at least nine days in the chassis of a motor
truck driven twice a day from a farm to a dairy (Twining 1949). A
third nested in a shed where workmen were constantly sawing and
hammering during the daylight hours. As I sat watching the family
after the young had fledged, one of them approached and perched on
my knee and then on my shoulder. The mother also came within a
foot or two of my face as she searched for food. The familiarity with
man which old and young had acquired inhibited the utterance of
the warning chitters which usually prevent any intimacy with young
wrens. " How use doth breed a habit in a bird! "[2]

The widespread notion that putting a finger into the nest causes
a wren to desert is a myth, probably originating through the majority
of nests not being used for breeding (p. 139). Some wrens, indeed,
will tolerate extensive interference, as for example, when I recon-
structed the entrance to a nest in order to fit a recording instrument.
Occasionally a wren will desert for no apparent reason. Sitting a dozen
yards from a nest in the dim light of dawn, I watched a bird emerge

after spending the night on the eggs. She never returned. Two other birds deserted after being flushed from their nests, but one of them had already been sitting twenty-six days on infertile eggs and was perhaps about to desert in any case.

DRINKING AND BATHING

Wrens are seldom seen drinking, but, when they do so, they dip and raise the bill like most birds. On the only occasion when I witnessed a wren bathing, the bird jumped in and out of a shallow, herbage-fringed stream in a curious, nervous way. Shortly afterwards I heard it uttering its alarm and a rat came into view, but I could not be certain that there was any connection between the bird's hurried manner of bathing and the presence of the rat. On another occasion I found a wren perched on a twig beside a small pond diligently preening his wet plumage, having just emerged from his bath. Grinnell and Storer (1924) noticed that a western winter wren splashed in a pool for a few seconds at a time, returning after each dip to its perch. Finally, it spent a few minutes preening.

A wren was once seen swimming in a rain-water tank in water two feet deep. It flew off on finding its activities observed, but soon returned, perched on the iron rim, and then launched forth, swimming in a semi-circle back to the rim, riding buoyantly and fluttering its wings as it swam. It moved around several times " doing all the motions of a bird bathing " when it reached the rim again (Tritton 1947). When I startled a brood of newly-fledged wrens on the bank of a reservoir a chick flew out over it and dropped into the water. It struggled towards the bank and I lifted it out, none the worse. Most passerine birds can propel themselves in water to some extent though, of course, it is unusual for them to choose to do so. A mistle thrush has been seen swimming in a pool (Olivier 1949), and stock doves have been watched repeatedly alighting on a lake (Crackles 1948). In spite of the wren's buoyancy three of the few recoveries of ringed individuals concern birds found drowned (p. 250).

Early one misty morning, when every twig glittered and heavy drops pattered on the herbage throughout the wood, my attention was attracted to a tangle of hawthorn and wild rose in agitated movement. I found a wren enjoying a shower-bath, moving here and there, some- times hanging momentarily upside-down, so that my first thought was that the bird was a tit. It was shaking drops on to its fluffed-out plumage and continued to do so for two or three minutes. Wren-tits are among the few birds which commonly bathe in wet foliage (Erickson 1938), but some, such as the blackbird, willow warbler, whitethroat, swallow and Bahama honey-creeper, dew-bathe (Nichols 1921; Staton 1950; Mitchell 1950). Pale-bellied house wrens (*Troglodytes musculus clarus*) perch singing with ruffled feathers, spread tail and trembling wings as they take a shower-bath in the rain (Fr. Haverschmidt, *in litt.*). Bathing in rain or snow has been recorded of various other birds (Shaw 1944; Nice 1943; Clague and Goodwin 1949).

An account has been published of a pair of wrens opening a milk bottle and one of them bathing in the milk, but it can hardly be doubted that there was some error in identification. Probably the observer caught a glimpse of tits drinking the milk.

Sun-Bathing and Dust-Bathing

I have seen juvenile and adult wrens sun-bathing. A male surprised basking on a gate went off singing. Like many other passerines, wrens sprawl in the sun with plumage fluffed and wings and tail spread (Jackman 1947; Heinroth and Heinroth 1924-33). St. Kilda wrens also sunbathe in this posture (Harrison and Buchan 1936).

Mr. J. E. M. Mellor has sent me the following description of a wren's sun-bathing procedure:

> When reclining in my hammock after lunch on what was a sultry but bright afternoon, a wren came on to the seat of my garden bench, put her head and bill into a horizontal position flat on the bench, spread her wings fan-wise so that their tips almost met in front of her beak, spread her tail like a fan, ruffled up all the feathers of her back and, after a second or two in that posture, darted forward 3-4 inches like a mouse, rested and darted forward again, and so forth for one or two minutes or a little more. Then up on to the side of the bench to have a peck or two at her shoulders, and then off to the shade of the hedge for 5-10 minutes. This was repeated some ten or more times. . . .
>
> She gaped each time towards the end of the sunning period. As pleasing a sight as could be wished and left a gem of a miniature on the mind.

House wrens (Nice 1943), pale-bellied house wrens (Haverschmidt, *in litt.*) and Bewick's wrens (Miller 1941) bathe in dust as well as water. Wrens do so also (Niethammer 1937-38), but I have only once witnessed this. Woods (1948) states that he has never seen northern cactus wrens bathing in dust, though one would expect desert-dwelling birds to do so. When taking a bath they go about it gingerly and only wet the breast feathers.

PREENING

Presumably because cobwebs and particles of dirt frequently become attached to their plumage European wrens often pause to preen. They do so at intervals as they feed or between sexual chases in winter or at dusk when one bird is waiting for another. Like many other birds wrens preen almost immediately when released after being ringed—probably due as much to agitation as to the impulse to arrange the disordered plumage. A Shetland wren, frightened from her nest in a turf-cutter's hut, gave much attention to her plumage as she perched on a rafter before returning to incubate. This behaviour was obviously occasioned by the conflict of the impulses to flee and to incubate. Such "displacement-preening" (Armstrong 1950b) is common in situations of this kind. Another displacement activity sometimes performed by excited birds, including wrens, is to wipe the bill on a twig or other object. A very excited wren will even attack and strike a branch.[3]

The following note, made in March, describes a wren's toilet procedure:

> At 07.30* a wren was singing antiphonally against a rival. He preened for five minutes or more, bursting into song two or three times during his toilet. He stretched his bill round to the oil-gland and then preened elsewhere, including the stretched-out wing. I particularly noticed that when he reached to the oil-gland the tail was quivered as if the oil were being extruded. Twice he paused to dig the tip of his beak into an adjacent twig, and also on three occasions he grasped a twig momentarily—presumably to clean the mandibles. Rain was falling.

During preening Bewick's wren also appears to obtain oil from the oil-gland (Miller 1941).

No species of wren is known to ant-bathe, squatting among ants and placing them in the plumage (Chisholm 1944; Lane 1948), but a wren, as well as a robin and a blue tit, frequented a wryneck's nest, picking up ants which had escaped from the mouthfuls brought by the parents to the young (M.D. England, *in litt.*). In captivity young dippers picked up ants and passed them through their feathers (Heinroth and Heinroth 1924-33).

*All times mentioned are G.M.T.

CHAPTER 5

TERRITORY

It also is a bird that roves alone, and never flies
in flocks; nay more, so often as it meets another of
its own kind it forthwith declares war and fights.

WILLIAM TURNER, 1544

SIZE OF TERRITORY

IF WE TAKE into consideration the size of the area occupied as well
as the persistence and vehemence with which it is defended, we must
number the male European wren among the most territorial birds.
The female, however, does not normally defend territory. Although
territorialism is somewhat relaxed when the birds are moulting in
summer and during hard weather in winter, it is approximately correct
to say that the male maintains territory throughout the year. This,
of course, is true only of the areas in which the European wren is non-
migratory and where severe weather due to high latitude or altitude
does not drive the birds from their breeding resorts. Observations
which I made in Algeria during November suggest that *Troglodytes t.
kabylorum* may maintain territory at this season. Some other races are
less territorial than the European wren.

A tendency towards sustained territorialism is characteristic of
other species of wren. In some areas Bewick's wren is territorial the
year round (Miller 1941), and probably this is true also of the
Carolina wren. The fact that a cactus wren was retrapped three years
later at the place where it had been ringed (Cooke 1950) indicates
that these birds may retain territory. Sturgis (1928) mentions a
chestnut-backed wren (*Thryothorus rufalbus castanonotus*) which lived and
sang in the same place at Panama for three years and presumably
held territory during this period. Very little is known of the size of
the territories of tropical wrens, but Dickey and Van Rossem (1938)
heard three Santa Ana rufous-browed wrens (*Troglodytes rufociliatus
nannoides*) singing at the same time in the cloud-forest of Salvador.
Perhaps we can infer from this that their territories are no larger
than those of the European wren. A pair of rufous-tailed wrens
(*Thryothorus mystacalis ruficaudatus*) reigned unchallenged throughout

31

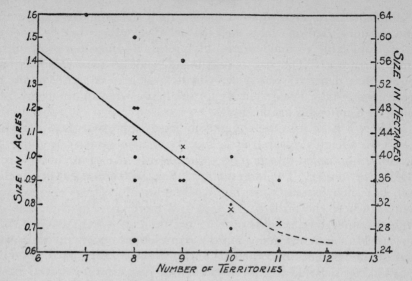

Fig. 5. Graph showing the relation between size and number of house wren territories. Each dot represents the average size for one breeding period, and each cross represents the average size for all breeding periods with the same number of territories. (*After Kendeigh 1941.*)

an extensive area around an observation point in Venezuela but spent three-fourths of their time not more than one hundred yards away (Beebe 1950).

Like most passerines wrens often appropriate more ground than they will defend when challenged. In suburban Cambridge males unrestrained by rivals in territories marching with their own, patrol and sing over an area of six or seven acres, and in some Scottish glens I have noticed birds singing about a quarter of a mile apart along the course of a burn. Shetland wrens sometimes have territories of this length along a stream. An isolated Iceland wren may patrol between sixty and ninety acres, but in particularly favourable areas the territories are much smaller. In Greenland the territories of snow buntings are at first of comparable size, but also become greatly reduced as newcomers compete with males already established (Tinbergen 1939). Wheatears may also establish themselves in extensive areas. These territories are among the largest recorded for small passerines. Perhaps a large area over which a bird wanders and sings with no rival within earshot should be distinguished from an area which a bird can be observed to defend, and described as a " patrolling range," but so far as most species are concerned this would be an unnecessary subtlety. Kluijver's conception of a bird's

" domicile " (1951) as an area smaller than the range and larger than the territory, within which the bird sleeps as well as breeds, does not seem applicable to male wrens although they sometimes roost outside their territories. The size of territories tends to vary inversely with population density. This rule, which is of general application, has been demonstrated more clearly for the house wren than for any other bird, as Kendeigh's graph shows.

There is a limit to the compressibility of territory. At Gates Mills, Ohio, Kendeigh's research area, this was reached when ten to thirteen territories occupied fifteen acres. The average size of the house wren's holding is an acre. The largest recorded was 3.6 acres and the smallest .08, but such extremes are highly exceptional. Vigors's wrens, in a canyon where the birds could have had more space had they needed it, maintained territories of rather more than an acre in extent (Miller 1941). Monogamous male, prairie marsh wrens occupy .3 of an acre, but bigamous birds hold double this area.

Where St. Kilda wrens are numerous their territories are, apparently, about four acres, but when nestlings are being fed the area defended diminishes. Reduction of territorialism as domestic responsibilities increase is common among passerines. During the period after the young have hatched, a male European wren may pay not the slightest attention to a potential rival, represented by a mounted specimen placed so near to the nest aperture that he rubs against it every time he brings food, though he may attack it when set near to a nest under construction (p. 97).

At Stein in Holland the smallest territory was .75 of an acre and the largest three acres. In both my observation areas this maximum has been exceeded and in neither of them has this minimum been reached. I refer, of course, to breeding territories, and not to territories in course of being established, as in late summer and autumn, or domains diminished after the birds had bred. From August onwards territories tend to decrease as pressure from intruding birds increases, and even apart from such competition the area of ground occupied by established birds is reduced. In such circumstances some territories are much smaller than breeding territories and, when a newcomer first insinuates himself at this season, his *pied-à-terre* may be very small.

The research area at Stein of approximately 17.5 acres held in successive years twelve, eight and eight territories. A few of these extended outside the garden and some of the garden area was unoccupied. A rough estimate shows that the average size of territories varied from about one and a half acres when wrens were numerous to somewhat over two when the population was less dense.

In Wren Wood, slightly over four acres in extent, there were never more than three males in occupation of breeding territories, and sometimes only one. Taking into account the surrounding garden area which was included in the birds' territories, though resorted to much less than the wood, breeding territories were between two and three acres in area when there was competition, but if a single male was in occupation he toured the whole wood and to a minor extent the gardens, so that his domain included approximately six and a half acres. The " control " area around and near my house was shared by two males every season, apart from one year when a single male ranged singing over the whole seven acres.

In comparing the size of the territories at Stein and Cambridge we must bear in mind that a higher proportion of Wren Wood was occupied by pond than in the Dutch garden. On the other hand, at Stein there was open water while the Cambridge pond was a mass of reeds, so these differences tend to cancel each other. There was also some open ground at Stein. The Wren Wood territories averaged larger than those in Holland, but this can be accounted for, to some extent, by there being in some years fewer wrens than the wood could accommodate.

The tendency for territories to be even larger near my home may be attributed to this locality being less favourable. There was no standing water and it contained fewer nesting and roosting niches. The smaller average size of the territories at Stein, in comparison with those in Cambridge, may have been due partly to the Dutch garden being a very congenial habitat for wrens, and also to several mild winters having enabled the Dutch wren population to increase. However, as territories at Stein during two years averaged slightly over two acres, and at Wren Wood, when there were three males in occupation, territories were under three acres, the discrepancy between the size of territories in the two areas is not as great as it might at first appear.

The territories of warblers and many other small passerines are small compared with the wren's territory. Reed warblers hold areas of less than 500 square yards (Brown 1946), blackcaps and garden warblers average .5 acre (Raines 1945), willow warblers .3 (May 1947a), and redstarts rather more than one acre (Buxton 1950), but marsh tits' freeholds range from one to sixteen acres, averaging about six acres (Southern and Morley 1950).

Counts of territories in a wood near Amsterdam in 1943 and 1945, show that the wren population is so liable to serious reduction by bad weather, that where the birds are resident in the northerly regions of the European wren's range there must be many seasons when by no means all the ground which might support the species is occupied. In 1943, after two successive fairly hard winters, there were only four, but in 1945 there were .22 in the area of 75 hectares (187.5 acres) (Sluiters 1947). The winter and spring of 1948-49 in Iceland were exceptionally severe and wrens were absent from some of their usual haunts. The two males I saw were in territories two miles apart. Song sparrows (Nice 1937), robins (Lack 1948b) and, according to my own rather limited observations, snow buntings, settle by choice close to other birds of their species, but Iceland wrens apparently prefer not to have close neighbours. Aristotle commented that gods and wild beasts love solitude, but whatever may be true of the inhabitants of Olympus, this is not valid of most birds in spite of their zeal in keeping their territories inviolate.

ASSESSING THE EXTENT OF TERRITORIES

Occasionally at the beginning of the breeding season ground may pass from the possession of one bird to another in such a way that one cannot be certain for some time to which bird the area belongs. Also, the presence of a female in a territory may stimulate a rival to encroach temporarily. More abrupt changes in dominance occur during the territorial flights in which two prairie horned larks or snow buntings participate, flying first to one side, then to the other, the pursuer chasing the pursued by flying after him into his territory (Pickwell 1931; Tinbergen 1939).

It sometimes happens that early in the year an apparently " strange" wren is heard singing in the corner of an occupied territory. Such birds may come from territories some little distance off, they may be males investigating the possibilities of invasion, or they may be transients on the lookout for an untenanted or weakly defended area in which to settle. It seems most probable that, some of them, like the house wrens which Kendeigh noticed around occupied territories, are males not yet fully mature. He found that some nine per cent remained unmated throughout the season. As ardent males in spring will sometimes suddenly take wing and start to sing in a distant corner of the territory, a single observer is occasionally puzzled as to how many birds are in the area. At such times I regretted not having a collaborator, but, on the whole, a detailed field study of a bird is best done alone. The presence of a companion, however congenial, is apt to deflect one's attention at critical moments, and, much more serious, prevents that meditative absorption into the bird's world which is essential to an intuitive appreciation of the significance of its activities.

A male wren is often most active in one sector of his territory at certain periods, especially during the breeding cycle, so that sometimes it is doubtful how effectively some other areas are incorporated. In spite of these and other complications, it is possible to estimate the extent of territories with considerable accuracy, mainly by noting and mapping the points at which the birds are heard singing and calling.

OCCUPATION OF TERRITORY

Migratory birds in spring naturally occupy territory very soon after they arrive. As about 75 per cent of adult house wrens return to nest within 1000 feet of where they bred the previous season, and a high percentage to the same box in which they nested, they are the better able to establish themselves without delay preparatory to nesting again. The procedure of resident species varies but tends to be such as to facilitate breeding as soon as climatic conditions permit. Gregarious species sometimes mate while in the flock and later establish territories; the blackbird secures territory in autumn and often pairs in winter (Lack and Light 1941). Robins occupy individual autumn territories, but form pairs mainly in winter, usually in the male's territory (Lack 1946a). British starlings pair and seize territories in autumn, but continental birds in this country do not (Bullough 1942).

As the European wren maintains territory practically throughout the year, we may best describe the procedure involved in its acquisition by beginning our account when territorialism is at a low ebb in summer. Towards the end of June, and increasingly through July and August, male sexual ardour and related activities, such as nest-building, display and song diminish, though preoccupation with the young tends to increase. If there is pressure from invaders the area defended shrinks, each male retires to a particularly favourable sector of his once larger domain and there establishes his citadel or " refuge area," singing from time to time in broken accents and making occasional sallies to defy the encroaching enemy.

The first invaders of established territories during the summer are evidently first-brood birds of the year, precocious in developing song and territorial impulses. They may appear as early as the end of June, though when they first begin to sing their crude jingles they will tolerate another wren within a few yards of them. Thus song is prior to territorial isolationism. It is doubtful whether the resident males recognise these intermittent ejaculations as the incipient songs of potential rivals (p. 85). By the second week of July some intruders may have managed to encroach on the established territories, but it is not until August that the tide of invasion is flowing strongly. Although the two types of imperfect song uttered respectively by maturing birds of the year and by moulting adults often resemble each other closely the trained ear can usually distinguish them. Invaders may also be recognised by their persistent exploratory activity and frequent snatches of song. Residents, in low condition after breeding and during the moult, are less active in movement and utterance. Even where the wren population is dense the increasing vigour and insistence of the young birds enable them to establish a footing among their elders. Thus in autumn an area may hold twice as many males as in spring.

Newcomers execute accepted military strategy, insinuating themselves at the junction of territories and gradually extending and consolidating their ground (Fig. 6). Other species, such as prairie horned larks, magpie larks, reed buntings and lapwings, also invade where boundaries meet, and drive a wedge between two holdings (Pickwell 1931; Robinson 1946-47; Howard 1920). Similar procedure is characteristic of some non-passerine birds and even of fish (Baerends and Baerends-Van Roon 1950). Like the camel in the fable which, having politely asked permission, thrust its nose, then its head, and after that its ample neck into the Arab's tent, and eventually ordered him to get out, wrens intrude where their presence is least objectionable and gradually become more truculent. House wrens adopt a rather different procedure. They sometimes appropriate a nesting site outside existing territories and then try to expand their domain at the expense of their neighbours. In Greenland, snow buntings carve out territories within those of established birds (Tinbergen 1939).

Apparently many of the invaders are unsuccessful in establishing a permanent foothold, but when birds are discovered to be missing in autumn and winter we seldom know whether their disappearance is to be attributed to expulsion, death, or even, perhaps, to an impulse to go elsewhere. Some birds, particularly those hatched the previous year, are driven out in the early months of the year. That established males endeavour to hold their ground is shown by the Dutch records. Of eight identifiable males in the garden at Stein in November, 1938, five were still maintaining their territories, some of them enlarged, in the following February. Only one of the wrens ringed there, the vigorous male No. 42 who had a specially favourable area, retained his territory for four years; another held his for three, and three others maintained holdings, with some modifications in size and area, for two seasons. My records show that one wren, Silver, held the same territory for not less than two years and another, Yellow-and-Black,

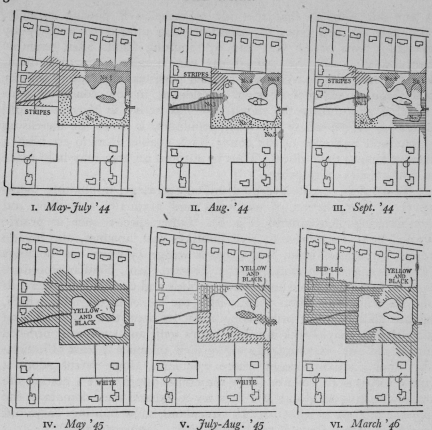

I. *May–July '44*   II. *Aug. '44*   III. *Sept. '44*

IV. *May '45*   V. *July–Aug. '45*   VI. *March '46*

FIG. 6. Plans showing wren territories in Wren Wood, Cambridge, from 1944 to 1949.

occupied in a second year half of the previous year's territory (p. 104). Normally males, having established their claim to a congenial domain, do not vacate it except under duress. However, evictions frequently occur. Similarly among house wrens Kendeigh found that eleven out of seventeen attempts by late-arriving males to usurp all or part of another male's territory were successful. I have pointed out elsewhere (1947) that some ornithologists have assumed too readily that possession of a territory renders a bird nearly or quite invincible.

As already mentioned, some young wrens remain at least a few months near where they were reared and, possibly, now and then, a bird establishes a territory and remains for its lifetime, as a robin may do. This is not surprising, as even among migratory passerines, such as the house wren, a sprinkling of first-year birds returns to the

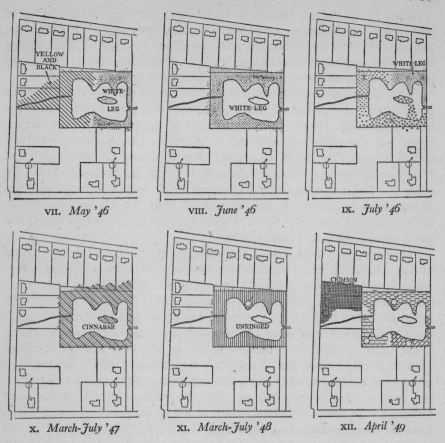

VII. *May '46*   VIII. *June '46*   IX. *July '46*

X. *March-July '47*   XI. *March-July '48*   XII. *April '49*

locality where they were reared, though they tend to scatter over the surrounding countryside much more than adults. The Dutch observers obtained the following data:

TABLE I

NUMBER OF RINGED NESTLINGS REMAINING WHERE REARED

Year	Number of nestlings ringed	Number remaining the winter
1936	65	2
1937	81	5
1938	49	3

Two of the 1938 juveniles established themselves in extensive territories, but although both were holding ground in January, one had disappeared by February and the other by April. This agrees with other evidence covering a variety of species, that older birds often have the advantage in competition with their juniors.

The alterations in territorial boundaries in Wren Wood which took place during my period of study are shown in maps I to XII. Observations were made almost daily over most of the period, except during 1950, but the plans are selected to illustrate at significant intervals modifications of the areas occupied. The territories are shown stippled with various devices and not represented simply as enclosed areas. By using the latter system some writers on other species have sometimes unintentionally conveyed the impression that the boundaries of the birds' estates, especially those where ownership is unchallenged, are more precise than they actually are.

In the Wren Wood area a precise territorial frontier seldom existed except where the wood abutted on pasture and at those places where males came into competition. The gardens outside the wood, being fairly recently established and without dense cover, were not such congenial wren habitats as the wood itself and were frequented much less—with the exception of the wooded gardens to the south which, apart from a small area bordering the wood, were always occupied by a male other than one of those holding territory in the wood. The pond area, although full of reeds and with some fallen willows stretching out into it, was comparatively little frequented by the wrens, and although they fed to a limited extent in the reeds, and females gathered food for their young along its banks, the wrens did not compete with the sedge warblers and occasional reed warblers which bred in the reeds. No altercations between these birds and the wrens were observed, nor did disputes about food occur with any other species. In the maps showing breeding territories the pond area is not stippled because singing and calling were infrequent there, and other territorial activities practically non-existent. On the other hand, as activity was sometimes considerable in this area during the invasion of territories late in the year, stippling is used to indicate this state of affairs. The island was not much frequented by wrens and no nest was ever found there, although it offered good cover, suitable nesting sites and greater security from ground predators. I did not observe that it was any less frequented by wrens when sparrowhawks were nesting there than when they were absent. In late summer and autumn, when boundaries were undergoing considerable alteration owing to the activities of intruders, some of the birds, especially those which had held spring territories, patrolled and sang in comparatively small areas and vocal competition was less than in spring. Frontiers were unstable and less clearly demarcated than during the early breeding season. This state of affairs is indicated on the maps by the blank buffer areas fringing territories.

When I first definitely ascertained the territorial boundaries at the end of May 1944, there were three wrens in occupation (Fig. 6, map 1), but, as a male was singing unchallenged along the north side a week earlier, it is possible that the bird holding the N.E. corner had driven the occupant, Stripes, into the N.W. corner shortly before these observations were made. At that time none of the wrens was ringed, but towards the end of July I succeeded in ringing Stripes and this simplified identification as his territory lay between the other two. However, during the first week of August an intruder, No. 3, established a small territory where Stripes's estate marched with that of No. 2. This intruder sang a great deal and most of his neighbours' singing was in reply. During this month other invaders staked claims so that by 31 August Nos. 4 and 5 could be heard at the points indicated on map 11. Birds sang on the island and at the N.W. corner of the pond, but they may have stayed only a day or two. No. 3 consolidated his gains in the wood and extended his sway into the garden to the west. A newcomer, No. 5, who sang tentatively for a few days at the S.E. corner, later occupied almost the whole of the S.E. section of the wood (map III). During October and November there was little change and, with the reduction in the amount of song, it became increasingly difficult to plot the boundaries of territories.

Although the maps show the extent of the territories with sufficient accuracy it must be emphasised that it was impossible to trap and ring invaders as they arrived, so it is only an assumption that the birds in the various locations were not supplanted by other individuals. However, as observations were made almost every day and the encroachment of intruders was recorded stage by stage, it is very unlikely that their places were taken by others without my knowledge. Even if this assumption were unjustified the maps depict accurately the pattern of territorial adjustments during summer and autumn.

In spite of my having ringed six wrens in the wood during the autumn and winter of 1944 only one of them, White, was present in the spring of 1945 and his territory was in the garden to the south. In March most of the wood, except the north-western sector, was held by a bird which I ringed Yellow-and-Black. Although by May he had the whole wood and surrounding area to himself he did not breed (map IV). An invader, B, appeared early in July and occupied the south side, while Yellow-and-Black retreated into the N.E. corner. This sector, which had thick cover, became a " refuge area " from invaders every year. Later in July other intruders appeared at the N.W. corner, on the island and mainland to the south (map v). This situation continued into December, except that in September the island wren disappeared.

In the spring of 1946 Wren Wood was held by two males; Yellow-and-Black in the east had enlarged his domain outside the refuge area, and a bird, Red-leg, caught on 26 February 1946, who may have been an invader of the previous year, was found to be established in the western half of the wood and the adjoining gardens (map vi). It seemed as though the wrens had reached a satisfactory *status quo*, but on 25 April an intruder, White-leg, seized the N.E. corner and soon occupied the whole eastern sector. Yellow-and-Black, expelled from his territory, forced his way into Red-leg's domain, ousted him and established himself there (map vii). After mid-June when Yellow-and-Black was driven right away by White-leg this usurper occupied the whole area (map viii) until July when two newcomers arrived and White-leg retreated to the refuge corner (map ix). One of these intruders had disappeared by August and the territories changed little throughout the summer and autumn.

In 1947 and 1948, when wrens were rather scarce after the severe winter of 1946-47, territorial adjustments were simple. A single polygamous male, Cinnabar, held the area throughout the 1947 breeding season (map x), retreating to the citadel area when intruders arrived in the autumn. In 1948 an unringed bird was in possession (map xi) and gave up most of his ground to an intruder in the late summer, apparently retiring like his predecessor to the N.E. corner.

In the spring of 1949 there were three males in the wood, one on the north side and two on the south. A ringed bird, Crimson, held territory in the gardens to the west of the wood (map xii). Three, if not four, of these birds nested successfully, but I was unable to follow the birds' fortunes as closely as in other years. Early in 1950 the wood was almost equally divided between two males, one on the north side, the other on the south.

TERRITORIAL BOUNDARIES

Contrary to what I expected of a bird so fond of thick cover, I found that wide roads do not automatically constitute frontiers as they do for willow warblers (May 1947a). Occasionally boundaries are formed by roads, but commonly they are incorporated in territories. A bird with a large territory will cross a main road to " trail his coat " at a rival and may even build a nest within a few yards of the other bird's ground. I have known a wren invade ground across a wide highway and so dominate a neighbour as to cause him to leave (p. 73). A territory may include both banks of a river or, in Iceland, extend across a river gorge. Shetland wrens will nest where they have to fly across more than a hundred yards of rough pasture to the main feeding area—a cliff or burn. House wren territories may sometimes include areas on both sides of a road, but for Vigors's wrens open spaces and even trails through brushwood or particularly dense growths of chaparral constitute boundaries (Miller 1941).

In spite of the exceptions mentioned, European wren frontiers are mainly determined by topographical features, though often in a somewhat indirect way. Thus boundaries apparently come into existence, not so much because of some gap in the vegetation—in some instances quite small—as because such a reduction of cover is situated between two areas of relatively dense cover which constitute the citadels of two territories. These places or areas become frontier regions apparently because the wrens on either side find them insufficiently attractive to arouse the determined pugnacity necessary to transgress them and defy the defender on the other side.

A small densely-wooded patch in the midst of sparser growth is seldom or never shared by two wrens, and a thinly wooded area, or even a slight break in the cover, may form a boundary if there is thick cover on either side of it. An opening of only two or three yards between the trees on the west, where a tiny stream flows into Wren Wood, tended to constitute a frontier, and where the stream issues from the wood on the east, in an area with comparatively meagre cover, another boundary was often demarcated in spring or autumn, or at both seasons. Although there are trees and shrubs occupying the ten yards between my neighbour's house and my own, five successive couples of rival males established their territorial limits at this gap between the houses. No doubt this was largely due to friction between the birds becoming concentrated at the opening where they could defy each other. It was here that I witnessed one of the two fights mentioned later (p. 48).

It might seem contradictory that open spaces sometimes constitute boundaries and sometimes do not, and that a river should be included in one territory and a ditch mark the frontier of another, but these apparent anomalies can usually be accounted for when we take into consideration the location of citadel areas as well as breaks in the cover. This aspect of territory has not received sufficient attention. With most species the immediate neighbourhood of the nest, when it is built, becomes the citadel area, but with wrens the situation is complicated by multiple nest-building. None the less, these birds seem to have a tendency to build their first nests of the season in the citadel area—the sector to which they will retreat in autumn when challenged by intruders.

Where domains are contiguous there is apt to be frequent pressure as one of the birds seeks to enlarge his territory at the expense of the other. Across a narrow strip of no-man's-land rivals shout defiance. Such buffer areas are recorded of many species of bird, and also of man, for Darwin (1845) noticed that in Tierra del Fuego neutral tracts existed between the hunting-grounds of rival tribes.

Among birds fighting is greatly reduced through its formalisation or ritualisation. Calls, songs, threat postures and associated adornments have the effect of preventing birds coming to grips, and sometimes are socially and sexually stimulating. What might be described as a buffer-strip, perhaps only an inch or two across, comes into being when two birds menace each other. Territorialism may be regarded as the localisation of formalised defensive posturing and utterances in connection with a specific, consistently guarded area, which may be separated from another territory by a buffer-strip corresponding to the threat distance between two defiant birds. These two types of buffer-area merge when birds at a lek, or social display arena, threaten each other from stances separated by a short distance. When this distance between territories is reduced to a minimum, as on a ruffs' " hill," visual demonstrations predominate over vocal threats (Armstrong 1947). On the other hand, territorial birds with domains sufficiently large and endowed with cover in which they spend most of their time out of the sight of rivals, tend, like the wren, to have highly developed songs or calls.

In general, territories surrounded by others are smaller than those with a frontier on one or more sides unmenaced by rivals. When birds, such as robins (Lack 1946a), wren-tits (Erickson 1938) and wrens are relieved of the necessity to defend the whole perimeter they are naturally able to conduct offensive and defensive operations advantageously against rivals, and so secure unusually large territories.

THE PATROLLING OF THE TERRITORY

In the breeding season wrens patrol their territories, sometimes with remarkable regularity, singing as they go, and from time to time visiting, inspecting and titivating their nests. I have taken advantage of this trait in setting traps and lying in wait for birds I wished to ring. Gait (1946) was able to secure his photographs of a male (Pl. IIIb,

p. 109) by placing his camera in position twenty minutes before one of the customary visiting hours, which were at 06.00, 10.00, midday and 16.00.

Early in the year, as I have already mentioned, male wrens are particularly active in their territories, singing for a short time in one place and then flying some distance across the domain to sing again. The Iceland wren also behaves in this way. Keeping in touch with the movements of a male in the half-mile of birch scrub about which he roamed taxed the hearing and agility of my two companions and myself. This bird sometimes sang as much as 500 yards from the point at which he had previously been noted, and just when the observer most strategically placed had reached a point of vantage close to where the wren had settled, the song would again be heard far away. This procedure may be of advantage to the species in enabling the male to make his presence known to wandering females throughout an extensive area and thus attract them to his domain. It may correspond to the wide-ranging song-flights characteristic of many waders.

TERRITORY AND THE FEMALE

Among passerines the male usually has more strongly developed territorial impulses than his mate. When both defend the territory commonly male defies male and female defies female. Such behaviour was first recorded of the solitaire (*Pezophaps solitarius*) which became extinct about 200 years ago (Leguat 1708; Armstrong 1953c). In some species, of which the wren is one, the female leaves territorial defiance to the male. Indeed, she seems unaware of territorial boundaries. A female wren may become attached to a congenial locality and remain there even when the male who has been courting her moves his territory (p. 105), but she does not defend the area, so it cannot properly be styled territory. Very rarely she may manifest some kind of territorial behaviour, such as song (p. 91), and some females will defend the nest, and perhaps a tiny area around it, against a putative intruder, as shown by their attacking a mounted specimen placed near to it. Marples (1940) describes a somewhat confused situation in the course of which the female apparently defended territory, but he was not quite certain of the sexes of the birds involved.

Female house wrens defend the nest but not the territory. They have little knowledge of the frontiers demarcating the male's holding. When two males were competing for another male's territory and mate before eggs had been laid, the female's mate led her to another territory, displacing the owner. In another instance when two males exchanged territories for the second brood the previous partner of one of them rejoined him in the new territory. Female Vigors's wrens have not been observed to take any part in repelling intruders on the male's ground, but they must know its boundaries as they do not go outside. The female constantly accompanies her mate and thus has ample opportunity to learn the extent of his freehold (Miller 1941).

SURREPTITIOUS TRESPASSING

Now and then a cock wren may be detected sneaking into a neighbour's territory. He utters no sound and probably is able to avoid a contretemps with the proprietor by exploring a sector away from where the latter is advertising his presence by song and calls. Perhaps on such scouting expeditions a bird may notice roosting places to be sought in winter when territorial boundaries are openly transgressed. Similar quiet reconnaissances are undertaken by house wrens. Marsh tits (Southern and Morley 1950) and, no doubt, other passerines, also become silent when they trespass.

EXPULSION FROM TERRITORY

A wren may be dispossessed of his territory by gradual usurpation or by more or less abrupt domination and eviction (p. 74). We have already noted that from mid-July onwards encroachment is usually gradual as none of the birds, old or young, is in full vigour. Earlier in the season resistance, as a rule, is stronger and the break-down of defence, when it occurs, tends to be more precipitate and drastic. As territorial altercations are usually carried on vocally the procedure involved will be discussed in the next chapter.

Most mornings in 1945 I had occasion to pass along a lightly-wooded area divided by a stream from a large meadow. Early in the year there were three birds in occupation. On 3 May I found that the centre bird's territory was being threatened with invasion from both sides. A week later further encroachments had occurred, so that his territory had become one of the smallest I have recorded—about one acre. He was involved in vigorous song duels. On the 22nd he had been pushed into a yet smaller wooded patch and he and one of his neighbours were building. Three days later the aggressor to the east was seen accompanying a newly-fledged brood; and the aggressor to the west and their victim were adding to their nests. The dominated bird was found with a fledged brood on 6 June, and it was then apparent that he had been concentrating on the defence of the fragment of his territory in which the nest was situated. On 27 June he had disappeared, and one of his adversaries had appropriated the whole of his domain. Thus, after the young had been reared to independence, he capitulated. In mid-July his vanquisher was being forced by another intruder to occupy a smaller domain. Such evictions are not unusual where wrens are numerous.

A remarkable account of a Carolina wren's intrusion into the territory of a breeding pair is given by Laskey (1950). When the birds were feeding nestlings six days old another male appeared. He began singing in the male's territory, courting the female and piling nesting-material on the young birds. The male of the breeding pair was so intimidated that he seldom brought food to the nest. The intruder was trapped and deported (p. 21), but if his activities had not suffered interference he might have mated with the resident female. It is suggested that this bird had established himself in a territory early in the year, but owing to Carolina wrens being decimated by the previous exceptionally severe winter had been unable to secure a mate, and so had wandered about until he found a territory where he was able to dominate, though not to expel, the resident male.

Among passerines the most usual type of territorial altercation is, of course, boundary pressure. Forceful intrusion such as that by the Carolina wren is much less frequent, but unmated redstarts and robins without domains are sometimes extremely persistent in trespassing on the territories of established birds (Buxton 1950).

Threat Display and Fighting

The wren's intimidatory display need be only briefly mentioned here as it is not elaborate and is alluded to in other contexts. Threats are mainly vocal, and so far as threat posturing is concerned, the principal activity is a quick flipping in and out of the wings, varying from a mere twitch to raising them vertically (Pl. III, p. 109). Such behaviour is seen when a territorial dispute reaches a vehement pitch and the birds approach each other, moving actively from twig to twig. Flipping, however, is an expression of various kinds of excitement and may be performed when a wren—usually a male—is alarmed, or even during courtship. A thoroughly excited bird darts from this perch to that, stands at times with legs at full stretch, as if on tiptoe, cocks high his tail and erects the plumage nearly all over his body. Such enlargement of the contours in threat display is, of course, characteristic of many organisms, vertebrate and invertebrate. Songs and calls usually accompany these demonstrations.

It is unusual for a male to pursue another in flight, and when this happens the chase is brief as both are apt to alight to call, sing and posture. Once when two wrens were close together, engaged in a song duel, the defending bird sang frequent, broken passages of subsong and displayed as to a female, pirouetting with fluttering wings on a pollard willow—apparently a form of displacement activity (p. 285). I have seen analogous posturing by a nuthatch frightened at the nest. Willow warblers also flap their wings in displacement courtship display, sometimes after the adversary has disappeared (May 1947a; 1949). An Iceland wren continued to display after the female had flown away.

When the attention of a cock Hebridean or Shetland wren is attracted by a strange object he sometimes crouches low with partially spread and depressed tail in what may be a threat attitude. It is rather similar to the threat attitude of the house wren and also bears some resemblance to the soliciting posture of the female wren (Fig. 17, p. 130). The male house wren " intently watches every movement of the other, flattens himself out on a branch, erects his back feathers, lowers his tail almost vertically and fans it out, and partially spreads or droops his wings " (Kendeigh 1941). I have seen a male European wren, excitedly regarding his mate as she foraged for the fledged young, assume repeatedly a somewhat similar attitude, though without flattening himself on his various perches.

Apparently the prairie marsh wren's posturing in courting the female and threatening a male are somewhat similar. In courtship he perches a foot or two above the object of his attentions and, in addition to erecting his plumage, cocks his tail over his back so that he resembles a ball of feathers; in threat display the fluffing of the plumage follows a challenging song and is succeeded by a dash at the intruder.

Despite William Turner's statement quoted at the head of this chapter, fighting between wrens, as distinct from skirmishing with menacing postures, is rare. On one occasion, when I was experimenting with a mount, a cock wren, with his plumage standing on end, twice bumped the dummy with his breast after singing frenziedly at it. He was apparently bewildered by the presence of a live female beside the mount. I have witnessed real fighting only on two occasions. The first was during my boyhood in Ireland when I saw two birds grappling with one another fall at my feet from a branch; the second was on 10 September 1949, when two males, after hurling snatches of song at one another, twice scuffled together in the air. Howard (1935) saw wrens, clutching each other, fall at his feet. One of them sang perched on his rival's body. Howard noted that " nothing strange arrested the victor's attention or turned him from his purpose." Mr. R. Perry noticed wrens fighting and singing at one another on 31 August and 2 September, and Major A. Buxton watched a midwinter altercation between two birds on the sea shore. Another correspondent, Dr. B. Campbell, tells me that on 30 November he saw a wren holding another on the ground, pecking it for about two minutes. Both birds held their wings outspread and a very shrill call was uttered, like a shrew's squeak amplified. On 12 September 1944, Williamson (1947a) found two Faeroe wrens sparring, leaping a foot or more from the ground and uttering harsh notes. One bird sang short snatches.

The most remarkable account of fighting between wrens was recorded by Murton (1869). He found two wrens scuffling on an ivy-covered rock and twice captured one of them, placing it under a hat, but when the bird was released the duel was resumed. Challenge notes or songs were uttered between the bouts. The wrens gripped each other's feet and fought with their bills. Apparently this fighting was in connection with the invasion of territory early in the year.

Pursuits and fighting are more frequent among house wrens than wrens. These birds will even destroy each other's eggs and young. They, too, fight with feet interlocked and tumble on the ground so that occasionally they may nearly be captured (Kendeigh 1941). One of the combatants may even be killed (Sherman 1925). Altercations are apparently exacerbated by the presence of the female. This is true to some extent also of the wren's belligerent demonstrations. One of the most serious quarrels I have seen was in October. While the males displayed aggressively, sang and cursed, the female perched on top of a fence looking on, interested but not perturbed. When an altercation is taking place between pale-bellied house wrens three birds may be involved (Haverschmidt 1952). Such situations are by no means confined to wrens. A female spectator has the effect of accentuating assertiveness and the vigour of pugnacious display among organisms as various as spiders (Crane 1949) and human beings.

TERRITORY AND POLYGAMY

I have never known a polygamous wren's mates to lay in nests close to one another when they could choose sites farther apart. In 1947, for example, the two mates of the male Cinnabar occupied nests at diagonally opposite corners of Wren Wood. Where there are two female prairie marsh wrens in a territory they nest as far from each other as possible. In this species the correlation between bigamy and the possession of a large territory is due, according to Welter, to the intolerance of the male's mates. A bigamous male may own a holding nearly twice the size of that held by a bird with one partner. Female house wrens mated to one male do not fight, but sometimes occupy boxes at opposite ends of the territory. Similar avoidance of one another by the two females of one male has been noticed in other species. One of the mates of a Nuttall white-crowned sparrow defended a subdivision of his domain against his other mate (Blanchard 1936, 1941), and the partners of a robin appropriated separate portions of his territory (Lack 1939a). However, occasionally two female robins mated to one male nest close to one another (Shepperd 1953). Antagonism between mates of bigamous males has also been recorded of the pied flycatcher, blackbird, starling and Montagu harrier (Haartman 1951; Kochs 1935; Freitag 1936; Dent 1939). Each of the two mates of a great reed warbler would not allow the other to approach her nest (Kluijver 1949). The mates of a red-winged blackbird tolerate each other when nesting is under way but repulse visits to the nest (Nero and Emlen 1951). Mutual toleration is probably much less frequent, but sometimes occurs among American robins, song sparrows, spotted flycatchers, mute swans and white storks (Brooks 1932; Nice 1943; Gosnell 1949; Ringleben 1936; Ellis 1936; Dewar 1936; Hoffmann 1935). When two female birds use the same nest they may co-operate in rearing the young, but no instance of wrens doing so has been recorded. Greenshanks may lay in the same nest or close together, but in this species the breeding and feeding territories may be separate (Nethersole-Thompson 1951).

Kendeigh's data provide some evidence that bigamous house wrens tend to own relatively large territories. The only bigamous male known to have attempted to secure a third mate held the largest territory shown on his maps, and there is no instance of a bigamous bird possessing an unusually small domain relative to those of neighbouring contemporaries. Non-breeding house wrens, mostly first-year birds, hold the least favourable areas, and four out of six unmated males had small territories. As females were seen to visit such males without remaining to breed a correlation is evident between reproductive vigour and size of territory. A male holding .08 of an acre did not secure a mate until late in June. As the prairie marsh wren nests in a more homogeneous type of habitat than either the wren or the house wren the relationship between area of territory and number of mates is most apparent in this species. Kluijver (1949) found that bigamous great reed warblers held favourable territories and sometimes had unmated birds as neighbours.

While data are insufficient to show whether the average territory of a polygamous European wren is larger than that of a monogamous bird there are some indications that this may be so. Undoubtedly there is a correlation between the nature and size of territory and reproductive vigour. Thus while the strongly polygamous Dutch male

No. 42 possessed a very favourable domain, another male, No. 23, was driven out of his small estate and then established a new territory in a rather unsuitable location. He did not secure a mate. Next year he enlarged his domain and eventually paired, but only after his neighbour, No. 42, had secured three partners.

There is evidence from various other species that breeding failure is commonest among young birds and that mature birds crowd out yearlings from the most suitable habitats. Haartman (1951) found that every polygamous pied flycatcher in his study area was at least two years old. About 50 per cent of the one-year-old males remain unpaired but only 10 per cent of the older birds do not find mates. A first-year bird acquired two females, but after they had begun to build they departed. Eventually the male raised a brood with another female. Only a small proportion of first-year collared flycatchers are polygamous (Löhrl 1949).

An already-mated prairie marsh wren fought another male for a female and the area where she had settled, and so secured two mates and a large territory before his adversary had paired. In 1946, as we have seen, the two males sharing Wren Wood were expelled in succession by the intruder White-leg, who eventually secured three mates.

Winter Territory

Lack (1946a) considers that the winter territory of the robin has no useful function and May (1947b) is of the same opinion in regard to the mute swan's winter territory. The arguments advanced are not convincing, for they do not take adequate account of territory as an area facilitating functions other than feeding, such as the maintenance of the pair-bond and roosting. The winter territory of the wren has an important rôle. Its functions are as follows: (1) A wren maintaining his breeding territory, or part of it, in winter, is able to use some of his nests for roosting and has the advantage over a newcomer of being familiar with other snug nooks suitable as sleeping places. (Bewick wrens which hold territory throughout the year roost in cavities and scold other hole-nesting birds which investigate the holes (Thomas 1946). Thus these birds defend their roosts to some extent.) (2) A bird in an area with which it is familiar can find food in winter more readily than a newcomer. That birds as various as chats and humming-birds establish winter territories indicates a relationship between foraging and defence, for they do so where the food supply is meagre. Swanberg (1951) has shown that the chief importance of winter territory for the nutcracker is as an area in which the bird is familiar

with localities where food is obtainable. Before the winter it caches
nuts where they can be sought later. (3) Wrens maintaining territory
throughout the year are able to begin nest-building earlier, make more
nests and *ceteris paribus* secure more mates and leave more numerous
progeny than late arrivals. Association between male and female in
the territory early in the season offers opportunity for mutual stimulation and pairing-up so that the nesting cycle may be initiated without
undue delay. In some species a direct relationship has been shown
to exist between early breeding and nesting success (Haverschmidt
1949).

CHAPTER 6

SONG AND CALLS

This Bird, in my opinion is a pretty, sweet, dapper
Songster, being of a Nature cheerful; as he is
pleasant to the Ear, so he is to the Eye; and when
he sings cocks up his Tail, and throws out his notes
with so much alacrity and pleasure that I know not
any Bird of its bigness more delights the sense of
Hearing.

NICHOLAS COX, 1678

THE WREN'S SONG shows every gradation from a loud and vehement
clear-cut phrase, through softer, sweeter and more varied subsong
to a very tender, quiet warble, and finally a " whisper song " of
sibilant notes which may be audible no more than a few inches from
the bird. There is also another modification of the loud, stereotyped
phrase—a congested, excited, rapidly delivered utterance which is
heard when two males suddenly meet. This type of song is identificatory and intimidatory. The sweet forms of subsong are heard during
courtship, but whisper song is usually, though not invariably, connected
with " domestic " situations. Fig. 7 gives an indication of the
relationship between, and functions of, these types of song:

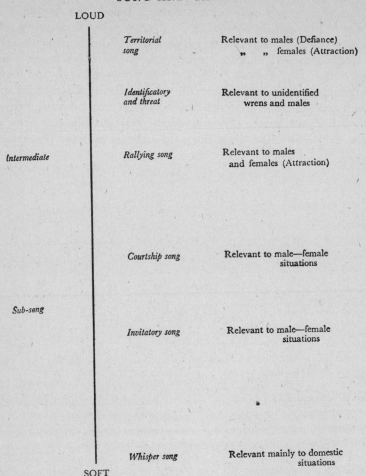

LOUD

Territorial   Relevant to males (Defiance)
song   „   „   females (Attraction)

Identificatory   Relevant to unidentified
and threat   wrens and males

Intermediate

Rallying song   Relevant to males
                   and females (Attraction)

Courtship song   Relevant to male—female
                        situations

Sub-song

Invitatory song   Relevant to male—female
                        situations

Whisper song   Relevant mainly to domestic
                        situations

SOFT

Fig. 7. Diagram illustrating the gradations in volume and corresponding changes in function of the wren's song. It should not be regarded as indicating that whisper song is known to be a modification of territorial song. The volume of each type of song varies considerably.

Pattern

The European wren's well-known, ebullient territorial song is loud, clear and vehement. It impresses the listener as cheerful and, indeed, the Breton name for the wren is " the cheerful one." " The wren never sings except to say it is the best of all possible worlds," wrote Robert Lynd. Viscount Grey's anecdote of the boy at his lessons who complained of " that shattering wren " emphasises the vigour of

FIG. 8. THE SONG OF THE WREN

Musical analysis of the wren's song by Miss Gladys Page-Wood based on what may be distinguished in the song of the living bird by the human ear. It will be noted that transcription No. 3 bears the closest resemblance to the sound spectrogram (Fig 9).

The method of transcription is that suggested by M. E. W. North (Cf. *Ibis* 92: 99-114). The octaves are numbered from the lowest to the highest perceptible to the human ear, middle C being the first note of octave 5. The syllables are suggested by, and adapted from, the *Handbook of British Birds* (1: xvii) and the introductory chapter of *Songs of the Birds* by W. Garstang (1923).

I. Characteristic territorial song. Loud, clear and staccato.

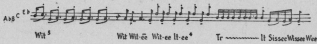

Duration 5 seconds. Speed ♩ = 132. Five songs to the minute. Range Ab8—Eb9 = 7 semitones.

II. A long phrase with some full-toned, canary-like notes. Probably courtship song. Brent Knoll, Somerset. June 1951.

Duration 8 seconds. Speed ♩ = 150. Three songs to the minute. Range C9—Ab9 = 8 semitones. During courtship song there appears to be an appreciable amount of variation in pitch and intervals used by individual birds as well as in the components making up the phrase and the order in which they occur.

III. A sweet, full-toned song. The female was sitting. Cloutsham, Exmoor. May, 1951.

Duration 4 seconds. Speed ♩ = 180. Six songs to the minute. Range G8—D9 = 7 semitones.

The song consists of about seven well-defined components which vary considerably.

1.   Single notes, or notes with scarcely perceptible grace-notes, clear and staccato, uttered a varying number of times, five being common. The pitch varies.

Whit⁵   or   Tee⁵   or   See   or   Wheet

2.   Two notes, generally uneven, but sometimes even, the interval varying. Often uttered five or more times.

lt-ee³   or   lt-ee²   or   lt-y²   or   Whit-ee

3.   A long, rapid trill, length and number of notes varying, often ending with a staccato note of same pitch or higher. It is often uttered at the end of the song.   Tr 〰〰〰〰〰〰〰 lt

4.   A shorter, slower trill, varying in the same way as No. 3. Sometimes it occurs in addition to it, at other times in place of it at the end of the song.   Tr 〰〰〰〰〰

5.   A trill. The interval is often very small.

6.   A halting turn, akin to syncopation.

7.   Two uneven, full-toned notes, the first higher than the second and the interval varying.    Chee-ah²   or   Chee-oo²

8.   A single whistled note is occasionally interpolated in the middle of the phrase.

the song; Grey also aptly suggests the unfinished character of the
phrase by comparing the wren's utterance to the efforts of the lady
who concluded her address at a public meeting with the words, " But
still . . ." and sat down. The high-pitched notes dance up and down,
settling momentarily into a trill two or three times during the phrase,
the number of trills varying according to the duration of the phrase.
The swift delivery makes it difficult to apprehend the exact relationship of the components. Indeed, there are more notes than the human
ear is capable of discriminating. Miss Gladys Page-Wood has kindly
provided the musical analysis of the song on pages 54-55.

Electronic recordings of the winter wren, the American subspecies
most closely resembling our bird in appearance and song, show that
there are about 130 notes in its phrase of 7.6 seconds although the ear
only registers thirty to fifty notes (P. P. Kellogg, *in litt.*; Saunders
1929; Brand 1938).

The wren's normal phrase occupies five to six seconds with five
to six seconds pause after each, so that a bird in full song averages
five to six phrases per minute (Armstrong 1944). The song phrases
are usually shorter in winter than in summer and the final trill is
often lacking, although even in spring and summer it may sometimes
be omitted. The Hebridean and Shetland wren's phrases are also
variable, but typically of about five to six seconds' duration, and the
majority of the Iceland wren's songs are within the range of four to
seven seconds, though longer and shorter phrases are frequent.

The frequency distribution of the wren's song intervals—defined
by Clark (1949) as the time between the commencement of successive
phrases—was studied throughout five days in successive months (Fig
10). He found that curtailed songs of less than five seconds formed
about seven per cent of the songs uttered and only six out of 4,500
were of more than fifteen seconds' duration. The shortening of the
song-interval of curtailed songs is probably due to the abbreviation
of the song itself rather than variation between the end of one song
and the beginning of the next. Various factors influence the duration
of the rests between songs. In February they are sometimes rather
short, and later in the year when birds sing as they flit here and
there picking caterpillars from the leaves their songs are naturally
less regular than when the song is uttered again and again from a
perch during the song-peak hours in May and June.

According to my observations the Iceland wren's pauses between
songs are more irregular than those of the Shetland or European wren.
This impression may be due to peculiarities in the songs of the birds
I heard, but perhaps the irregularities may be an adaptation to the

greater diurnal " spread " of song during the prolonged daylight near the Arctic Circle.

Pitch

Wren song notes are of very high frequency. Brand (1938) has shown that Nicholson and Koch's calculation of between 3000 and 5100 cycles per second is probably an under-estimate attributable to the deficiencies of the recording apparatus. Even so, among British birds, only the wood warbler and grasshopper warbler (Weisman 1950) are known to exceed these frequencies, and of the 58 North American species whose songs were analysed by Brand (1935) only four surpass the maximum of about 8775 cycles of the winter wren. This bird's song averages about 4000 cycles—the highest note of the piano.

Volume

In good conditions a wren may certainly be heard at 600 yards, but this cannot be the extreme range. St. Kilda wrens are audible at least half a mile away and Hebridean, Shetland and Iceland wrens may be heard at a great distance when the bird is perched on or near a cliff which reflects the sound, but possibly the European wren's song is more powerful than the songs of these birds. The difficulty in assessing the relative loudness of the utterances of the different races is due to their being subject to much variation of volume as well as the damping or amplifying effect of the surroundings. Close at hand, as when a wren perches on the naturalist's hiding-tent, his utterance, like that of the pale-bellied house wren, " can be felt on the ear-drums as a physical impact " (Belcher and Smooker 1937). I can endorse this description of the latter bird's song as a pair nested in my bedroom in Trinidad. The Chippewa Indian name for the house wren signifies " a big noise for its size."

Attitude during Song and Flight-Song

The wren's tail is not always cocked while singing but only when the bird is excited, as, for example, by the intrusion of a human being, the appearance of some strange, suspicious-looking or potentially dangerous object or creature, during disputes with a rival or when a female arouses sexual interest (Pls. III and IV, pp. 109 and 116). The house wren commonly sings with his tail depressed (Saunders 1929). According to my observations of the Panama house wren the male cocks his tail comparatively seldom. However, the attitude with tail elevated is characteristic to some extent of many wren species. While singing consistently from a perch, as a wren will do in the morning

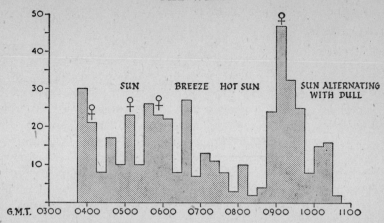

Fig. 9. Histograms showing song output of a wren (Cinnabar.) (a *above*) Number of songs during the morning of 11 May; (b *above, opposite*) total number of songs on 26 May, and (c *below, opposite*) total number of songs on 4 June. The vertical scale shows the number of songs per quarter-hour. The sign ♀ on (a) and (b) indicates that the male and female were known to be close to one another. No correlation between song output and weather changes is apparent

when in an ardent state, he turns his head from side to side so that the sound is broadcast far and wide. Birds as different as the nightjar and grasshopper warbler act thus. A singing wren's yellow gape is clearly visible but, contrary to many artists' conceptions, the tongue is not exposed (Pl. iii, p. 109).

Occasionally, especially when in the " stimulated " phase or period of fullest song, the European wren will sing in flight as he goes a short distance from one perch to another. Probably this is true of all races, as well as of such other species as the house wren (Brackbill 1948), pale-bellied house wren, prairie marsh wren and Costa Rica banded wren (Skutch 1935). As we shall see, the flight-song of the Shetland wren, and perhaps also of the Hebridean, has a special significance in the nest-invitation ceremony. Flight-song seems to play a more important part among the insular races than among European wrens.

Seasonal Song

The European wren is sometimes given rather more credit for persistent songfulness than is his due. *Nulla dies sine linea* is an exaggeration except when the winter is mild and wrens numerous. Gilbert White's comment: " All the year, hard frost excepted," is apt in that there is no day when one may not hope to hear a wren, but as Grey

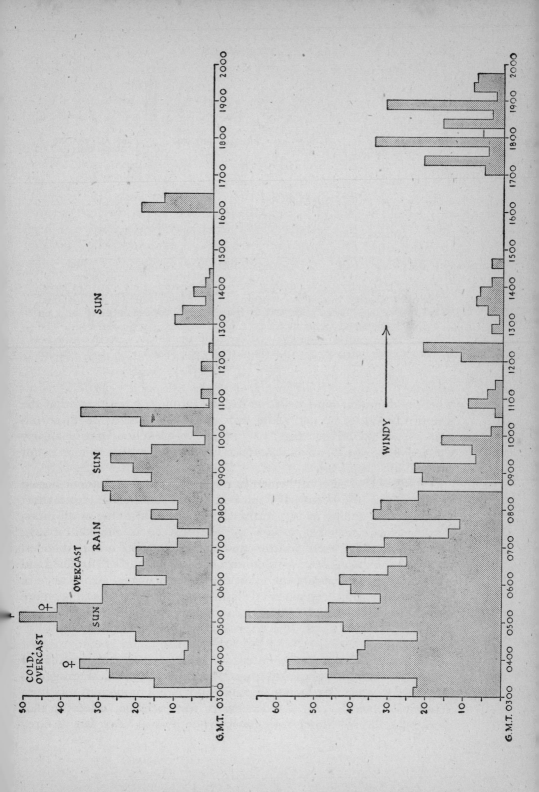

characteristically remarked: "There are times when this is not accomplished without trouble and anxiety." During the winters of 1946-47 and 1952-53 there were periods of several weeks when I did not succeed in hearing a wren, but there were few songless days during the mild winter of 1948-49. On some days in January 1949, there were song duels early and late, and even a little song early in the afternoon. Data sent me by Mr. R. Poulding of Clifton, Bristol, show that in 1943 there were only two weeks—at the end of August—when a wren was not heard on at least one day in the week. In 1944 only one week at the end of January was songless. When the cold weather which inhibits song, except "rallying song" (p. 85), abates, wrens are soon heard again. In spite of ten days' hard weather in January 1945, the first song uttered by Silver (10 February) was only a day later than his first song the previous year when the winter was mild. Alexander (1942) refers to a delay in the recovery of song after severe weather, but in 1947 wrens came into song a few days after the thaw which began on 26 February.

The Annual Cycle of Song

Usually there is little song in January apart from occasional imperfect phrases, lacking in verve, during the day, especially in the morning if the weather is mild, and some rallying songs at dusk, if it is severe. Individuals vary. Although the first fortnight of 1950 was mild I never heard a wren, but Mr. E. Mytum tells me of a bird which, on 8 January of that year, sang 200 phrases in two hours in the London area. Occasionally two birds sing for a time, replying to one another, but such behaviour is exceptional until the beginning of March. Favourable weather in February elicits a fair amount of morning song, a song or two in the afternoon, as in mid-January, and a little regular song before roosting. During an inclement February or March the progress of song is retarded, but there is a sudden increase when it becomes milder. Song tends to be inhibited early in February if a couple of frosty days occur, but to persist during a short cold spell in March. With increased temperature the song threshold becomes lower towards the breeding season, as with many other species. If the weather is relatively warm in March there is intermittent singing for two or three hours in the morning, an increase in the evening output and a general advance towards day-long song. About the middle of the month song becomes fairly frequent in the afternoon. Throughout this early period of the year there is a tendency for several songs to be uttered in close succession and then for silence to be maintained for some minutes. By March the phrases are loud and clear, and towards

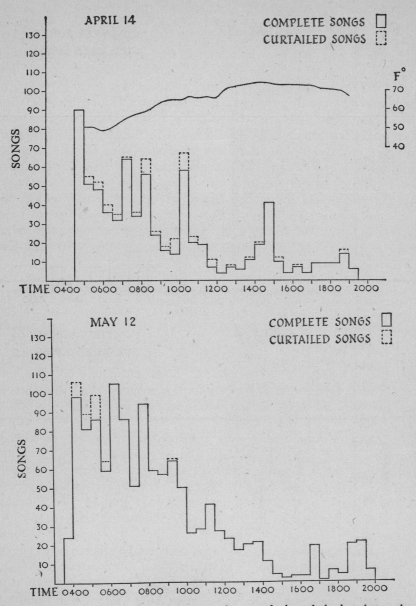

Fig. 10. Histograms showing song output of a wren during whole-day observations in April, May, June, July, and August. The vertical scale indicates songs per half-hour. (*After Clark 1949*)

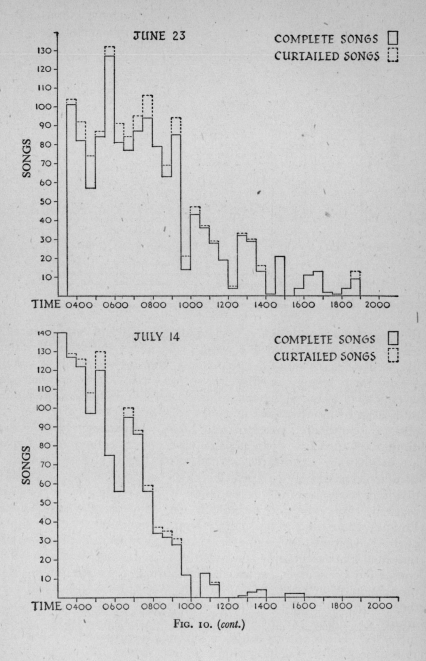

FIG. 10. (*cont.*)

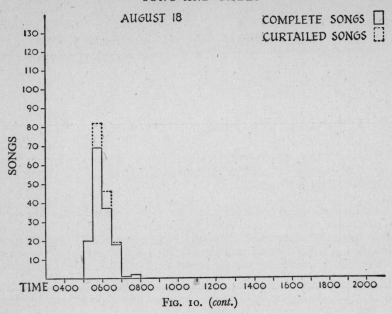

FIG. 10. (*cont.*)

the end of the month, when nest-building has begun, song is in every way well developed. As the wrens' vehemence increases they tend, like birds of many other species, to sing from higher points of vantage —sometimes as high as fifty feet, or even, in an exceptional case, seventy feet. In April there is still more territorial song and often much broken and subdued courtship song (p. 89), but on days when the birds are building the output is reduced. Apparently there is some diminution in May, when nest-building continues and most females are incubating, or, towards the end of the month, feeding young. It is difficult accurately to assess the output of song at this stage as individuals vary according to the phase of the breeding cycle they have reached, their diligence as builders and their fortune with females. Probably there are two peaks in the wren's song output at the inception of the two broods, but owing to polygamy and multiple nest-building this situation has become somewhat obscured. The evidence will be considered presently. In June many birds reach their highest daily production of song and a few young wrens begin to sing at the end of the month. During July song decreases and deteriorates, and some adults go almost out of song, but the number of juveniles singing increases. The moult in August is accompanied by an abrupt diminution of song, so far as most adults are concerned, but the birds of the year frequently utter their broken ditties, mainly during the hour and

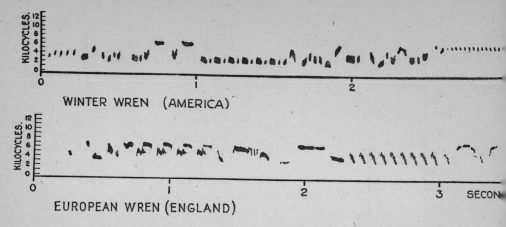

WINTER WREN (AMERICA)

EUROPEAN WREN (ENGLAND)

FIG. 11. (*cont.*) Note that the sound spectrogram and the oscillograph recording (Fig. 12) of the
half consists of five components. The first half is higher pitched and the two high, prolonged

Comparison between the two sound spectrograms suggests that the European wren's co
of five main components, each involving reiterations. The effect given by the winter-wren's s
greater speed of the winter wren's song and the higher pitch of the second half conveying an in

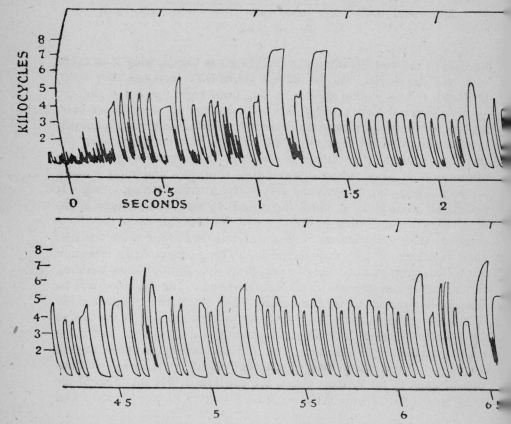

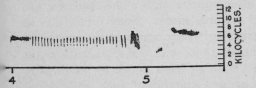

FIG. 11. Sound spectrograms prepared by Dr. W. H. Thorpe of songs of (above) eastern winter wren and (below) European wren. The recording of the winter wren's song was made by Dr. P. P. Kellogg.

song show that, with some modifications, the second half of the song repeats the first half. Each recur in the second half. The central and final trills are closely similar. corresponds to the first half of the winter wren's song. It will be noted that the former consists more warbling and less mechanical than the European wren's would seem to be due to the greater variability.

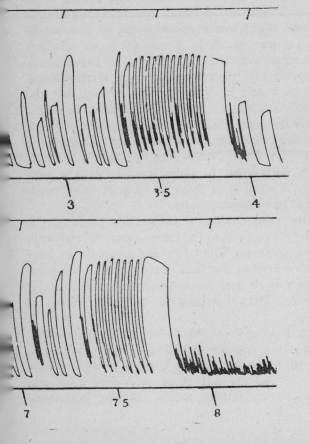

FIG. 12. Oscillogram of the song of the eastern winter wren prepared by Dr. W. R. Fish from a tape recording by Dr. P. P. Kellogg. The vertical scale indicates frequency in kilocycles, the horizontal scale duration in time. Amplitude is not shown. Note the similarities between the first half of the song (above) and the second half (below.) Comparison with the sound spectrogram of another song by the same bird (Fig. 11) shows that the song-pattern is closely similar. For technical details of the method employed and an oscillogram of Bewick's wren's song see the paper by Dr. Fish in *Condor*, 55: 250-257

a half after sunrise. This may continue until about the beginning of October when song becomes bolder and clearer, though still incomplete. It may be heard occasionally in the afternoon as well as the morning. Territorial rivalry at this season stimulates song and calls. In November, if the weather is open, there is little change: wrens are heard for about half an hour after sunrise and a few phrases are uttered in the late afternoon and towards sunset. Song diminishes in December, but even when it is freezing wrens occasionally engage in song duels. At 15.30 on 21 December 1950, with the temperature just above freezing, I watched a wren dashing from perch to perch after another. He uttered vigorous, congested snatches of song while doing so, and after driving off his adversary sang in flight on his way to a hedge-bottom to feed. Thus even in midwinter there may be vigorous defence of territory.

As a group wrens tend to have a protracted period of songfulness. In the thirteenth century Albertus Magnus noted that wrens sing during cold weather in winter. Hebridean, St. Kilda and Alaska wrens also sing during the winter (Dixon 1888; Heath 1920), but apparently Japanese wrens do not (Jahn 1942), and Shetland wrens are not usually heard in December and January (L. S. V. Venables, *in litt.*). There is only one record of an Iceland wren singing in the snow (Faber 1822). Such reduction in song probably implies reduction in territorialism. In Anatolia wrens may be heard in November (Kummerlowe and Niethammer 1934). Carolina wrens sing virtually all the year round (Saunders 1948b). It may be that, like some tropical species of wren, they remain paired from one breeding season to the next. More than all other birds of the American tropics wrens sing throughout the year (Skutch 1940b). This is correlated, in some species, with a long breeding season either in the sense of as many as three or four broods in succession or a wide spread of nesting dates.

The song-charts or histograms enable the maturation of song to be considered in more detail. They refer to the male Cinnabar and show the number of songs uttered during some morning hours on 11 May 1947, as well as complete records of this bird's singing on 26 May and 4 June. The incomplete record was obtained by Mrs. H. L. K. Whitehouse; the whole-day data by both of us taking turns of observation.

An attempt to obtain a song-chart on 1 August was frustrated owing to the meagreness of the bird's song output. Watch was kept from well before dawn until 13.00 and during that time phrases were heard around 04.25 (11), 05.00 (4) and 06.20 (1). The male was diligently helping his mate to feed fledged young—at times surpassing her in the number of visits to them. The correlation between reduction of song and accentuation of concern for the young is evident. The abridged chronicle of this bird's doings during the breeding season of 1947 (p. 164) will enable the reader to compare the progress of his breeding activities with his song output as depicted in the histograms.

The data show an increase in song to a maximum in June and a rapid decline in July to a minimum in August. They also indicate that, as the song impulse declines, singing tends to be concentrated mainly in the morning hours. We have already noted that there is increasing song from March to April. Probably owing to 1947 being a late season Cinnabar's breeding-cycle was a week or more behind the average, and we may be justified in regarding the histograms of 11 May as more typical of the end of April.

If the histograms constructed by Clark (1949) from data obtained in 1946 on one day each month from April to August are compared with my records there is seen to be considerable agreement. Cox's histogram (1944) based on the number of birds heard singing during twenty-five-minute walks, morning and evening, shows an April peak subordinate to that in June and a trough in May. His results must have been affected by the alteration in recording times in April from Summer Time to Double Summer Time, but perhaps not very materially if the high song-peak at the beginning of the bird's day does not develop until towards the end of May. Apart from the May trough his histogram agrees substantially with those obtained by Clark, Mrs. Whitehouse and myself. Further observations are needed to determine whether this trough is characteristic or whether song increases until June.

This matter is of interest in connection with the evolution of polygamy. In many species the males go out of song or greatly reduce the output when the young hatch, if not earlier in the nesting cycle, but there is often a recrudescence when the second brood is initiated. As the European wren is double-brooded we should expect two peaks of song, one in April and the other in June, as shown in Cox's histogram, but the effect of polygamy and the continued efforts of ardent males to secure additional mates over a long period would be to accentuate song between the two nesting-periods, and reduce the May trough. It may well be found that some individuals sing vigorously in May, but that song-census methods such as those of Cox reveal that in the species as a whole there is at this time a reduction in song, as some of the males are occupied with helping to feed the young. It is significant that there is a marked diminution in the amount of song uttered by the Shetland wren when the young hatch and the

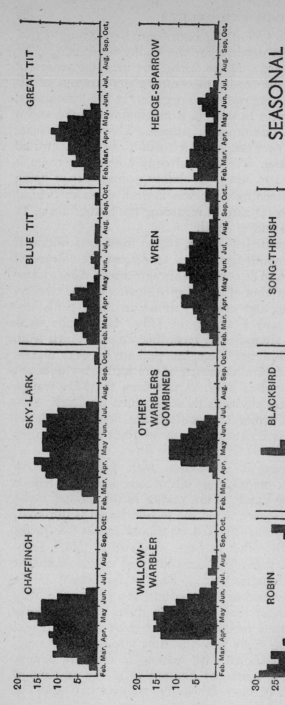

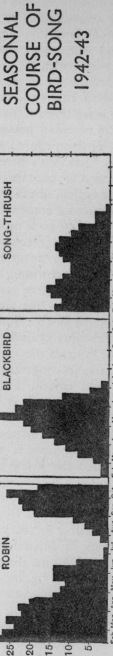

FIG. 13. Histograms showing the variation in the number of individuals of different species singing during daily morning and evening transects from February to October. It will be noted that the wren is the only bird shown to be always in song during this period. (*After Cox 1944*)

male starts to feed them. The male house wren reduces his song-output while feeding nestlings or fledged young, but at the beginning of the second nesting cycle he sings vigorously (Burns 1937). When a male does not assist in feeding the young he comes into song at once. Contrary to the behaviour of many European wrens the male house wren feeds the young in the nest more assiduously than after they have fledged.

On days when a wren is building his song output may be considerably reduced. Rollin (1951) records that a mated bird on 22 June, when building was in progress sang 407 songs. If a male is courting ardently the pattern of the histogram may show unusual peaks and troughs. Thus on 11 May at 09.00 when Cinnabar increased his singing tempo from his previous maximum of 30 to 47 phrases per $\frac{1}{4}$-hour, he was leading a female to one of his nests (No. 5) and so excited that he sang in flight and pounced on her. The complexity of his activities that day is indicated by some further details. At 05.14 and 05.29 he visited and stayed some time in nest No. 5, and at 06.55 the female, Silverband, whom earlier he had been enticing to enter, did so, and then brought some feathers to line it. At 07.02 and 07.45 he again inspected it. Nest No. 4 to which he led the female at 13.00 was in another part of his domain. This female later laid in Nest No. 5. Cinnabar's other mate, Scarlet, was at this time in process of completing her clutch in No. 6. At 13.30 he spent quarter of an hour adding to nest No. 5. Such varied activities modify the song output to an extent difficult to estimate. Similarly, the considerable outburst of song in the evening of 4 June occurred when Cinnabar was actively chevying Scarlet sexually as she fed the nestlings.

DAILY CYCLE OF SONG

Different species vary greatly in the relative amounts of morning and evening utterance during the seasonal development of song. Not until the song thrush has been in song for a month or two does he add the evening performance, but the blackbird begins with serenades and gradually extends his singing to earlier hours so that after a month it reaches back into the forenoon (Burkitt 1935; Cox 1944).

The peak of wren song is always in the morning, with the possible exception of a few cold days in winter when a bird may be silent in the morning and sing a few signal songs before seeking the roost (p. 278). This is evident from our histograms and is clearly shown in Clark's song-charts. My histograms reveal a minor song-peak in the evening. During most of the year the wren tends to sing a little in the evening, even if it be only a phrase or two.

Many bird activities, including song, show a pronounced morning and evening peak with the evening peak usually lower than that in the morning (Klockars 1941; Palmgren 1932, 1949). The significance of the latter may be as a declaration to rivals before retiring for the night that the territory is occupied. It has been ascertained in regard to a number of passerines, including the wren, that a territory, silent through misadventure to the proprietor, is soon invaded. Moreover, Brown and Davies (1949) observed three episodes in which male reed warblers which did not respond vigorously to the singing of an unmated intruder were deserted by their mates. Thus there is no doubt of the importance of the proprietor's song in keeping a territory inviolate.

ORDER OF BIRD SONG

As a rule, birds which sing their first songs early in relation to other species sing their last songs later, in conformity with the principle, which has been found to be true of many birds, that early risers generally go late to roost, indicating, as will be discussed more fully later (p. 256), that light intensity is the critical factor. Craig (1943) says of the wood pewee that in the first half of the season he sings " progressively earlier in relation to clock time and even in relation to sunrise and morning twilight "; later in the season he sings " progressively later, even in relation to the sun's altitude."

From early times men noticed that some birds are earlier songsters than others. Most species sing before sunrise—the time when dreams are most prophetic, according to Dante:

> *Nell'ora che comincia i tristi lai*
> *la rondinella presso alla matina.*

> What time the swallow pours her plaintive strain,
> Saluting the approach of morning grey.

> *Purg.* ix.3.

The " bird clock " has been described by many naturalists (Allard 1930; Armstrong, in preparation) and it need not be discussed here. In my study of the wren I found this orderly song sequence of practical value. If I dressed quickly on hearing the first robin I could be out of doors in time to hear the first wren.

The place of the wren as a contributor to the dawn chorus is shown in Marples' table (1939b) in which he has estimated the average period before sunrise during several months when various birds are first heard:

TABLE II

SEQUENCE OF MORNING SONG AND VOCALISATION

Species								Minutes before sunrise
Blackbird ..	..	..	..	..	..	..	..	43.76
Song thrush	..	..	..	..	..	..	..	42.73
Woodpigeon	..	..	..	..	..	..	..	42.35
Robin ..	..	..	..	..	..	..	..	34.04
Mistle thrush	..	..	..	..	..	..	..	32.47
Turtle dove	..	..	..	..	..	..	..	27.00
Pheasant ..	..	..	..	..	..	..	..	23.36
Willow warbler	..	..	..	..	..	..	..	22.46
Wren ..	..	..	..	..	..	..	..	21.55
Great tit ..	..	..	..	..	..	..	..	17.44
House sparrow	..	..	..	..	..	..	..	16.62
Bullfinch ..	..	..	..	..	..	..	..	12.50
Green woodpecker	..	..	..	..	..	..	..	12.30
Blue tit ..	..	..	..	..	..	..	..	9.50
Chaffinch	..	..	..	..	..	..	..	8.69
Whitethroat	..	..	..	..	..	..	..	6.66

Not all lists purporting to show the order of song agree, for there are seasonal and individual variations as well as differences in listeners' acuity of hearing, but it will be noticed that the wren is a relatively early riser, though anticipated by birds of the thrush and dove families. My records show that the wren usually precedes the garden warbler, goldfinch and the arising clamour of rooks. The hedge sparrow is heard about the same time as the wren. Out of season anomalies occur; very occasionally in autumn I have heard the wren before the robin.

INTERVAL BETWEEN LEAVING ROOST AND SONG

Like many other birds, wrens tend to sing soon after leaving the roost. As the year advances the interval between flying out and singing diminishes, as the table on page 72 shows:

These observations refer to a single bird, Silver. Another wren sang rather more than six minutes after leaving the roost on 18 November 1944. The anomaly on 10 March 1944, was probably due to the thick ground mist. As there is no correlation apparent between the interval and temperature it would seem that its duration is determined rather by the bird's physiological state and the associated drive than by fluctuations in temperature. The times of cessation of the mocking-bird's evening song during winter and spring show

TABLE III

RELATIONSHIP OF FIRST SONG TO DEPARTURE FROM ROOST

Date	Intervals in seconds before song*	Temperature (°F.)	Weather
10/2/44	120	39	Windy
12/2/44	60	29	Cloudy
4/3/44	30	23	Clear
6/3/44	5	28	Clear
9/3/44	5	32	Overcast
10/3/44	120	29	Misty
22/3/44	5	41	Clear
9/2/45	180	37	Overcast
27/2/45	30	47	Clear
21/3/45	9	37	Clear
28/4/45	10	40	Sleet
17/5/45	16	57	Clear

*The periods are not quite exact as they were estimated by counting seconds. I could not take my eyes from the roosting-place lest, if there were another bird, I might miss its departure.

no significant correlation with temperature (Shaver and Walker 1930).

TYPES OF SONG

In the preceding pages we have been discussing the normal and most frequent form of song—the territorial song. Sometimes the term " advertising song " is used as if it were synonymous. This is undesirable as there are exceptional birds, such as the bearded tit (Koenig 1951), and brown thrasher (Saunders 1942), which utter song having the effect of attracting the female without being in possession of territory. Moreover, there are types of song not linked with territory, for instance, " rallying song " (p. 85), whose function is to advertise the presence and whereabouts of a bird.

The wren's territorial song is the typical, loud, frequent utterance which repels other males and attracts females, but it is modifiable to such an extent, as a means of intimidating individuals of the singer's sex and attracting the opposite sex, that these modifications can be defined as specific types of song. They are to be distinguished as much by the circumstances in which they are uttered as by the degree of modification. Naturally, absolute distinctions between the types cannot be drawn, but the functions they serve in their accentuated forms are so definite that they are best described under separate cross-headings.

DEFENSIVE AND INTIMIDATORY SONG

With song the wren registers his title deeds in the morning, endorses them during the day and confirms them before retiring. During his patrolling, especially in the morning, he often sings on favourite trees or bushes near where his territory adjoins that of a rival. Even when a hundred yards or more of pasture land separate territories the birds perch near the boundaries of their domains and shout defiance. In the breeding season song-duels are frequent, and I have known an intruder disappear from the neighbourhood of a male's territory after the proprietor had withstood him in a vigorous vocal altercation; probably they never saw each other. Similarly, an intruding robin may decamp at the mere sound of an opponent's song (Lack 1939a). Belligerence is thus diverted into vituperation. Birds, such as vireos, which sing a great deal during the summer, seldom fight one another (Sutton 1949).

Song is a weapon of offence as well as defence, but with birds as with men, an absolute distinction between the two functions is seldom possible. Nevertheless incidents may be observed in which the behaviour of the singing birds makes it evident which is the aggressor. Two such episodes may be briefly described.

White-leg, who had successfully driven Yellow-and-Black from the eastern half of Wren Wood (p. 41), was discovered singing tentatively near their common frontier. His rival replied. Suddenly there was a very urgent, prolonged, ringing " churr " from a bush. Yellow-and-Black had been roused. There were some rather subdued and abbreviated songs and another churr from Yellow-and-Black, then a ten-minute song-duel with the birds ten yards apart, mainly counter-singing. White-leg, singing lower in the bushes than Yellow-and-Black, moved gradually away, but a fortnight later he had supplanted his adversary. White-leg's insistent encroachment, rather than the out-come of this or any other altercation, determined the outcome.

Sometimes the dominant wren sings more powerfully than his opponent. A specially vigorous bird may have a particularly loud song, as Kluijver noted. Kendeigh observed that of two competing house wrens the bird which sang most rapidly was the victor, and Conder (1948) found that the most songful goldfinches held the largest territories. Obviously there is a close correlation between song and the possession of a favourable territory.

For some weeks Cherry had been singing in my garden against a

T.W.   F neighbour across the road. One morning I found him, silent and subdued, in a tree on the domain's boundary intently watching his rival, who was behaving in a peculiar fashion. Head in air, tail vertical, wings drooped and quivering, he sang lustily. Had I not known Cherry to be a male I would have supposed this to be some accentuated form of courtship display. I had caught and ringed him while he was building a few weeks earlier. The two birds flew from twig to twig maintaining a distance of two or three feet while the truculent intruder displayed here and there. Cherry's deportment conveyed an impression of curiosity, subservience and " gormlessness." The climax was reached when the excited intruder pirouetted slowly as he sang on one of the topmost twigs of the apple tree with quivering wings outspread and rear feathers fluffed, revolving like a mannequin displaying a gown. Cherry stood as if spellbound; then he retreated and, when he was well into his territory, began to sing. The other went back into his domain over the road, also singing. The next day Cherry was seen courting a female, but before a week had elapsed he vacated his territory. Some weeks later I found him in possession of another piece of ground 400 yards away in the opposite direction to that in which his adversary's territory lay. I have no doubt that his departure was due to intimidation. His rival courted, and I believe secured, the female in whom Cherry had been interested.

Lack (1946a) records three instances in which robins, after being subjected to song-assaults, relapsed into quiet song and then abandoned their freehold to the importunate newcomer.

Mrs. J. C. Maples tells me of an episode in which a wren behaved in a manner resembling that of Cherry's adversary. A hawfinch settled on a bird-bath immediately below a wren's nest and the owner, singing vehemently and with wings outspread, turned a complete circle around the entrance. Two aggressive wrens were seen on a mild mid-February day singing excitedly, " heads in air, wings waving, tails fanned and depressed. They jockeyed around each other at about two feet apart, now facing one another, now turning round apparently displaying the tail, each occasionally singing, both constantly ' ticking '." (M. D. England, in litt.). A wren seen by Mr. D. J. May sang at another with beak and tail high and made clicking sounds with his mandibles.

Pale-bellied house wrens posture in a somewhat similar way. Haverschmidt (1952) saw one singing with drooped wings and beak pointed upwards while another perched silently close by.

Mrs. Aubrey de Selincourt's account may perhaps refer to quarrelling between males rather than courtship (de la Mare 1943):

" The lovely burst of song was suddenly at my very ear. I looked up, startled, and saw them—two wrens. He sang to her, loud and clear. She answered a little softlier (I thought). He crept a little nearer, singing again. She retired a little, answering. . . . It went on for about five minutes. Each time he advanced with his little bouquet of song, she retired, giving note for note, but softlier. Each time they sang, both of them, they pointed their little heads right up to the sky, as if only so could they pronounce the exquisiteness of their rapture. At the end they *both* sang softly. Usually their utterance is sweet and loud and clear, gem-like, unless you admit as song the little inward warbling which the mother-bird makes to herself when she is on the nest."

An ardent male wren will sometimes sing when startled by a person approaching, but the song uttered is the territorial phrase rather than the congested challenge song.

CHALLENGE AND IDENTIFICATORY SONG

Territorial song not only repels rivals and attracts potential mates but also serves to indicate the location, identity, vigour and sex of the singer. Its effect is to call forth response which reveals these particulars in regard to neighbouring males. When phrases are uttered in an accentuated manner directed at a strange bird we have what can best be styled " challenge song." It serves to compel the intruder to reveal his sex, if he is a male, by returning the challenge or fleeing.

Like many other birds in which the appearance of the sexes is similar, wrens distinguish sex by behaviour, not by plumage. A female wren challenged by a male is known as a potential mate by her apparent nonchalance, neither singing nor retreating. In the breeding season a female entering a male's territory may also be identified by her chittering call. Close encounters between wrens occur most frequently in late summer and autumn when newcomers are trying to establish themselves; then snatches of song, spit-hiss calls and other strange notes are heard in the undergrowth.

Challenge song is distinguishable from territorial song by being stifled, congested and somewhat harsh. The songs of fighting robins, blackbirds, song thrushes and many other birds undergo similar modification, as if the birds were choking with rage. This form of behaviour is most readily observed by exposing a mounted specimen where the owner of a territory will see it, or by placing a mirror where the bird can catch a glimpse of his own reflection. A male wren approaches the mount, flipping his wings excitedly, and after uttering one or more brief challenge songs may copulate with it, the reaction being based on the principle that a wren which does not declare itself male must be female. Silence gives consent. As a mirror image, reacted to as an adversary, disappears now and then as the wren hops excitedly around, the thwarted bird, unable to come to terms with his elusive opponent, may intercalate displacement activities such as twig-pecking or bill-wiping with his challenge songs (p. 30).

AMBIGUOUS SONG

I have already referred to the activities performed " out of context," usually in an incomplete or abnormal manner, which are elicited when an animal is thwarted or disconcerted in some way. Such displacement activities are common among birds, rather less prominent in the behaviour of mammals and have been noted among spiders and insects. The difficulty with regard to ascertaining whether some forms of song should be regarded as due to a thwarted drive is that, as so much song has an aggressive element, some of the apparently incongruous utterances of startled birds might be considered expressions of defiance rather than as caused by a conflict of drives. This interpretation can hardly be adopted when the song uttered is that associated with courtship rather than defiance. Thus, after I frightened a wren from an air-raid shelter, to escape from which he had to fly close over my head, he sang a series of subsongs. When a male sings on being released after being ringed the " displacement " character of the utterance is not so clear. The interpretation of some situations is puzzling because the birds themselves seem confused. I have even heard an excited song dueller utter courtship subsong, apparently " in error."

THE EFFECTIVENESS OF TERRITORIAL SONG

The function of the wren's territorial song and its integration with other patterns of behaviour are illustrated by the biography of a male observed by the Dutch students. In 1936 he wandered about without establishing a definite territory, singing seldom and abnormally. Next year he seized a small territory from which he was soon evicted, but he then occupied another whose owner had disappeared shortly before. It was an undesirable wren habitat with little cover; evidently the bird was making the best of what he could get. Although he built one or two nests he failed to secure a mate. During the winter and early spring he again became a nomad and was never heard to sing. In April 1938, however, he settled again in his 1937 territory, enlarged it, built seven nests and at last, in June, secured a mate. Meanwhile a robust neighbour had obtained three mates. Similarly, a prairie marsh wren, forced to occupy a rather unfavourable habitat, was late in pairing. Some first-year house wrens do not breed. They lurk in cover near the territories of established birds and seldom sing. Sometimes one of these birds seizes a small territory for a few days and then relinquishes it. Females often visit birds with small territories but do not stay to breed. These facts suggest that some non-breeding male European wrens may be first-year birds which have not attained full maturity.

Red-leg, who occupied the western end of Wren Wood in the spring of 1946, sang at first in a peculiar wheezy way, though, as usually happens in such cases, after some weeks the song became normal. He built two nests, but was driven out before he was able to obtain a mate. It may be that other males react with more confident aggressiveness against deficient singers, so that, were they inadequate in no other respect, they would be handicapped. Experimental injections of hormone preparations have shown that song, aggressiveness, dominance and territorialism constitute a complex of impulses dependent for their adequate expression on the bird's physiological state and, more particularly, the condition of the endocrine glands. Thus breeding inadequacy may manifest itself in behaviour at different levels, varying from complete absence of some or all of the appropriate activities to a slight deficiency in one or more of them. Such deficiencies seem to be fairly commonly manifested by juveniles. Howard (1920, 1929) observed that of three reed buntings the bird which sang imperfectly was not the last, but the second to pair, and that a yellowhammer came into full song only after his mate had laid her eggs. He argues from such data that song variations exercise no influence on the course of pairing, but, so far as wrens and house wrens are concerned, the evidence is in the contrary direction. In connection with the attractiveness of the house wren's song for the female, Kendeigh remarks: " The male, whose song is most stimulating to her ears, would seem to have the advantage." In both species it is noticeable that the presence of a female often accentuates the song-rivalry of neighbouring birds. It has sometimes seemed to me that when a wren was heard uttering his courtship song a rival was aroused to more vigorous territorial song.

We know that in some species, notably the southern cormorant, deficient posturing is a handicap, for the female tends to pair with the male exhibiting the most vigorous display (Kortlandt 1940). A female heron will pass from one to another of three displaying males, her behaviour suggesting that she is influenced by the effectiveness of the potential mate's performance (Verwey 1930). We have already noted that a reed warbler will desert her mate for a rival singing more vigorously (p. 70). Apparently, imperfection either in display or song reduces a bird's chances of mating. Thus male rivalry is not only for territory but for a partner (Armstrong 1947). Howard's belief that the young are not at a disadvantage in securing territory as compared with the adults is incorrect.

COUNTER-SINGING, ANTIPHONAL AND UNISON SONG

The vocal duels of European wrens often consist of counter-singing, the phrase of one bird being uttered in the pause after the other bird's phrase (Marples 1939a; Armstrong 1944). Hebridean, Shetland and St. Kilda wrens, and no doubt wrens of other races, also sing in this manner. Owing to the phrases and pauses not being exactly equal the birds frequently get " out of step." Then one may desist for a short space and begin again in alternation. It is as if a wren liked to be able to hear his rival replying. Such song is not unusual among birds which sing clear-cut phrases. The domestic cock, for example, waits a few seconds before replying to a rival and so an orderly alternation is maintained.

In order to make a distinction between the type of territorial song just described and responsive song in which mated birds are involved, I suggest that this inter-sexual song be called antiphonal. It occurs principally among forest-dwelling and nocturnal species, particularly those which remain paired from season to season (Armstrong 1947), and is well developed among tropical wrens. Male and female of some species time their responses so exactly that the duet sounds like a continuous song. Such duets are distinct from the true song of the species (Skutch 1940a, b).

Antiphonal song in the strict sense is not recorded of any species of *Troglodytes*, though when male neotropical or southern house wrens (*T. musculus*) sing exuberantly the female may answer with a shy twitter or trill (Skutch 1940a). The two sexes of Cabanis's wren (*Thryothorus m. modestus*) duet antiphonally, one singing *chean, cheery* and the other *gwee*. The rufous-tailed wren (*Thryothorus mystacalis ruficaudatus*) (Beebe 1950) and Galbraith's wren (*Thryothorus leucotis galbraithii*) are also fine duettists. Lawrence's song wren (*Leucolepis phaeocephala lawrencii*) pipes seven or eight vibrant notes, rising in pitch, while the responding bird, presumably the female, chuckles *cutta, cutta, cutta* . . . (Chapman 1930). The female Chiriqui or highland wood wren (*Henicorhina leucophrys collina*), singing in the nest, responds to her mate. The two birds sing back and forth, but are rather casual in timing their replies to one another (Skutch 1940a). Other species of the genus *Henicorhina* also sing duets (Fuertes 1916). White-bellied wrens (*Uropsila leucogastra*) are also duettists, and both male and female sing after copulating (Sutton 1948). The complementary songs of male and female tawny-bellied spotted-throated wren (*Thryothorus rutilus hyperythrus*) make up a continuous refrain, but male and female hooded or rufous-naped cactus wrens (*Campylorhynchus rufinucha capistratus*) sing so perfectly in unison that it is difficult to believe two birds are involved. The sexes of the Chiapas cactus wren (*C. rufinucha chiapensis*) and the banded cactus wren (*C. zonatus*) also sing together (Skutch 1935, 1940a; Dickey and Van Rossem 1938). The cock *C. bicolor* gurgles, "Keep your feet wet," and his mate perched a few inches away sings, "What d'you care?" (Fuertes 1916). Such responsive songs evidently play an important part in maintaining contact between the birds.

A Comparison of Wren Songs

Although comparative estimates of bird song are notoriously subjective, and there are discrepancies and contradictions between different naturalists' descriptions, the generalisation may be made that whatever minor differences exist the song of *Troglodytes troglodytes* is identifiable as such in any part of the world by a practised observer.

Apart from the variability of song according to function individual idiosyncrasies are noted occasionally. I have already mentioned Red-leg's wheezing song (p. 77). Another Cambridge bird began his song for some weeks with a trilled reiteration of a single note resembling a great tit's, simulating an electric bell. Individuals in Cumberland, Lundy and elsewhere have been heard uttering a song incorporating a chatter like that of a sedge warbler (R. Perry, *in litt.*). Turner (1929) noticed a Sutherland bird piping a ditty which seemed to be a mixture of blackcap and linnet song. A wren in Abernethy Forest in the Grampians uttered a chirrupy phrase which I thought might be a geographical dialect, until three weeks later I heard a similar song in Suffolk. Late in the season it is not unusual for birds to sing a-typically.

The Hebridean wren's song includes a remarkable reel which renders it the most distinctive wren song I have heard. It is sweeter and less shrill than that of the European wren. The St. Kilda wren's song differs from both. To my ear, the songs of the Iceland and Shetland wrens bear more similarity to one another than to the song of the European wren, from which they are easily distinguishable. They seem less reiterative and strident. Mr. L. S. V. Venables noticed that the Faeroe wren's utterance was very similar to that of the Shetland bird, and Feilden (1872) thought it louder and more melodious than the European wren's song. Dr. P. Westall tells me no difference can be detected between the song of wrens in England and those of southern Spain. In my notes on the wren in Corsica (*Troglodytes t. koenigi*) I find the comment, " The song seemed sweeter and of higher pitch," but my observations were made before I took a critical interest in the variations of wren song. However, if the song had been highly distinctive I would have made notes to this effect. Trevor-Battye (1913) noted a difference of phrasing in the song of the Cretan race (*T. t. stresemanni*). The song of *T. t. mülleri* in the Balearic Islands is described as weak (Munn 1931), and that of *T. t. juniperi* as vigorous, varied and rich (Hartert 1910).

It would be interesting if racial differences in song could be correlated with the length of time the races have been isolated, but the geological data are inadequate. In the present state of knowledge it would be rash to explain the distinctiveness of the Hebridean wren's song by the survival of the bird in Hebridean refugia during the Ice Age, though the apparently slight differences between the song of the Corsican wren and that of the European wren may, perhaps, be due to a relatively short period of isolation.

The song of *T. t. nipalensis* is said to resemble the phrases of wrens in Pekin and also of the European wren (David and Oustalet 1877). According to Jouy (1883) Japanese wrens (*T. t. fumigatus*) sing exactly like winter wrens while Jahn (1942) considers the song identical with that of the European wren. Probably it differs somewhat from both.

Comparison between the songs of our wren and the winter wren is of special interest because of the probability that the winter wren is close to the (evolved) ancestral stock of the races in Europe and Asia. Some naturalists who have heard both subspecies hold that the songs are similar, but this is incorrect. Comparing the two Burroughs (1895) wrote of the European wren's song:

> It is far superior to our house wren. It approaches very nearly to our winter wren, if it does not equal it. Without hearing the two birds together, it would be impossible to decide which was the better songster. Its strain has the same gushing, lyrical character, and the shape, colour and manner of the two birds are nearly identical. It is very common, sings everywhere and therefore contributes much more to the general entertainment than does our bird.

I have heard an excellent recording of the eastern winter wren's song, kindly sent me by Dr. P. Kellogg. It is more animated and varied, less mechanical and percussive than the song of the European bird and seems more closely akin to the song of the Iceland wren.

The western winter wren is said to sing like the eastern subspecies

(Brandt 1943; Bent 1948). Strangely enough, the song of the Santa Ana rufous-browed wren (*Troglodytes rufociliatus nannoides*) which inhabits the darkest groves of the cloud-forest in Salvador resembles that of the winter wren (Dickey and Van Rossem 1938).

The songs of the various races of Bewick's wren also differ to a noticeable extent.

The house wren's song, which I know from a recording, consists of rapidly repeated notes in a phrase which could not be confused with the wren's, although some similarity is apparent. It lasts only one and two fifths to two and three fifths seconds and is uttered with several changes of pitch (Saunders 1948a). Occasional variants are noticed. The Panama house wren's song impressed me as being sweet and lively, with a trill reminiscent of a canary, as well as some sedge warbler notes. As the bird sings his throat quivers and his mandibles vibrate. Like the European wren he readily breaks off before finishing his song. A few weeks after becoming familiar with the utterance of this bird I was in Trinidad and frequently heard the song of the pale-bellied house wren, but I did not note any difference in the phrases of the two races.

There is immense variety in the songs of the different species of the Troglodytidae. The rufous and white wren (*Thryothorus r. rufalbus*) utters deep hoots like an owl (Dickey and Van Rossem 1938). Some wrens sing clear, separate notes quite dissimilar from our bird's song. The Carolina wren's utterance, known to me also from a recording, is a somewhat variable, bright yodel. The riverside bay wren (*Thryothorus nigricapillus semibadius*) utters clear, ringing notes and the wood wren (*Henicorhina prostheleuca*) " compelling whistles " (Skutch 1946). Passing along a trail in the rain-forest of Barro Colorado Island I was surprised by the loud, urgent oriole-like whistles of the Panama black-bellied wren (*Thryothorus fasciatoventris albigularis*) low down near me in the undergrowth. In such forests the naturalist is impressed by the contrast between the brilliantly-hued but raucous-voiced birds of the canopy and the sober-suited wrens of the low zone with their remarkable songs. He becomes much more readily acquainted with the forest wrens as vagrant voices than as figures in the field of his binoculars. This species and the rufous-breasted wren (*Thryothorus r. rutilus*) I knew by voice alone.

Gould's white-bellied wren (*Uropsila leucogastra*) warbles a faint " dainty, tinkling song " (Sutton and Pettingill 1942). According to Chapman (1930) the bay wren (*Thryothorus nigricapillus castaneus*) is as brilliant a performer as the nightingale, but some of the melodious notes of the chestnut-backed wren (*Thryothorus rufalbus castanonotus*) resemble " a subdued bugle call " (Sturgis 1928). It is a superlative singer. Chapman, after referring to the songs of other species of wren, says of this bird's song:

> But all these songs and calls sank to insignificance before one of the most arresting performances that I have ever heard from the throat of a bird. It was not its volume that commanded one's attention. It was not a loud song; the tone, indeed, was a low contralto; but so full-throated, so mellow, so rich, and the song itself was of such marked musical distinction and executed so flawlessly that it completely dominated the senses.

All naturalists who have listened to the songs of tropical wrens have been immensely impressed by them. Fuertes (1916) wrote: " Perhaps no songs heard in the tropics are so characteristic or make such a strong impression on the mind and desires of a naturalist as these romantic and mysterious wren songs."

The song of the Cayenne wren or organ bird (*Leucolepis a. arada*)* of the Amazonian forests is described as of exquisite beauty:

> Listening, one remains at the same time rooted to the spot as its notes, which can be compared to the sound of a glass bell continuously modulated with the strictest regard to the intervals, are blended into one regular melody, which falls lightly and slowly on the ear from the topmost branches of the trees. There is something so indescribably soft, one might say ethereal, in this bell-music, the charm of which is enhanced by the desert stillness of the broad forest and the invisibility of the excessively small singer (Pöppig 1874.).

Haviland (1926) describes this bird under the name of the quadrille wren:

> The sweetest songster of the Guiana forest, and perhaps in the world, is the quadrille wren which haunts low dark undergrowth. No pen can do justice to its delicious melody, which is neither a whistle nor a warble but has a mysterious finished charm unlike that of any other bird music with which I am acquainted. Clear and deliberate, it suggests some elfin singer, sitting aloof in the dim thicket and improvising on silver panpipes.

Bates (1864) gives this account of the song:

> When its singular notes strike the ear for the first time, the impression cannot be resisted that they are produced by a human voice. Some musical boy must be gathering fruit in the thickets, and is singing a few notes to cheer himself. The notes become more fluty and plaintive; they are now those of a flageolet, and notwithstanding the utter impossi-

*Elsewhere in South America other species of wren may be called " organista " (Zimmer 1930).

bility of the thing, one is for the moment convinced that someone is playing that instrument. . . . The ending of the song is rather disappointing. It begins with a few very slow and mellow notes, following each other like the commencement of an air; one listens expecting to hear a complete strain, but an abrupt pause occurs, and then the song breaks down, finishing with a number of clicking, unmusical sounds like a piping barrel-organ out of wind and tune . . . it is the only songster which makes an impression on the natives, who sometimes rest their paddles whilst travelling in their small canoes along the shady by-streams, as if struck by the mysterious sounds.

Hudson's description in *Green Mansions* of Rima's voice was obviously influenced by the account of the organ bird's song given by Bates and other travellers:

> Its greatest charm was its resemblance to the human voice—a voice purified and brightened to something almost angelic. . . . The blood rushed to my heart as I listened; my nerves tingled with a strange new delight, the rapture produced by such music heightened by a sense of mystery.

In another context Hudson wrote:

> When I listen to Rima's voice . . . I hear . . . the gurgling running water . . . the organ-bird singing far, far away in the shadows of the trees.

There can be little doubt that Rima herself is in large part a transmuted, imaginative embodiment of Bates's account of the enchanting bird voice which Hudson had never heard, representing in female form the idealised Nature which was Hudson's first love.

Beebe (1917) describes one of these birds singing from time to time before returning to incubate. As it is improbable that the male incubates or that the female sings like the male, one must assume that he refers to anxiety utterances rather than song.

VOCAL MIMICRY

Some species of birds utter the normal song without ever hearing another individual sing it, others learn it to a greater or lesser extent by imitating others. The degree to which birds are imitative is therefore of considerable interest.

Although European wrens occasionally sing in such a way as to resemble other species they do not mimic them. Occasional similarities to the song of the hedge sparrow are accidental. The late Hugh Wormald, who reared young wrens in an aviary where they could not hear birds of their own species, told me that they sang typically. As nestlings they might have heard the male, but it is improbable that wrens acquire their song in this way. Saunders (1929) mentions a winter wren which " came very near to singing ' The girl I left behind me,' " but such aberrations should not be regarded as indicating a capacity for vocal mimicry. Bewick's wren is said to be an accomplished mimic (Howell and Oldys 1907), and a bird has been heard uttering the songs of this species and the house wren (Thomas 1943). The closely-related Seattle wren (*Thryomanes bewickii calophonus*) sometimes calls like a chickadee (Pearse 1948). The opinions of American naturalists differ in regard to the imitativeness of the Carolina wren (McAtee 1950). The notes of many species have been detected in the song (Nuttall 1932), but it is doubtful to what extent the similarities are accidental. On the whole, wrens as a group seem little prone to add to their repertoire by imitation.

Exploratory Song

A wren exploring a sector of a newly-acquired territory or investigating some locality in the countryside which might prove suitable in which to establish himself, may utter a subdued warbling rather similar to the courtship song (p. 89), but distinguishable from it, apart from the absence of the female, by lack of excitement in the utterance. He goes along soliloquising sweetly as if too uncertain of unknown hazards to express himself vociferously. With tail horizontal —not erected, as when moved with erotic fervour—he progresses in fits and starts slowly through the undergrowth. On 30 April a wren, White-leg, which had occupied another's territory four days earlier, sang the exploratory subsong as he investigated a corner of his domain, and on 21 September I found a bird warbling in low, sweet tones as he crept tentatively along a hedge in an area offering too little cover to be a permanent wren habitat. I was reminded of a California thrasher which I had seen moving along the ground in the chaparral one day in January singing his rich song.

The behaviour of some other wren species is rather similar. House wrens newly-arrived in their breeding quarters sing imperfectly, but improve quickly in competition with other males. Prairie marsh wrens tend to be silent on their first day in the breeding area while they select and explore a territory. Quiet or incomplete song by birds acquiring territories has been recorded of snow buntings (Tinbergen 1939), Galapagos finches (Lack 1945), and song sparrows (Nice 1937). In some species song reaches perfection more rapidly where competition is intense than in areas where individuals are isolated.

Song of the Young

The young of many species exhibit precocious display, nest-building and other behaviour (Armstrong 1947), and nestling passerines such as the blackcap (Lorenz 1943), oven bird (Hudson 1892), song thrush and dipper (Heinroth and Heinroth 1924-33) have been heard singing. A naturalist who had not paid special attention to the development of wren song would not recognise the first crude jingles of the juveniles, and probably the adults do not respond to them (p. 36). Once I heard a young bird sing a series of very crude songs when accompanied by another juvenile, probably of the same brood. The songs elicited no territorial reactions, though, of course, the companion may have been a young female.

As competition between birds of the year and adults develops the songs of the juveniles graduate from the ejaculation of a few scratchy, splintered notes to a more definite phrase, but for some time these phrases are uttered in quick and irregular succession and vary from loud jingles to sweet subsong. Sometimes the crude gush of squeaky notes resembles the hedge sparrow's song, just as the wren's subsong bears some similarity to the subsong of this bird. Not infrequently the crude songs develop into louder and more typical phrases approximating to what I call the " itty-chee " song uttered from time to time by adults not in full singing form. It is shorter than the usual song, rather slovenly, and contains the phrase after which I have named it.

The young house wren utters an " indefinite warble," and immature cactus wrens warble so quietly that they are inaudible at a distance of more than a few feet (Woods 1948). The songs of young prairie marsh wrens, first heard in August, are squeaky and rasping, " entirely different from those of the adult " (Kendeigh 1941).

The " nonsense songs " of young birds usually differ from territorial song in two respects. They are neither as loud nor as precise and stereotyped in pattern, thus showing negatively that the qualities of territorial song are loudness and distinctiveness.

Rallying Song

During hard weather in winter wrens may be heard in the gloaming chittering and uttering sharp calls or grating notes. Suddenly there rings out from among the trees a song, rather jingly, but clear. A little later one or two other songs are heard and a few sharp notes. Then silence. Unless you know where the roost is situated you may wait until the stars are bright in the frosty sky without seeing or hearing anything more of the birds. If, however, having located the dormitory, you conceal yourself near it one evening you may see the wrens in a scattered party flying to adjacent twigs, teetering here and there, then popping inside.

Birds such as long-tailed tits and pied wagtails which seek a communal roost in company maintain touch by means of call-notes—travel-talk—but the use of song as a rallying signal, especially by such territorial birds as wrens, is surprising. The utterance which was a threat no longer intimidates; the signal of defiance becomes a call to assemble. On a winter evening I have listened to two birds replying to one another in song and then seen one of them fly towards where the other was singing, deliberately entering his song sphere. How is this reversal of function of song to be explained?

Although the rallying song is usually of a rather jumbled pattern compared with the normal phrase it cannot be assumed that, as such, it is recognised by the birds as distinctively different from the territorial song. A similar type of song may be heard occasionally during the day in winter. It sometimes approaches the clarity of spring song. Possibly the reversal of response on the part of the males is due to their reverting to some extent, physiologically and psychologically, to a juvenile or " female " condition and becoming temporarily positively responsive to song. In severe wintry weather male wrens become non-territorial and utter calls which approximate to those of the female. When these usually intolerant and unsociable birds assemble in closest contiguity in a nest they are acting, not only as they did as nestlings and fledglings, but also as the female in charge of a brood sometimes does. In Holland birdcatchers use chaffinches, artificially brought into song in autumn, as decoys for male and female migrating chaffinches. Perhaps it is the temporary modification of the male wren's masculinity which transforms the isolated defender of a territory into a gregarious creature. However, as male wrens occasionally chase one another and dispute territory in wintry weather it is doubtful whether any explanation of these reversals of behaviour in physiological terms is adequate.

Calls are uttered at the roost by most passerine birds which roost communally and sometimes the utterances approximate to song, as with starlings and redwings. With blackbirds and some other birds which usually roost alone such calls appear to be a proclamation of territory but, among owls, calling at the roost is probably an invitation to a female. Few birds except those which roost socially in inaccessible situations utter loud calls or songs at the roost itself, for birds doing so would betray their resting-place to predators. Wrens do not normally sing at the roosting-site though they often do so while approaching it. It is unusual for birds to be attracted to a roosting place by the movements and calls of other species, but this occurred in Ireland when a variety of birds flocked to roost in an Aga cooker during cold weather (Wilkinson 1945).

NOCTURNAL SONG

On rare occasions European wrens sing at night. The winter wren has also been heard at night (Saunders 1929). I have listened to the Iceland wren singing in the pale light of midsummer midnight, and Dr. B. Løppenthin tells me that in N.W. Iceland the birds kept him awake. Short-billed sedge wrens sometimes sing as persistently by night as during the day (Walkinshaw 1935) and long-billed and prairie marsh wrens are heard in the darkness (Hunt 1904; Welter 1935). Nocturnal song probably has selective advantage for these birds and some other migratory species, such as the corncrake, in which the females fly by night and arrive after the males, because birds which haunt particularly dense vegetation have most need to proclaim their presence. It is interesting to note that the American marsh-frequenting wrens and the European warblers which occupy similar ecological niches, sing during darkness.

MIGRATORY SONG

Wrens, like many other birds, sometimes sing during halts on migration, as at Heligoland, and even birds of the year may sing on autumn passage (Weigold 1926). Observers on the Isle of May have never noted song by visiting wrens, and individuals of *Troglodytes t. idius* in winter quarters near Shanghai do not sing (Wilkinson 1929). As the wren has bred on Heligoland (Drost 1927), song at halts on migration may indicate a tendency to establish a territory. According to Kendeigh the nearer returning house wrens approach to their destination the more persistently they tend to sing. There is a close correlation between such song and sexual development.

ATTRACTION OF THE FEMALE

Early in the breeding season it is easy to ascertain that the territorial song of the male wren is effective in attracting females. Soon after a male begins to sing a female may be heard calling, and presently she appears close to where he is singing. I have known two females to be thus attracted to one male. A wren with three mates will continue to sing vigorously and apparently would take yet another should one present herself.

Birds whose pair-bond may best be described as successive polygamy tend to remain in song longer than monogamous species as they continue persistently inviting females to join them. Thus, of the eight British species shown in *The Handbook* charts as having the longest song season—the starling, corn bunting, cirl bunting, robin, hedge sparrow, wren, dipper and woodpigeon—the corn bunting and wren are polygamous. The cirl bunting may, perhaps, sometimes be polygamous. Of course, long-continued song is not necessarily indicative of polygamy. It may be associated with persistent defence of territory, as with the dipper, or a prolonged breeding season, as with the woodpigeon.

Observations by Tinbergen (1939) show the connection between song and the attraction of several mates. The snow bunting is normally monogamous, but an unusually highly sexed male whose mate was incubating began to sing and paired with another female. Song was inhibited until the day the first egg was laid and the second female refused to copulate. He now behaved like an unmated male, singing and trying to force unwilling females. Similarly a bigamous mocking-bird sang exuberantly before and after one mate had laid her eggs and some days later when his second mate was laying (Laskey, *in litt.*). The presence of female birds near males early in the season tends to stimulate song. A Bewick's wren watched during nearly an hour and a half sang only twice; on both occasions before copulating (Williams 1941).

Among wren species there appears to be some correlation between the persistence of song and the extent of polygamy. Male prairie marsh wrens intensify their singing when the females arrive, but song decreases with the beginning of nest-making by the female and continues to diminish as incubation proceeds. There is a slight recrudescence when the young fledge, but a week later song has practically ceased. An unmated male of this and other species continues his song when mated neighbours have reduced theirs.

Male house wrens, arriving about nine days before the females, reiterate their songs in a mechanical kind of way, but when a female appears, and especially when she inspects a nest, their utterance becomes more vigorous, the shrill, squeaky " mating song " is interspersed and neighbouring males compete. A western house wren has been seen courting a female " with wings and tail spread and head thrown back pouring out a flood of rapturous song " (Bent 1948). After pairing the " nesting song " is heard and it is maintained until the birds migrate—a softer, lower-pitched, less rapidly repeated and more variable version of the nesting song. The types of song uttered by the wren in similar circumstances approximate to the three types of house wren song distinguished by Kendeigh—territorial, mating and nesting—but not to such an extent that they can be included in like categories. The house wren's " mating song " has as counterparts " courtship " and " nest-invitation " song, though the character of the utterance is closer to that of the wren's challenge song. The quality of the house wren's " nesting song " resembles the modified territorial song, intermediate between it and courtship subsong, often sung by male wrens interested in a female, but, as has already been emphasised, the fact of pairing does not initiate a permanent alteration in the type of song as it does with house wrens.

COURTSHIP SONG

The two types of song just mentioned, " courtship " and " nest-invitation," are relevant to the female and distinct from territorial song. As with the types of song uttered by the house wren there is intergradation from the stereotyped, vigorous phrase of territorial song through broken, irregular forms to subsong and a warble, culminating in the exquisitely beautiful, subdued, nest-invitation song.

The wren's sweet subsong, unlike the subsongs of song thrush, blackbird and many other birds is not the utterance of birds coming into song:

> Songs yet half devised in the dim drear
> First beginnings of the year.

It is elicited by the presence of a female. When a wren is courting, whether it be a bird long resident in the area or a recent arrival, the modification in his song is so noticeable that I have often said to myself on entering Wren Wood, " He is busy with a female." Courtship songs in general are sweeter, softer and more warbling than most territorial songs. " How silver-sweet sound lovers' tongues! " The dipper (Serle and Bryson 1935) and hedge sparrow utter a dulcet warble, the brown thrasher and American robin sing very quietly (Saunders 1929), and the rose-breasted grosbeak dances around twittering a song so soft and low that some of the notes can only just be heard two feet away (Ivor 1944).

A wren concerned with a female does not sing subsong all the time, but frequently utters some form of broken song. The usual territorial phrase may be heard from time to time, but instead of being constantly reiterated there is irregularity. Sometimes the phrase is abruptly interrupted, sometimes phrases modified into a warble are run together so that there is all but continuous, quiet song for a minute or two. Occasionally I have known such song to continue uninterruptedly for half a minute or even forty seconds. The strain may begin very softly

T.W. G

and end loudly or start vigorously and dwindle to nothingness. In the presence of the female the wren's shout of defiance is modified to a melodious whisper and brief amorous warblings. The Hebridean, Shetland and St. Kilda wrens, and probably other races, also utter soft, sweet song when courting. The courtship subsong of the Iceland wren seemed to me the sweetest of them all, but probably my judgment was influenced by the wild beauty of the valley in which I heard it (1950a, c). Occasionally, when no female is present, a European wren patrolling his territory or engaged in building will sing courtship or exploratory subsong " absent-mindedly "; or it may be when visiting an unoccupied nest he will murmur a few soft strophes as if imagining a partner with him. A wren entering a roost where he had copulated with a mount the previous evening sang a sweet phrase. Another approaching a winter roost sang " a slender unexpected strain " when the female with whom he shared the roosting-nest drew near. Even when feeding fledged young in the absence of his mate a wren will very occasionally sing a subdued song.

NEST-INVITATION SONG

The naturalist can scarcely hope for a more delightful experience than to behold the lovely courtship ritual when the wren with quivering wings, and uttering his sweetest songs, postures on a twig before the nest inviting the female to inspect it. The song is not different in kind from courtship subsong, but is rather the most finished development of it. As the procedure is described in Chapter VIII, I would call attention here only to the fact that while the " courtship " utterances of insects, amphibia and mammals are generally unmelodious, the courtship songs of birds are usually beautiful, according to human standards. In contrast, the female bird's expression of sexual receptivity is seldom musical.

THE SONG OF THE FEMALE

Female wrens utter whisper songs, but I have known only one sing challenge song. The circumstances were exceptional. She had her brood in a shed at Girton College and the male was never observed near the nest. Although the bird was not ringed the possibility of error in regard to sex was negligible as the nest was under frequent observation by the gardeners working in the shed, the garden steward, some of the students, myself and some other friends. Moreover, in a number of respects the bird's behaviour was not typical of the male. On the occasion of the first of my experiments the wren was going in and out through a hole in the wall when the door was closed, or, sometimes, by a chink under the door. I placed a mount in an attitude somewhat resembling that of a female soliciting a male immediately outside the aperture while the wren was inside. To my amazement, the instant she alighted at the opening she sang a short, stifled song, and immediately flew out uttering an abbreviated, rather harsh, song. On several occasions I elicited song by setting the mount or a mirror near the hole—sometimes loud phrases and on other occasions brief, subdued, excited snatches. With repetition her reactions tended to wane. The bird's appearance as she sang, still retaining food for the young in her bill, was extraordinary; every feather seemed to stand on end so that, as a companion remarked, she reminded her of an angry cat.[4]

Using this and another mount I experimented with a number of other females, but never succeeded in evoking song. Usually the mount was ignored; occasionally it was attacked. No other instance of full territorial and challenge song by a female wren is on record though a singing female may have been involved in episodes recorded by Macgillivray (1837-52) and Marples (1940).

Evidence is accumulating that occasional females of very many species sing. Often the capacity is latent and manifested only by exceptional individuals. Such birds are not necessarily so masculine as to preclude normal breeding. The Girton wren reared her brood and singing hen chaffinches have been known to invite coition and rear young (Tucker 1944; England 1945). If, in such birds, song is due to an excess of male hormone or to a different hormone threshold of the nervous system it is insufficient to disorganise the breeding cycle. It is not surprising that an occasional female wren should be able to sing in view of the number of tropical wren species in which both sexes sing.

WHISPER SONG

He sings to the wide world and she to her nest
In the nice ear of Nature which song is best?

J. R. LOWELL

Although full song by female wrens is very exceptional, whisper song is common. It may be uttered by them in at least five types of situation—when the bird is brooding, feeding nestlings or fledged young; leading chicks from the nest or into the roost, and by males during territorial quarrels. Even when all is quiet around it is audible, at most, only a few yards away. So similar are the notes to the distant twitter of a swallow and so difficult to locate are they that, on more than one occasion, I have looked up expecting to see one of these birds overhead, only to discover eventually that the notes emanated from a wren six to eight feet away.

The song may vary from single notes uttered occasionally, as when the syllable "whit" is whispered, to a succession of such notes constituting a fairly sustained twittering. Occasionally subdued but harsh " skreeks " are uttered.

Sometimes an incubating female wren sings whisper songs on the eggs (Rendell 1946) comparable in quietness and the circumstances in which it is uttered to the very subdued " nest-songs " of some corvine species and the siskin, red-backed shrike and male blackcap.

The tendency to utter whisper song apparently becomes stronger after the eggs hatch. At a nest in an observation box so arranged that I could watch the interior from a few inches away I noticed that the female, before giving food to the two-day old nestlings, uttered a few very soft " whit " notes—incipient or abbreviated whisper song. Even when so close to the bird I was unable to detect any movement of the mandibles or throat. These calls stimulate the young to beg and so facilitate feeding in the dim interior of the nest. Similar notes are uttered by many birds, particularly dome-building and cavity-nesting species, such as some of the tits. A brood of wrens was successfully reared in a nest, the entrance to which I obscured experimentally so that the interior was in almost, if not quite, complete darkness, proving that feeding may be conducted with little or no help from visual cues. When the chicks are older and after the young have fledged the song may be uttered as the parent approaches with food. Some females utter a brief " swallow song " (p. 222) on alighting at the nest.

It is not easy to determine precisely what kinds of stimuli are most important in eliciting begging by the young at various stages, for the arrival of the parent may be heralded by the sound of her wings, the impact as well as the slight sound of her feet on the threshold, any utterance she may make and the darkening of the interior as she enters, but as the swallow song is often omitted when the young are sufficiently advanced to be fed at the nest-entrance it is not an essential item in the procedure which releases begging. At three nests of the Shetland wren I listened while the young were being fed, but did not hear it, but I noticed a harsh rendering at a Hebridean wren's nest. Whisper-song or subdued small-talk when birds have young is probably much commoner than the few records in the literature indicate. According to Sherman (1929) young house wrens during their first few days react to the male's song as a signal to open their mouths.

Whisper song is only very occasionally uttered by male wrens. I have heard it from two males during a territorial dispute in October. It may, perhaps, be uttered in other circumstances. While a wren's mate was incubating he began to feed a brood of great tits nine feet away. The day before they fledged he sang a very subdued song and then the swallow song was heard, presumably sung by this male. My informant, Mr. H. M. Heybroek, independently compared it with the notes of a swallow. Next day this bird's behaviour was unusual, for he sang broken song and displayed without any visible stimulus. He also perched for minutes at a time uttering calls. Next he went to the tits' nesting-box, sat a long time on the perch while the swallow song was heard, and then flew to the nest, where he sang a very quiet song. The observer was so placed that he could not ascertain exactly from which nest the swallow song emanated, but the male may well have been responsible.

CALLS

Thinks he that the chirping of a wren
By crying comfort from a hollow breast
Can chase away the first-conceived sound?
2 *Hen. VI.* III. ii. 42

Wrens have a large and complex vocabulary. My notebooks are sprinkled with syllabic renderings of these calls, but detailed enumeration and discussion of them would require more space than is available here. Table IV is over-simplified and includes only the commonest and most significant types of utterance. It must be borne in mind that calls may intergrade with one another and even intergrade with song. Moreover, a call appropriate to a particular situation may sometimes be elicited in other circumstances. Thus, for example, although the *kreeee* call is definitely associated with the presence of a ground predator, another note may sometimes be uttered. Furthermore, a human being or an owl occasionally evokes this call.

To a considerable extent the calls so frequently heard in autumn take the place of, and function as, song. Vituperative calls are nearly always emitted in thick cover so that it is difficult to ascertain which sex is responsible for particular utterances, and even when the observer is close to two wrens it is often impossible to determine which bird called or its sex.

Such calls as I have heard uttered by the Iceland wren differed from those of the European wren though they were obviously related to its utterances. The Hebridean, St. Kilda and Shetland wrens' calls bear a close affinity to our bird's. These insular races perhaps call less frequently than *T. t. troglodytes*. In Korea, during the winter, wrens live asocially (Wolfe 1950). They sometimes utter a "churr" like the European wren (F. S. 1951). Descriptions of the house wren's calls and my recollection of the notes of the pale-bellied and Panama races indicate a broad similarity to the main types of *Troglodytes* utterance. The sharp, loud call-notes of many species of wren play a vital part in their life, for audible means of *rapport* are important to cryptically coloured birds inhabiting dense vegetation or rocky areas where they are inconspicuous. Thus the canyon wren, which I have seen creeping about like a hedge sparrow below bushes in the chaparral of California utters penetrating call-notes, besides being able to sing loudly.

TABLE IV

WREN CALL-NOTES

GENERAL

Call	Character	Sex	Occasion	Function
Tick or chirp-churr.	Single, double or repeated sharp notes like large pebbles knocked together.	♂ ♀ (Rarely)	Patrolling territory. Intervals of nest-building or courting. When predator present, etc. Common in autumn and winter.	Indicates presence and identity. Expresses excitement. Signal to young when following male. Functions as warning.
Churr	Short, rapid succession of notes as above.	♂ ♀ (Rarely)	As above. By ♂ when escaping capture or on being released after capture.	Indicates higher level of excitement than above.
Ringing churr	Prolonged drumming or throbbing churr.	♂	When in highly stimulated condition, especially before, or during intervals of, nest-building or courting.	Indicates still higher excitation associated with breeding activities.
Chit	High-pitched tick, like beads knocked together.	♂ ♀	When moving around. Common in autumn and winter.	Indicates presence and identity. Serves to maintain *rapport*.

GENERAL (*Continued*)

Call	Character	Sex	Occasion	Function
Chitter	Short, rapid succession of chits. Higher pitched than churr.	♂ (Occasionally) ♀	In many situations. Often by ♀ with young.	General excitement. Alarm and warning. Uttered by ♀ to attract ♂ and when predator present, etc.
Chatter	Loud, rapid succession of low-pitched, rather harsh notes.	♀ ♂ (Rarely)	By ♀ in nest; sometimes on approach of ♂.	Excitement. Means of *rapport* between ♀ and ♂.
Chleep	Slightly grating chit.	♂ ♀	When wrens are seeking winter roost.	Means of maintaining contact.
Kreeee	Regular succession of reeling chitters at intervals of 1-3 seconds.	♂ ♀	When predator present — usually quadruped.	Signals presence of ground predator and warns other wrens and sometimes other species.
Squeak and mandible snipping	High-pitched soft call.	♂ ♀	When in hand after capture.	Protest.

SEXUAL

Call	Character	Sex	Occasion	Function
Grating note	Harsh and low-pitched. Resembles grating note of house sparrow.	♂ ♀ (Rarely)	When ♂ makes sexual pounce.	Expresses sexual excitement and, possibly, thwarting.
Weech-eech-eech . . .	Sharp, high-pitched urgent series in quick succession. Somewhat squealing.	♀	When ♂ in neighbourhood.	Sexual solicitation.

Call	Character	Sex	Occasion	Function
Wheeze, wheezy squeal, spit-hiss, etch note and glass-squeak.	A variety of urgent, vituperative, angry-sounding utterances.	♂ ♀ (Extent to which any of these calls confined to one sex unknown).	When wrens meet. Commonly in autumn.	Intimidation and " annoyance."

JUVENILE

Call	Character	Sex	Occasion	Function
Squeak	High-pitched squeak uttered by nestlings and fledglings.	♂ ♀	Especially when parent approaches with food.	Expression of hunger. Means of social contact.
Chitter	Resembles adult chitter but less vigorous.	♂ ♀	When intruder approaches.	Expression of uneasiness or alarm.

CHAPTER 7

RECOGNITION, PAIR-FORMATION AND POLYGAMY

Orchilos infestus . . . floricomis hymenaeis
AVIENUS. *Arat.*, 1763

MUCH of the social and sexual behaviour of birds is of a more " mechanical " character than has generally been realised and is elicited through the movements performed, adornments displayed or calls uttered by one bird calling forth or "releasing" correlated reactions in a companion (Lorenz 1935, 1950).

SPECIES RECOGNITION

A bird-like object must have certain characteristics if it is to elicit from a wren the typical reactions appropriate to a contact with a member of its own species. What are the factors concerned? Framing the question somewhat differently: Within what limits may a wren-like object vary from the norm and yet be reacted to as a wren? Attempts to answer this question are limited by practical difficulties as reactions to experimental objects placed near the nest need special interpretation according to the stage of the breeding cycle. Most of my experiments were made near a roost early in the season.

Summarising the results of these experiments, I found that a mounted wren with wings slightly raised, approximating to the attitude of a soliciting female, elicited copulation from males in the appropriate state, though it was attacked by a nest-building male. A rather bedraggled mount in normal posture called forth sharp notes and a few brief songs while the wren hopped around in a quizzical way, but not enough experiments were conducted to determine whether such reactions were typical. A fir cone equipped with wings from a dead wren evoked only momentary curiosity. The wren quickly picked the wings off and then lost interest. A mount with hens' feathers fixed in the crown of its head and its tail disconcerted the male wren Silver. He alighted close to it and in quick succession made two short flights backwards. He then flew off and did not return to the roost for many

97

weeks. However, before the experiment he was not frequenting it regularly.

Female wrens only occasionally attack a mount placed close to the nest. Males and females ardently feeding young will disregard a mount at the nest entrance.

Inadequate as were these experiments they suggest that, so far as appearance is concerned, as distinct from posturing and utterance, the general pattern is more important than any outstanding feature. The wren, in contradistinction to the robin, with its red breast, has no specific adornment which in isolation may evoke a particular kind of behaviour from another bird of its own species, though the position and movement of the tail may have a releaser function in determining the nature of another wren's response.

In experiments with a house wren Noble and Vogt (1935) found that he copulated as readily with a mounted winter wren as with a mount of his own species, but not with a stuffed long-billed marsh wren, which differs more in appearance from the other two than they do from each other. Thus, up to a certain point, the house wren is able to discriminate its own species by appearance alone. Probably this is also true of the European wren. In Central America, where the breeding areas of two species of wren may overlap, differences in appearance and voice prevent inter-breeding. Even in such circumstances habitat preferences tend to separate the species (Skutch 1951).

SEX RECOGNITION

In species, such as the wren, in which male and female are similarly adorned, sex recognition is by behaviour. As an element in this behaviour song is of major importance. If the response to the challenge song is another song the sequence of reactions will be aggressive; if there is no retaliatory song, courtship and coitional behaviour may follow if the male is in the requisite physiological condition. Each item in the sequence has a correlate which, if it is forthcoming, elicits its correlate, and so to consummation—expulsion of the rival or courtship and copulation with the female. It is by her demure deportment that Jenny Wren reveals her sex and evokes the courtship behaviour of the male.

An excerpt from my notes dealing with an experiment made on 8 March describes the kind of response which occurred when a male caught sight of the open-winged mount. I had placed the specimen on a trellis-bar near the roost frequented by Silver:

He perched on the middle of the bar, hopped nearer to the mount and flipped his wings out and in vigorously, then he bounced over the specimen to the other side and sang with beak open looking up at its head. His song was thin, short and excited. Immediately he leaped to the base of the mount's tail and copulated. The contact was hardly more than momentary, but I later found a deposit of semen. When he fluttered off he stood a foot distant, facing the mount. Then he perched on a rose twig with his tail cocked forward so that it was at an angle of some 60°, and at times 45°, to his back. The feathers of the cloacal region were fluffed up and his posterior kept working in slow rhythm, partly from side to side and partly up and down, with the tail rotating slowly from side to side while he raised and lowered himself comparatively slowly as compared with his usual bobbing movements.

This odd, slow movement of the rear of the body and tail accompanies intense sexual excitement and occurs sometimes shortly before, as well as after, coition. Another male, who had been ardently courting a female, found the mount ten minutes after it had been set up under a tree in his territory, sang a short, congested song and immediately alighted on it to copulate. Such song should be regarded as challenge song, not courtship. As the mount remains silent and motionless, approximating to a complaisant female, coitional behaviour is released. When two males meet and the challenge song is reciprocated skirmishing or chasing, with further song, is the sequel. As we have already noted (p. 75), such song expresses defiance and facilitates identification.

As one would expect, in experiments with a mirror placed so that a male wren catches sight of his reflection, song is evoked; the bird hops here and there seeking an adversary, but he easily loses sight of his image as he moves so he usually soon desists. Particularly vigorous reactions were elicited by placing a mirror behind the mount. In experiments of this kind a wren will sometimes attempt copulation twice within a few minutes.

EXPERIMENTS ON SONG RECOGNITION

Most of my experiments designed to furnish positive proof of the function of song in determining the reactions of male wrens were inconclusive, probably owing to the inadequate reproduction of Koch's recording on a portable gramophone and the difficulty of placing the instrument sufficiently near to the subject of the experiment. When it was ten feet from a wren building his nest there was no response; nor was there a definite reaction when the record was played the same distance from a bird going to roost. Barraud (1948-49) obtained " immediate and strong response " from a male which flew near to where the same record was being played, " flinging himself into a fury of song "; but on other occasions the bird continued unheedingly on his way. Perhaps, so far as the wren's appreciation is concerned, the rendering is so inadequate that only when the bird is in a stimulated condition does it elicit reaction. It is well known that many species will respond to an inadequate mount only when the threshold of response is low, and this may well be true of song also.

The only reactions which I succeeded in eliciting by means of the gramophone record were with the singing female mentioned earlier (p. 90). The circumstances were particularly favourable as it was possible to play the disc inside the shed in which the bird's nest was situated. The song sounded much louder than in the open and the wren could not but hear the recording. On the first occasion she sang one normal territorial phrase on the roof immediately after flying out; on the second, I rushed after her as she flew out so that I might see what she would do—and almost collided with her at the door as she returned. Although the results were not as conclusive as I should have liked, there was no doubt that her response was of a territorial character.

Occasionally wrens will respond to an imitation of their ticking or " chit " notes. When my small son was repeatedly pulling the trigger of a toy pistol at a first-floor window a wren chittered and flew up to the parapet just out of his reach.

FORMATION OF THE PAIR-BOND

Apart from whatever co-operation there may be between a pair of wrens in tending the young—sometimes almost or quite negligible—and, possibly, a tendency for two individuals of unlike sex to seek roosting quarters together at the onset of severe weather (p. 277), male and female rarely associate except when their interest is sexual rather than social.

It is not very unusual for pairs of wrens to be seen together in autumn, due apparently to a precocious ebullition of sexuality in birds of the year or a recrudescence in older individuals. On snowy afternoons in winter two wrens may sometimes be seen feeding together along a hedgerow or ditch. No doubt such associations are advantageous as the birds can go to roost together at dusk and thus keep each other warm, but it should not be assumed that they are paired. Wilson (1948) referring to observations on Attu in the Aleutians remarks: " Even in winter I saw what I believe to be paired birds." It is improbable that *T. t. meligerus* differs from other races in this respect. However, Bewick's and Vigors's wrens may maintain the pair-bond during the winter (Thomas 1946; Miller 1941), and some tropical species, such as the white-bellied wren (*Uropsila leucogastra*), probably remain in pairs throughout the year (Todd and Carriker 1922).

Although Kluijver noted that a male and female remained together for two broods in one year and the first brood the next year, partnership between the same birds in successive years is exceptional. None of my five identifiable female wrens re-mated with the same male in a subsequent season. When such re-mating occurs it is due, apparently, to the contiguity resulting from the retention of territory by the male, together with the female's persistence in a familiar habitat, rather than to any affective bond between the birds. Kendeigh found that notwithstanding the vicissitudes of migration 13 per cent of male house wrens and 22 per cent of females nested in a subsequent year with a former mate. Even for second broods in the same year wrens commonly change partners. In four years Kluijver recorded only two instances of wrens remaining mated for two successive broods, apart from the pair just mentioned. I noted only one quite certain, and another probable, instance. Kendeigh found that in 40 per cent of second broods the same house wrens re-mated. As the whole mating procedure is repeated for each mating cycle he refers to re-mating, but the introductory procedure for the European wren's second brood can be so curtailed that, when the same two birds remain together, it would be more accurate to speak of the continuation of the pair-bond from one brood to the next (p. 226).

No doubt a male and female which have roosted together in winter sometimes pair and rear a family. I had reason to believe this was so in one instance. The fact that Dunsheath and Doncaster (1941) found couples in roosts most frequently from February onwards may point in this direction. However, two birds of opposite sex may occupy a roost together as late as the end of March without nesting together. A couple spent successive nights together in January, and I once heard the male sing the courtship subsong as he and the female approached the roost one frosty evening, but later I found the female mated to another male who had been trapped roosting alone in the nest six weeks before I caught the other couple. Apart from other considerations winter casualties preclude a number of roosting associations from maturing into breeding partnerships. In some species, such as the starling, roosting together strengthens the pair-bond. A factor contributing to the " divorce " of a starling pair was their inability to spend the night in company owing to the only suitable hole being disputed by another pair (Morley 1939).

From the first week in January until 18 March 1944, there were two, and sometimes three, wrens roosting in the recesses between gnarled ivy stems on a wall. Almost every evening one of the birds would chase another, so that at first I thought the owner was trying to expel an intruder, but after a time it became apparent that no acrimony was involved. Possibly chasing began as an expression of hostility and acquired sexual significance.

When the female was the first to arrive she would sometimes wait for the male and then join in the frolic with him. The proceedings resembled the pre-roosting chases of paired blue tits, during which display and coition sometimes occur (Colquhoun 1942). On 4 March, after a pursuit, the male wren attempted coition, and again, five days later, the female, responding to the male's excited movements and song, elicited by an experimental mount, flew out of the ivy and squatted quiescent in a half-hearted invitatory posture. On 18 March the female sought roosting quarters elsewhere, but it was not until 18 April that the male deserted the roost. That day he was seen vigorously chasing a female, but I was unable to ascertain whether she was his winter partner. If the pair-bond had been firmly established one would have expected the birds to desert the roost together, but often, even when wrens are definitely paired, they roost separately.

Persistent courtship throughout some weeks may occur without wrens mating, and birds which have spent the winter together may not reach consummation until, after days or even weeks of mutual stimulation, their sexual rhythms have become synchronised. Late in the season pairing may take place without much ado, just as in many species a replacement nest may be built rapidly after disaster to the first.

It will be realised that it is not always easy to determine when a pair may be said to be formed, because the process is sometimes gradual. Pair-formation procedure among wrens may vary from association in the roost during autumn and winter maturing into a pair-bond, to a very brief summer courtship.

POLYGAMY

The type of polygamy characteristic of the European wren is best described as optional and successive—optional in that monogamous breeding also occurs, and successive, to distinguish it from the harem behaviour of some game birds and mammals such as the red deer and fur seal. The efficient integration of polygamy into the general pattern of the bird's behaviour is all the more remarkable as the number of males having more than one mate seems to be almost equal to the number of monogamous males. Kluijver and his colleagues found that one year six out of twelve males were polygamous, and two of these had three broods simultaneously. In the course of their research they noted three instances in which a male had three mates at the same time. Probably, as with pied and collared flycatchers (Haartman 1951) the older birds have the strongest polygamous tendencies.

In Wren Wood three of the eight males which occupied breeding territories during the five years I studied these relationships closely were bigamists, and as I shall presently describe, one of these, White-leg, had virtually three mates.

I observed further instances of wren bigamy in other areas of the Cambridge suburbs and estimate that the proportion of polygamous males in this locality, and probably other garden-woodland regions of England, is approximately similar to that noted in Holland. The reference by Fatio and Studer (1907) to the wren sometimes having three or four broods in Switzerland is probably a mistaken inference based on observations which, rightly interpreted, indicate polygamy.

The European wren is the most polygamous of the races, so far as our present knowledge goes, and indeed may be the most polygamous member of the family, though the winter wren also has polygamous proclivities. Thus only six per cent of house wrens are bigamous, and Kendeigh records but one instance of a male already possessing two mates trying to secure a third. Between a quarter and a third of the territories of prairie marsh wrens belong to bigamous males. One bird observed by Welter probably had three mates.

The biography of male No. 42, recorded by Kluijver, reveals him as an ardent polygamist. In 1937 this bird made ten nests. The first egg in one of them appeared on 10 April. Eighteen days later an egg was laid in each of two other nests. He was having sexual intercourse with two females contemporaneously, and was therefore a polygamist *sensu stricto*. In June he had three mates; they began their layings on the 1st, 10th and 21st. Thus he divided his energies between six females and during the period of his first brood three of his mates were occupied at their nests contemporaneously. This would also have been so during the second-brood period had not disaster befallen two of the nests.

The Biography of a Polygamist

The polygamous nature of the European wren can best be illustrated by chronicling briefly the activities of one male, White-leg, during 1946. In doing so I shall describe in greater detail the events which accompanied the territorial changes in Wren Wood represented on the maps for that year (Nos. VI, VII and VIII, pp. 38-9).

Red-leg, in the western half of the wood, whose wheezy song was sufficient to distinguish him from his rival Yellow-and-Black to the east, built part of his first nest on 30 March outside the wood and was seen courting a female, Bunty,* on 1 April and subsequent days. On 4 April there was much song duelling between the two males, both being interested in Pinkie, another female, who was moving about in the no-man's-land between their territories.

The situation remained unchanged for some time, apart from minor adjustments of the boundary between the territories, though on one occasion there was an exceptionally spirited song duel, but on 26 April I found there had been an abrupt alteration in the situation; the usurper White-leg had gained a footing in Yellow-and-Black's ground, this bird had moved into Red-leg's territory (which had been part of his own domain the previous year when he had the wood to himself), and Red-leg had disappeared *sans trace*. I ringed White-leg on 2 May at the nest he had begun two days earlier.

Three days later Yellow-and-Black was busy building his first nest in some ivy a few yards from a site used by him the previous year while Bunty loitered around, distracting him so much that at times he was torn between the impulses to woo and to build. Once she solicited coition with the characteristic pleading note. Next day, after visiting his nest in company with Bunty, he went off with her in his wake and laid the foundation of another nest in a low thorn stump; but he desisted after fifteen minutes and never completed the structure.

Meanwhile, a nest in my garden had been deserted and on 2 May I transferred the fresh clutch to a great tit's nest in White-leg's territory. The eggs hatched on 13 May and the young, thriving under the care of their foster-parents, fledged on 2 June. White-leg passed or perched now and then not far from where the nestlings could be heard calling in the nesting box, without taking any interest in them, so far as I could ascertain. However, a few hours after they emerged I saw him fly up and alight close to a youngster. He carried no food in his bill. The fledgling flew off in the opposite direction, apparently disconcerted by the cock's precipitate approach.

The great tits tended the young wrens, and I noticed that one of them successfully attracted a chick to a branch as high as twenty feet to be fed. To my surprise, four days after they had left the nest I found the party in a dense tangle of briars being supplied with food by Pinkie while White-leg sang and called around. From this time

*This wren was probably a bird which roosted with Red-leg but escaped when I trapped him and was never ringed. Thus it is not completely certain that the same female was involved in all the activities which I ascribe to Bunty, but various characteristics of her behaviour by which I believed I could identify her convince me that this is a justifiable assumption.

forth Pinkie and White-leg, who had been " keeping company," took over the care of the young wrens.

I believe that when the youngsters sought thick cover, as they naturally do, the great tits found approaching them so awkward that, after some attempts to deal with the situation, they surrendered the task to Pinkie. Presumably she had been attracted by the calls of the youngsters and been stimulated by their begging to feed them. She was constant in her attentions until 15 June, if not later, and led the foster-family to roost in the nest where she had been trapped on 12 December 1945. White-leg may have fed the young occasionally on 6 June and certainly did so on the 7th and 9th.

Meanwhile, Bunty had settled into Yellow-and-Black's nest in the western sector of the wood. She may have begun incubating on 14 May as on that date I flushed her from the nest. Now, however, it was Yellow-and-Black's turn to be evicted. On 9 June I noticed him singing vigorously against White-leg, but on the 10th, when the party of young wrens accompanied by White-leg and Pinkie wandered into Yellow-and-Black's territory, there was no protest. Next day I caught a glimpse of White-leg chasing Bunty from the bough where she had her nest. He uttered several subdued courtship songs. Before this he had been spending most of his time with Pinkie and the youngsters, occasionally pouncing erotically on her as she sought food for them. Not content with these flirtations I found him next morning pouncing on Bunty and also wooing a third, unringed female, at another of his nests, No. 2, built mainly on 24 May. He was thus courting three females at approximately three corners of the wood: Bunty, the mate of his defeated rival, Pinkie, busy with her foster-children, and the newly-arrived stranger. However, he was not so preoccupied with philandering as to neglect all other responsibilities, for he may have fed Bunty's brood on 13 June and undoubtedly did so on 15 June when they fledged. Probably he also fed them on subsequent days, but I was unable to continue daily observations.

On 15 June the stranger female laid her first egg in No. 2 nest. Her three eggs were infertile and I removed them on 12 July. Next day White-leg was again chasing and pouncing on this female, but she did not respond and was not seen again.

Pinkie was seen collecting insects on 18 July and flying off with them, but I did not succeed in finding the nest. The young fledged on 1 August and four days later Bunty appeared with her second brood. White-leg had fathered both these broods towards the end of June.

This condensed chronicle shows that the ardent male wren is ready to make sexual advances to any female who will endure them, but he is not promiscuous like some species of lek birds. He conducts potential partners to his nests, he remembers where the females which select them are ensconced, he visits occupied nests to see how things are going, and he usually interests himself in the fledged young, though often only to the extent of escorting them when they fledge, and, perhaps, giving them a little food.

Polygamy and the Availability of Food

Polygamy would be dysgenic for any species in which the female is incapable of rearing the young unaided. This implies, *ceteris paribus*, a greater availability of food than is necessary when both parents feed the nestlings. Theoretically, we should therefore expect polygamy not to occur where living conditions are bleak or marginal unless offset by some compensating factor such as small family-size. It is thus significant that the wrens of St. Kilda, Shetland and probably the Outer Hebrides, are normally monogamous and that in all three races the male usually helps the female to feed the nestlings. Presumably without his aid the young might lack sufficient food. Selection would operate against polygamous proclivities which tended to deflect males from tending the nestlings. The alternative of a smaller family, which it would be within the compass of one bird's powers to feed, would apparently involve too small an annual crop of young birds to replace casualties unless we postulate some exceptional compensating factor, of which we have no evidence among the birds with which we are concerned. Thus the wrens of the harshest habitats show least tendency to polygamy. This may hold not only of insular races but of wrens in some rather arid, mountainous regions, such as Sicily. The somewhat meagre evidence that the Iceland wren has polygamous tendencies is not in contradiction, for the birch scrub which it inhabits is often infested with caterpillars which are preyed upon by few other vertebrates and constitute, when at their peak, an abundant source of food for wrens. Young European wrens are not often found dead in the nest, but casualties among young St. Kilda wrens in the comparatively congested village area are sometimes high (Harrisson and Buchan 1934), and the circumstances suggest that there may be unusually great pressure on the food supply (Armstrong 1953b).

Polygamy in Other Species

The marsh harrier is bigamous fairly frequently and probably this is true of the bittern also. The penduline tit of southern Europe is polygamous and so are the tri-coloured redwing and red-winged blackbird of North America. As we have already noted, a good proportion of male prairie marsh wrens have more than one mate. Perhaps it is more than coincidence that these species frequent marshy habitats, but Montagu's harrier, which sometimes breeds on heaths, also has bigamous tendencies and, as Haartman (1951) has pointed out, polygamy has been recorded of the collared, pied and spotted flycatchers, and the snow, yellow and corn buntings. However, a male snow bunting's bigamy resulted in some of the young perishing (Tinbergen 1939).

The corn bunting is even more polygamous than the wren. Ryves (1934a, b), who studied it in Cornwall, found that two males had each seven females, and fifteen males were mated with fifty-one females, while Mr. L. S. V. Venables tells me that in preliminary investigations in Shetland he discovered two bigamous males. If further study of the species shows that polygamy is less general among corn buntings in bleak northern habitats than in the south of England it would support the evidence which a study of the wren provides that there is a correlation between polygamy and food supply.

Theoretically we might expect that if the size of the family and availability of food were such that an unaided female could rear the brood successfully the male might develop polygamous tendencies owing to being " at a loose end." Carrick (1949) found that a male starling with a brood too small to stimulate his activity in providing food may begin nest-building and court other females. Similarly Kessel (1950) noticed that a starling which had five females during the nesting season manifested building activity but did not feed the young. Among house wrens the males which go off to build a new nest while the female is incubating are most likely to secure another mate (Baldwin and Kendeigh 1927). In some species of bunting and warbler the male may not help to feed the nestlings if the brood is small. Such observations suggest that polygamy in some species may have evolved through prolongation or recrudescence of behaviour originally associated with the inception of the breeding cycle. If the energy of the male is not expended at the nest, in consequence of the female being able to procure sufficient food for the nestlings without his assistance, he may seek to form another alliance. When a male pied flycatcher was removed the number of meals given to the nestlings was at least as great as when both sexes worked together (Haartman 1951). Thus bigamy in this species does not necessarily jeopardise the successful rearing of the brood even when entire responsibility rests with the female. However, the successive bigamy of the pied flycatcher is such that the male, after establishing his second mate in a nesting-place, may return to help feed the young of his first mate. Owing to the short period during which the male great reed warbler is in condition for coition physiological considerations set a limit to the extent polygamy is possible and parental impulses become dominant more readily than in wrens. Thus a male will feed young in the nests of two mates (Kluijver 1949); so, too, will a bigamous collared flycatcher (Löhrl 1949), but a whitethroat neglected the brood of one of his two mates (Armington 1951) and no wren has been known to feed two contemporaneous broods of nestlings.

OCCASIONAL BIGAMY

Many monogamous species are occasionally bigamous—even birds such as the mute swan in which the pair-bond is maintained year after year (Dewar 1936; Ringleben 1936; Portielje 1936)—and species in which bigamy is frequent are sometimes polygamous, but there is an important distinction between birds, such as the European wren, in which other adaptations are so integrated as to promote successful polygamy and species of which this is not true. Sexual promiscuity among birds usually involves a pattern of adaptations of a different character from that which polygamy involves. Occasional bigamy may arise in a variety of ways. It may be due to a recrudescence of male ardour, as among snow buntings (Tinbergen 1939); chance association between a mated male and another female at a crucial point in the sexual cycle (Ewers 1942); the frequent intrusion of females into a male's territory (Rinkel 1940); building activity by the female outside her mate's territory (Kluijver 1949); a disparity in sex ratio, or to a male having too little to do owing to the small size of the brood, as we have just noted. Bigamy among collared fly-catchers is encouraged through pairing-up taking place before rivals have returned from winter quarters (Löhrl 1949). Pied flycatchers must be reckoned more than occasionally bigamous as thirteen per cent of the females are paired with bigamous males. The cock transfers his interest to the neighbourhood of another nesting cavity after his first mate begins to lay, so that he is apt to acquire another partner.

SEX RATIO

A differential sex ratio in favour of females or a preponderance of females in breeding condition may be correlated with polygamy or promiscuity, especially the latter, as is apparently true of some lek birds, game birds and ducks (Armstrong 1947). But there is little or no evidence of disproportion in the number of the sexes in breeding condition so far as European wrens are concerned. Kluijver does not think his data indicate an unbalanced sex ratio. The Rev. J. Lees

Plate IIIa (*above*). Wren in flight.

(*Eric Hosking*)

b (*right*). Male wren: threat display.

(*R. P. Gait*)

c (*below*). Wren singing. (*R. P. Gait*)

tells me that of seventy-three wrens he has trapped thirty-eight were females. At Cambridge and Stein unmated males were observed in the neighbourhood of polygamists. Although Bewick's wren is not polygamous Miller (1941) believes that the number of unmated males indicates that the sex ratio is in their favour. A comparison of mortality in game birds shows that the males of some polygamous species and the females of some monogamous species are most vulnerable to starvation and climatic extremes (Latham 1947). If this were true of wrens one would expect hard winters to accentuate polygamy, but the males' advantage over the females in being more familiar with the location of suitable roosts might tend to redress the balance. Among pied flycatchers there is no noticeable preponderance of either sex. Any attempt to explain polygamy among birds as due to a genetical aberration whereby females exceed males is too crude. Polygamy is an element in a highly integrated pattern of adaptation.

THE FUNCTION OF POLYGAMY AMONG WRENS

The European wren's polygamy represents an intermediate type. It is " optional " in the sense that broods are reared successfully alike when attended by one parent or both, and it may be contemporaneous or successive, as with the pied flycatcher, but is usually successive.

Whatever other functions it may serve polygamy appears to accentuate competition and give selective advantage to the most vigorous males. Those individuals whose energy, expressed in song, nest-building, display and other activities, is below average, are handicapped in securing mates in comparison with their more lively neighbours. Thus sexual selection is operative among wrens; the females are attracted to the males which build the most adequate and suitably situated nests in congenial territories. Among birds sexual selection is probably more important than has generally been admitted. Polygamy, as practised by the wren, involves a series of correlated adaptations in regard to song, multiple nest-building and so forth, all subject to female selection. The males which practise it most efficiently are those which co-ordinate these adaptations most effectively. They have reproductive advantage and leave most progeny. Thus Haartman (1951) found that a polygamous pied flycatcher fathered as many offspring in three years as a monogamous male in six. Apart from the possibility that mortality is much heavier among the offspring of polygamous wrens after fledging, or the operation of some other unknown factor affecting survival differentially, selection must operate in favour of polygamous males where food is relatively abundant.

CHAPTER 8

SEXUAL DISPLAY

For we are come here
To taste your good cheer
And the king is well dressed
In silks of the best.
He is from a cottager's stall
To a fine gilded hall.

WELSH WREN SONG

ALTHOUGH VERY LITTLE has been written on the wren's forms of display they are numerous, varied and lovely. Had " the wren with little quill " been larger and more flamboyant his posturings would not have been so scantily celebrated by poets and artists, and so neglected by naturalists.

THE SEXUAL PURSUIT AND POUNCE

The winter pre-roosting chases in which a male pursues a female flying about eighteen inches ahead of him (p. 102) seem to be rather unusual. In spring, however, pursuits, which may occur at any time of the day, become a characteristic activity and remain so to some extent so long as the male remains sexually ardent. Especially during the morning hours one may often catch glimpses of the two tiny birds speeding silently from bush to bush, the cock always in the rear. When the brief chase ends he may warble sweetly as he moves from twig to twig above the herbage in which the female has taken refuge, or he may go off through his territory singing and feeding. Commonly he makes a rush at the female where she has alighted on or near the ground; there is a quick mêlée, a grating note is heard, and usually, as the male flies up, he utters an excited snatch of song. This behaviour I describe as " pouncing." It is difficult to determine exactly what takes place during the mêlée, but sometimes, perhaps usually, there is no actual contact. On such occasions when I have been able to ascertain which bird uttered the harsh call it has been the male. Occasionally I have heard a more prolonged version of it, almost a screech, very similar to a harsh sparrow-like call uttered by the singing female wren when she was greatly excited by the mounted wren at the entrance to the shed in which her nest was situated (p. 91). This note may express frustration or aggression, for when coition has apparently been successfully accomplished I have not heard it or it has been uttered softly.

Pouncing frequently occurs without preliminary chasing, especially when the female is feeding newly-fledged young. It is also characteristic of the Carolina wren. When, during a pounce, a male actually struck his mate he uttered a loud song and she replied with a screech (Nice and Thomas 1948). The male white wagtail " charges " at the female and either male or female house sparrow may dart at the other in a manner suggesting a modified " pounce." The cock nightingale perches with ruddy tail fanned and flies down at the female, sometimes several times in succession (Daanje 1950). The rufous tail-coverts of both nightingale and wren are conspicuous in flight so that one suspects that study of the nightingale's displays might reveal further similarities with those of the wren. I have photographed a male singing and displaying at the nest in almost exactly the same posture as a nightingale photographed at the nest by Miss Turner (Armstrong 1947). Nice (1943) considers that the pouncing of the song sparrow, closely similar to that of the wren, has little immediate connection with copulation, but, so far as wrens are concerned, it may be that on the comparatively rare occasions when pouncing occurs and the female is receptive, coition takes place. She suggests that the cock song sparrow shows his prowess by pouncing, and that the procedure has biological value because it is advantageous for a female to mate with an aggressive male. " His courtship," she says, " may be symbolic of his readiness to defend her and her family." This interpretation could not apply to the wren, for in many instances he does not warn or make a show of defending his mate and the family until the young fledge, and sometimes not even then. Moreover, the most persistent pouncers among male wrens, being the most ardent sexually, are those which concern themselves least with the brood.

The simplest explanation of pouncing is that behaviour which may have been originally an attempt to copulate has come to have a function as a display activity stimulating the female sexually. The term " dominance " in reference to social hierarchy has been employed by various writers with different connotations so that it is desirable to avoid it in this context. Nice (1949) no longer considers it a valid concept as applied to behaviour at the establishment of the pair-bond. Let it suffice that in various degrees the self-assertion of the male is important in his efforts to secure a mate, and that in some species this may take the form of pseudo-aggressive display or even of violence to the female. It does not follow that because the male or female is assertive during some phase of the pair-bond relationship we can speak of one sex as being the dominant sex.

It has been assumed that when a male bird is seen pursuing a female he is the more ardent of the two, and this supposition might seem particularly justifiable in regard to the wren, as the male's songs are so persistent and his pursuits and pounces so conspicuous in comparison with the mousy shyness of the female. Undoubtedly in some such episodes he is ardent and she is sexually sluggish or unresponsive, but some females, far from waiting to be wooed, solicit the male at times in a vigorous, even frenzied manner.

Soon after dawn on 18 April some songs and a ringing churr attracted me to a nest. Close by I found Cinnabar with two females, Scarlet and Silverband. One of the females entered the nest and when she emerged there ensued much chasing and pouncing. Eventually Scarlet started uttering the solicitation calls, but Cinnabar did not respond and went off singing through the wood. Next morning I was at Wren Wood in time to trap Scarlet before she left her roosting place in this nest. I kept her in a glass jar until my observations were completed. Cinnabar spent the morning with the other female, Silverband, and only once performed the banner display (p. 118). There were no sexual calls from the female, no pursuits, no pounces or grating notes. Cinnabar merely sang in response to Silverband's chitters. She was obviously less mature sexually than Scarlet, as was confirmed when she began laying about ten days after Scarlet (p. 164). Undoubtedly Scarlet, (but not Silverband) had acted in such a way as to stimulate Cinnabar.

These observations suggest that, so far as these birds were concerned, the sexual pursuit was initiated by the female fleeing enticingly before the male. Like Virgil's nymph she did not seek to escape from him:

Et fugit ad salices et se cupit ante videri.

It is more frequently true that the female initiates chasing by the male than is commonly realised. The female house wren calls the male when she seeks coition and then flies off with him in pursuit. Watching pairs of hedge sparrows one often notices that it is only after the female takes flight that the male follows, though occasionally he tries unsuccessfully to induce the female to follow him. Female mallards sometimes attract the drakes to chase them by flying up and calling. Christoleit (1929a, b) concludes that this ensures fertilisation of the female by the most vigorous male. Whichever sex initiates the chase it is usually a means whereby the other sex is stimulated.

Howard (1929), basing his opinion on the sexual flights of buntings, chats, warblers and pipits, regarded " this crowning act of companionship " as a certain indication of pairing and interpreted the chase as indicating the sexual readiness of the male and the unreadiness of the female, but as Lack (1941, 1945) remarks, such chases may begin in some species weeks before coition occurs. A Galapagos finch will pursue a female after she has invited him to copulate and he has not responded. Thus the chasing of the female by the male was, in this instance at least, an indication of her, rather than his, ardour. Howard, however, emphasised correctly that epigamic display may be much more in evidence when one of a pair is unable to respond by coition. Thwarting increases display. Indeed, there is much to suggest that display and song are basically a by-product of conflicting drives.

FIG. 14. Male and female wren in accentuated pursuit flight.

Howard says that he never knew a female passerine to forsake a male after the sexual pursuit had occurred, but a female wren in Wren Wood deserted a male after this display had taken place repeatedly, both in the ordinary and accentuated form. As this male, Yellow-and-Black, remained unmated throughout this year he may not have been completely mature sexually.

These observations lend support to the view that the epigamic display of birds and probably other organisms has evolved partly through the ritualisation of intention and displacement movements performed when one partner is more ardent than the other. As such movements came to have a stimulating effect on the bird's partner they became stereotyped as display movements and postures. Similarly many threat, distraction and epigamic displays evolved through the ritualisation of the movements of birds subject to conflicting impulses —to approach and to flee.

Accentuated Pursuit Flight

In some organisms the pursuit of the female by the male could not be considered display. The male wasp *Bembex spinolae* perches watching the female and then chases and pounces on her in a manner not unlike that of the wren (Nielsen 1945). As it is not apparent that this behaviour and comparable behaviour by many other animals is more than an attempt by the male to copulate with the female we are not entitled to describe it as epigamic display, but when pursuit behaviour is ritualised and evidently has a stimulating effect on both male and female, as with wrens, it can legitimately be regarded as a form of display. Moreover, no clear distinction can be drawn between the pursuit flight of wrens and the accentuated pursuit flight, which involves the *ad hoc* display of adornments.

In the accentuated pursuit flight, which usually takes place in the early morning, the female precedes the male by about 18 inches, flying a few feet above the ground with moth-like, fluttering action, showing the rounded wings to full advantage. The male flies in similar fashion and both fan their tails. In the rays of the rising sun the russet plumage, attractively barred, glows prettily. The speed of flight is slower than in the ordinary sexual pursuit. I have only known this display to occur between the male Yellow-and-Black and a female who was the more ardent of the two, as her soliciting calls and general behaviour indicated. Moreover, as has already been remarked, Yellow-and-Black remained unpaired the whole season.

There appears to be an intensification of the ruddy coloration of the tail-coverts and tail feathers in spring which may be correlated with their display in pursuit flight and other posturings. If this is not a subjective impression, due to the manner in which these feathers are displayed, it may be attributable to the abrasion of the feathers, a process which, in a number of species, is known to result in an increase in vividness of plumage coloration independently of the moult. A partial pre-nuptial moult of the crown, facial and throat feathers has been recorded of many subspecies of *T. troglodytes* (Vaurie 1951), but the tail feathers are moulted only after breeding.

Wing Quivering

When a male is stimulated by the presence of a female his ardour is manifested, not only in sexual chases, pounces and the subdued courtship songs which have been described but also in characteristic posturing. Quotations from my notes will give a more vivid conception of these displays than a generalised description:

22/4/44   08.10.

Wren singing in the garden; one or two loud songs and some soft and broken. Found him on a high branch of a greengage leaning over, looking intently downwards, wings spread horizontally and half, or rather more than half, opened, quivering them and singing subsong. The female suddenly appeared and he made a dash after her. He returned to the tree and sang for nearly ten minutes.

11/5/44   05.30.

The male is constantly displaying, absolutely " electric," sometimes moving along a branch in a quick, hoppity way, as if gliding in tiny jerks, often holding out and quivering his wings, which vary from being draggled at the sides of his body to being raised more or less horizontally. He sings as he postures, sometimes continuing to sing while flying as much as 15 or 20 yards between trees. The song varies, often broken, sometimes crescendo, sometimes diminuendo.

16/4/45   10.00.

Wren displaying on branch with tremulous, widespread, nearly level wings and beautifully fanned tail, uttering somewhat subdued, excited and abbreviated song. He flies close to the ivy-twined trunk where the female is lurking. Shortly afterwards I hear a grating call. His wing-beats as he flew were rather slow; possibly also his wings were not fully spread. The sun shone luminously through them.

Later in the year, especially when the female is feeding young and the male is helping more or less intermittently, one sees various modifications of wing-quivering. The cock may perch here and there with wings slightly drooped uttering brief calls. One of my photographs shows a bird with food in his bill perched outside the nest in an almost upright position with wings and tail widely expanded, the undersides of the wings directed towards the nest. Mr. I. J. Ferguson-Lees tells me that he saw a St. Kilda wren with fledged young posing with spread tail, drooped and quivering wings, uttering a fragment of song. The wing-quivering displays of the Iceland wren (Armstrong 1950a) and western winter wren (Pearse 1933) are substantially similar to that of the European wren. The house wren also flutters his wings, particularly when leading the female to the nest. Mr. Job van Peppel's photograph (Pl. iv, p. 116) in which the female European wren is seen showing her excitement by slightly drooping her wings illustrates a form of display in front of the nest. This slight wing-drooping was also performed by the singing female when she had nearly become conditioned to the mount. It occurs in one or both sexes of a variety of other species—often as a low-intensity reaction.

The following excerpt from my notes describes a modification of wing-quivering when the male's normal reactions seemed somewhat inhibited.

3/7/48   17.00 to 19.00.

Male almost continually in semi-display. Nearly all the time his tail was more or less spread and depressed, sometimes very widely fanned. He was constantly looking for, or at, the female as she busied herself getting food for the fledglings, and sometimes raised his wings, slightly drooping. He uttered frequent " chlirp " notes and sang rather subdued and truncated strophes, sometimes while in the semi-display posture. Two or three times I saw him carrying mosquitoes for the chicks. Even when he was hunting for food he kept his tail incongruously spread.

If this curious behaviour was due, as it seemed to be, to a compromise between the impulses to feed the young and to court the female, it illustrates how modified display behaviour may be incongruously transferred to another kind of situation. When this occurs it may be, as in this instance, of no biological advantage, but it is possible that in some forms of diversionary display items of behaviour may be incorporated as " displacements " from other contexts, including epigamic display (Armstrong 1947: 1949a, b; 1950b). When such transference of behaviour-patterns to new contexts occurs the resulting form of behaviour may have survival value for the species.

There is a November record of a Faeroe wren moving about with spread tail and quivering wings (Williamson 1947a). The description suggests display behaviour in some respects resembling that of a wren I captured in its roost on a cold December night. After ringing the bird I placed it below the nest on a tree trunk. It clung vertically for five minutes with its tail fanned and quivering wings slightly drooped.

Such displays in November and December without any normal object to elicit them present a problem to those who regard other activities arising in conditions of minimal stimulus as " Leerlaufreaktionen " due to the building up of " action-specific-potential " to the point at which it must " explode " into expression (Lorenz 1950), for although some mild epigamic activity may occur in winter there is no evidence of a very low threshold of expression. Males which remain unmated the whole season have not been observed to perform overflow sexual display though they tend to sing more than mated birds, as if their primary sexual impulses found natural expression in this way.

Overflow epigamic display (Armstrong 1950b) tends to occur when

a

b

Plate IVa (*above*). Male wren courting female outside nest. (*J. Van Peppel*). *b* (*below*)
Young wrens about to leave the nest. The parent's excitement is indicated by the
upturned tail. (*M. D. England*)

a male is in a highly stimulated condition. Thus on 15 March 1951 I noticed a male singing excited snatches as he accompanied a female. He then left her, flying round to the front of my house. Here he spent two minutes hopping here and there feeding in the ivy and frequently uttering abbreviated phrases. Suddenly, as he sang excitedly, he went into display, spreading his tail and fluttering his wings rather haphazardly. Immediately he flew to the back of the house to rejoin the female and started courting her with similar displays and short songs. It was as if he had suddenly remembered the female he had left and displayed regardless of her absence. Such episodes suggest that birds may be able to form images of absent objects as some mammals, such as chimpanzees, are apparently able to do.

By means of the wing-quivering display, which may be repeated frequently, day after day, the male not only indicates his ardour to the female, but also stimulates her. In spite of her apparent indifference, creeping unobtrusively here and there, she is well aware of what is going on, as is shown by her readiness to follow the male and even to entice him. We may assume that the effect of the display, like the persistent erection of his ruff by the golden pheasant and many other forms of assiduous posturing performed by various species, is cumulative, and that the male is thus able to accelerate the female's responsiveness and synchronise her sexual rhythm with his own. It may even expedite the ripening of the ova. For her part the female, as we have noted, has her own ways of stimulating the male (pp. 112 and 130).

GREETING DISPLAY

When a mated pair of wrens meet at the nest there may be some reciprocal display, though it seems to be primarily misplaced " courtship " posturing rather than ritualised greeting display. The distinction is rather artificial as many greeting displays, in which both birds of a pair participate, are apparently adaptations of courtship display. None of the displays of this kind recorded of various races of *T. troglodytes* attain the degree of mutuality characteristic of some tropical wrens' greeting ceremonies. For example, at the reunion of hooded cactus wrens both sing with outspread tails and vibrating wings (Dickey and Van Rossem 1938). During the nest-building period of Irish dippers wing-quivering, accompanied by song, is the commonest form of display when a mated male and female meet (Rankin and Rankin 1940). Similar display is performed by other races of the dipper (Armstrong 1954).

As the males of the insular subspecies are more attentive at the nest than the male European wren it is not surprising that the tendency towards performing greeting display is more noticeable in them. The procedure amounts to an accentuation of the posturing already mentioned and illustrated in Plate IV, (p. 116). At a nest of the St. Kilda wren one bird greeted the other by spreading and vibrating its wings, making " queer chipping noises " (Atkinson 1949). Yeates (1948) noted that Shetland wrens " greeted each other with a charming little ceremony of mutual wing-quivering," but the only mutual display by a pair of these birds which I witnessed consisted of a brief song by a male standing with tail fanned while mildly quivering his raised wings. This display, which was performed when the birds first met in the morning, was " acknowledged " by his mate with even less drooping of the wings than that of the female in the illustration. Hebridean wrens display in a somewhat similar way, but the female may quiver her half-open wings while the male sings quietly and displays. The excitement of seeing an intruder at the nest may stimulate or accentuate this mutual posturing. Similarly a European wren disturbed at the nest by a human intruder may perform displacement epigamic display with wings quivering and tail expanded.

In the usual display of pale-bellied (southern) house wrens both birds quiver their wings, the male singing loudly and the female chirruping (Haverschmidt 1952). As this may occur when there are half-grown nestlings it may be a " courtship " display which functions as a greeting in connubial situations.

Banner Posture and Windmill Display

Occasionally a sexually excited male will perch with tail erect, but not fanned, and wings raised to about $45°$, or rather more, above the horizontal in a posture somewhat similar to that shown in Plate III (p. 109). (This photograph actually depicts a momentary attitude during threat display). The posture is maintained for only a second or so and the bird may perform several times in succession, changing his perch between displays. The light, shining through the wings, gives them a lovely, diaphanous appearance. These posturings may occur between pursuit flights and periods during which the male, squatting on a twig, gazes down where he knows the female to be skulking. When I watched a bird display thus a few inches from the entrance to a nest I was impressed by the effectiveness of the pose as a means of indicating to the female the whereabouts of the nest, but this is probably not its primary significance as it is assumed elsewhere and is not, so far as I have observed, an element in the normal nest-invitation display. The Faeroe wren also displays in the banner posture, perching with tail erect and wings uplifted in a deep V while singing near the female (Williamson 1947a). A very similar display is performed by the Irish dipper (Rankin and Rankin 1940).

A rather odd form of behaviour which looks like a half-hearted approximation to the banner posture is seen at certain times when a wren is in a sexually stimulated state. Momentarily he partially elevates his wings in a bedraggled way, almost as if he were preventing himself from over-balancing. The action seems to be an incomplete form of epigamic display, elicited by the appearance of an unexpected object. Probably it is an intention movement. It resembles the kind of behaviour which, in some species, has evolved into distraction display.

The most spectacular display of the male Shetland wren to the female consists of what might be considered an animated modification of the banner posture. While the bird perches in a prominent position he flaps his wings rapidly so that they appear almost to whirl about his body, thus rendering him very conspicuous. At the same time he sings excitedly. Although some of the display movements of the European wren bear some resemblance to this performance I have seen none exactly like it. So far as one can judge from a description the courtship display of the prairie marsh wren is rather similar, though less vigorous. He fluffs his breast feathers and tail coverts, tilts his tail over his back, flaps his partially-opened wings and sways his head from side to side.

DELAYED-ACTION FLIGHT

While the banner posture of the European wren looks rather like a " still " of the Shetland wren's windmill display the delayed-action flight suggests an accentuation of wing-quivering to the extent that the bird becomes airborne. Often this flight-display is brief; indeed, on the first two or three occasions when I noticed it, so momentary was the effect that I was uncertain whether my eyes had deceived me. Apparently the usual wing-beat is interrupted and a fluttering motion adopted in which the wings describe a curtailed arc. The beat, or rather flutter, is irregular. Delayed-action flight is sometimes performed in the midst of the usual courtship activities—wing-quivering, pouncing, subdued singing, and so forth. On beholding it one has a curious sense of buoyant slow motion—of time standing still for an instant. Nice and Thomas (1948) interpreted delayed-action flight by a Carolina wren as distraction display.

The Shetland wren's windmill display frequently ends in a flight during which the bird pounces on or near the female, and as the motion of the wings is so vigorous the flight appears the natural consummation of it. The bird's performance reminded me of a helicopter taking off.

The ordinary display-flights of birds can be roughly classified as the slow motion or " butterfly " type and the accelerated flutter or " moth " type. Some species, such as the oystercatcher and goldfinch, exhibit both forms. Conder (1948) regards the goldfinch's " moth " display as an extension into flight of the female solicitation posture, but it would seem possible that the solicitation posture of the goldfinch, wren and many other passerines is either an adaptation of inhibited flight or the chicks' begging posture. Watching the display-flights of birds one often gains an impression of inhibition or even lack of co-ordination, reminiscent of some injury-simulation and other diversionary displays. As it is probable that these flights are an outcome of mingled impulses, to defy and to flee, as with an injury-simulating bird, similarities between the two types of display need not surprise us. Indeed, we should expect to find, as we do in regard to the wren, willow warbler and other species, that the display-flight has the appearance of being evolved from an inhibited or accentuated form of ordinary flight due to a drive being impeded.

THE VOLPLANE

The " volplane " is so similar to the banner posture that it may be regarded as the adoption of this posture while airborne. As the bird concludes his flight, either from a high point to a lower perch or, very occasionally, high in the air from one part of the territory to another, he floats daintily down with wings tilted at an angle of 45°, giving a few wing-beats and a slight flutter before alighting. Once a male, followed by a female some twelve feet in the rear, flew at a height of about forty feet across a wide road and descended with a fluttering volplane. This aerial manœuvre is very pretty.

Mr. J. H. Owen tells me that he has seen a somewhat similar type of flight by a wren engaged in nest-building. Twice, when the bird dropped material, he floated down " with wings outspread, just like a falling leaf." He compares this behaviour with the slower and more leaf-like dropping flight of the red-backed shrike. In view of these observations it is just possible that the volplane is more a posture facilitating alighting after a vertical descent than a display figure, but as I have never seen it performed except by a sexually excited male in between displaying to a female in other ways it may be a flight posture which has acquired display function.

QUILL RATTLING

While watching a wren by the seashore in County Down on 26 September I noticed that during the wing-quivering display a series of rapid " snips " could be heard, a crepitation similar to that of a shower of electric sparks. A female followed him through the base of a low hedge, and twice, when she crept close to him, he sang subsong and shivered his wings in courtship display. When I first heard these sounds I thought that possibly the bird's wings might be touching leaves or twigs, but later, when the wren quivered his semi-horizontal wings as he perched on a bare tree-stump it was evident that the sounds were caused by the contact of the quills with one another. The morning was exceptionally still. It was so quiet that where I crouched six feet away I had no difficulty in hearing the impacts as the bird battered a caterpillar against a twig. Perhaps these " snippety " sounds are not so rare as this isolated episode would suggest. They could only be heard in a very quiet environment. Possibly they were due to, or accentuated by, some special condition of the wren's plumage after the moult. I was fully alive to the possibility that the sounds might be made by the bird's mandibles, for occasionally one may hear " snip " sounds as a wren closes its beak, but they were not caused in this way.

A familiar display of this kind is the quill-rattling performed by the peacock with his erected train. Many other kinds of mechanical sound are produced by various birds (Armstrong 1947), but the most interesting display comparable with, though much more elaborate than, that of the wren which I have observed is the performance of Gould's manakin in the Panamanian forest. It has been described in detail by Chapman (1935). The male makes " snip " and " snap " sounds with the enlarged quills of the wing feathers, as he leaps about in his " court " in the jungle. These noises serve to attract and stimulate the female. The wren's performance suggests that the origin of related types of display by other species may be traced to the accentuation, during the course of evolution, of slight noises incidental to display and the concomitant adaptation of associated structures, such as the wing-quills.

GUILLEMOT POSTURE

Sometimes an ardent male assumes a curious upright posture when approaching a female. One was seen crouching low, then stretching upright " like a guillemot," hopping quickly in this attitude with his tail dragging on the ground. He squatted again, then flew up singing

FIG. 15. Male wren in "guillemot" posture.

loudly, and alighted, again assuming the upright pose. Long trills accompanied these manœuvres. The female was some nine feet away feeding unconcernedly. The same observer saw two wrens perched on a hedge a yard apart facing each other with bills raised at an angle of 45° (Marples 1940). This posture is reminiscent of that adopted by dippers when *vis-à-vis*. Another male uttered a prolonged and powerful song, lacking the usual trills, and then approached the female with his neck extended to a grotesque extent " looking not unlike pictures of the bittern in alarm posture." The female thereupon posed in a similar way and the male attempted coition. When the male flew away the female remained quivering her wings and tail (Nelder 1948). The female prairie marsh wren points her bill upwards when soliciting her mate and a spotted-breasted wren (*Thryothorus m. maculipectus*) was seen with bill held skyward and spread tail quivering his wings in display to another wren (Wetmore 1944).

DISPLAY WITH NESTING MATERIAL

A great many species pick up or manipulate nesting material during display. This is a displacement activity which has become ritualised into their displays and acquired effectiveness in courtship, threat and other situations (Armstrong 1947, 1950b). In some species only the occasional desultory pecking at material occurs, in others the movements performed when holding material are stereotyped and elaborate. The European wren is one of the birds which merely pick up and carry material casually and infrequently. The procedure is not an essential element in any of the display "figures," but the species, like many others, apparently has the potentiality to evolve a specific, elaborate display with nesting material.

Morley (1938) describes seeing a male carrying some moss, his neck so elongated that it seemed half as long as his body. The neck feathers were erected and he sang snatches of subdued song, inter-mittently shivering his drooped wings. I have noticed display by a bird carrying material on a number of occasions. Three days after a female, accompanied by an excited male, had been seen lining a nest I heard the birds calling to one another. The female suddenly left off feeding and flew across an opening in the bushes to the male. He remained silent but soon crossed the clearing with a black object, which may have been a sodden, decayed leaf, dangling from his bill. She followed him. This performance was repeated five times and towards the end of the episode there was vigorous song from the male. Next day he was busy escorting a newly-fledged brood and pouncing on the female in charge.

On 29 April a cock wren, Yellow-and-Black, was building in a rather desultory fashion, spending from eight to twenty minutes in the nest. After a brief visit he sang a vigorous stifled and abbreviated song holding a leaf in his bill and quivering his horizontal wings. When the female suddenly appeared a short scuffle followed. He uttered some calls and then subsong, again holding leaves in his bill. Later I shall describe how a male, bewildered by the energetic building of his mate, frequently displayed while carrying material (p. 154).

Hearing alarm notes in Wren Wood one day I went to the spot from which they issued and found two wrens cursing two cats concealed below them. The male, who had a nest under construction, and possibly the female also, carried nesting material. On the occasion of a territorial quarrel during July between three males, one of them, possibly a bird of the year, sang a squeaky hedge sparrow-like song holding a rounded object in his bill. He was much excited and quivered his partly-extended wings.

In some of the episodes in which I have seen wrens holding material, building and courtship display were intermingled, but in others the behaviour may most plausibly be regarded as displacement activity. In many species materials used in nest-building have become ritually associated with display. The most interesting and unusual posturing of this kind which I have observed was in a Cambridge garden where, day after day, a female blackbird holding a bunch of leaves aloft in her bill, demonstrated against another in the centre of a lawn where the territorial boundary had been established. Circumstances may be imagined in which such behaviour, or the wren's tendency to display holding nesting material, might become as stereotyped as the courtship posturings with material of great crested grebes or the threat displays of the raven and herring gull in which grass is torn up with the beak.

Nest-Invitation Display

The nest-invitation display is a specific, localised form of wing-quivering. The procedure serves to guide the female to the nest, but also probably stimulates her and renders her more likely to choose it. I have never known a female to select a nest on her own initiative, that is, a nest at which no male was active. There is, however, as we shall see (p. 155), a possibility that on rare occasions when a female builds a nest she may choose the site herself.

Some resident females which have spent the winter and spring in and around a territory are aware of the situation of some of the nests belonging to the series built by the male before he discloses them ceremonially. It is not unusual to find a female roosting in an auxiliary nest. Many cocks sing and call in a significant way between spells of building, so that these intermittent bursts of song from a specific place betray the site of the nest to a human observer and probably also to interested females. Lying in bed I have noticed such characteristic song-bursts and been able later to walk straight to where the nest was being built. Several times I have seen a female visit a male while he was building, sometimes thereby confusing and disconcerting him.

One female led her young to roost in a nest built while she was feeding young in another nest twenty yards off. She could hardly have known where it was situated had she not noticed what her mate was up to while she was busy with her brood. Naturally, the full nest-invitation display may be curtailed when the female is already aware of the location of the nest, but some invitatory display may take place even at a nest used as a roost by the female (p. 112).

A male inviting a female to choose a nest leads the way, uttering songs and subsongs attentively around and ahead of her. His conspicuousness contrasts with the secretive character of her approach through the undergrowth. On reaching the near neighbourhood of the nest the male becomes increasingly animated, proceeding with staccato movements from twig to twig while uttering his fragmentary songs. Now, perched on a frond outside the nest he stands with spread tail and drooping wings all a-quiver, warbling sweet invitatory songs. Meanwhile, the female draws near, moving with diminutive hops, apparently preoccupied with the insects and spiders lurking in the herbage. Her suitor flies up to a branch and squats, vibrating his half-spread wings, leaning intently over, watching for her reappearance. Again he alights on the twig by the nest, singing his soft and slender song while holding his wings like a tremulous cloak about him. Suddenly he darts to the nest and pops inside. For some time—it may be a few seconds or several minutes—he stays there, then flies out uttering a ringing churr, flipping his wings as he stands on the twig. Quivering and warbling he faces the nest while the female hops and shuffles rather coyly towards it, cranes her neck to look in—and enters. He cannot contain his excitement but flies in and out again immediately, bobbing here and there. Later he may spend longer periods with her in the nest, perhaps inspecting or titivating it or just cuddling close to her. Probably, like the females of several passerines, who, when selecting a site for the nest, squat as if brooding in the crotch

FIG. 16. Nest-invitation display. (*After a photograph by the author.*)

of a branch, she settles into the bottom of the nest, experiencing something of what it would feel like to incubate there.

When the female is familiar with the nest the procedure is simpler. Sometimes the male, realising that a bird of opposite sex is near, comes bouncing along with loud, broken songs, entering the nest and emerging with a certain amount of display. A resident female may accompany a male to a nest again and again, but when two wrens appear at a nest it is difficult to determine which has taken the initiative. Often a considerable time elapses after the establishment of *rapport* between male and female early in the year, and the lining of a nest by the female. During this period, especially in the early morning, two females may be found near the nest with the male displaying from time to time to one or other. Perhaps the nest becomes, to some extent, a rendezvous, or the female sometimes joins the male on patrol as he visits the nest. Even when there is no prospective mate to escort and beguile with subsong and posturing a male will visit his nests from time to time (p. 44), occasionally whispering a fragment of quiet song as he goes in or comes out; or he may sing loudly and regularly outside the too-long-unoccupied dwelling.[5]

A wren will lead or accompany a female to an old nest built by his predecessor in the territory and display at it. Galapagos finches will go still farther and, although they build several nests, display regularly at nests of other species or even by a tuft of lichen (Lack 1945, 1947b).

Apparently a male and female may accompany each other on a nest-site selection expedition before a nest is built. Mr. P. Baldwin tells me that he once noticed a wren hopping around a nesting-box, singing frequently. The aperture was covered with spiders' webs so that obviously it had not been entered. The male peeped in from time to time. Then he grew bolder, going some little way inside, but backing out and then perching on the roof. At last he entered and came out head first. Now he went in and out repeatedly, even singing inside. Then a female, who had been lurking near at hand, hopped on to the box. Both stayed for about two minutes. The whole performance took half an hour. Later a nest was built and young reared.

The Shetland wren's invitation display is more conspicuous than that of the European wren. The male perches on a rock a few yards from where the nest is situated and then, singing lustily, flies ostentatiously to the site, creeps into the nest and, sometimes, stays there for some minutes. He will perform in this way several times in close succession. The display is evidently an accentuation of the European wren's nest-invitation adapted to the more open habitats of the Shetland race. One observation of the Hebridean wren's nest-invitation display suggests that it is similar. The evolution of this conspicuous display may be correlated with Shetland wrens being exposed to fewer predators than wrens in most parts of Britain or the continent, but perhaps the nest-invitation of European wrens in bleak habitats approximates to this display.[6] Where predators are scarce birds tend to make themselves more conspicuous at the nest than corresponding or closely related forms elsewhere. Thus display-building Galapagos finches perform a song-flight as they go back and forth (Lack 1945, 1947b).

The invitation ceremony of the house wren follows similar, but simpler, lines to that of the European wren. When the male returns from his winter quarters he pre-empts nesting cavities by placing materials in them. He flutters ahead of any female who joins him, perches near the entrance to the proposed nesting-place, and goes in and out. His song is more vigorous and frequent than usual, and he utters a squeaky, coaxing variant while she is near the nest. If she approves of the site she indicates this by bringing lining material. When she has settled into a routine of nest-lining the male reverts to his territorial song, uttered eagerly and excitedly.

Nest-Invitation Displays of Other Passerines

In nest-invitation displays in general the male makes himself conspicuous by movements or utterances—usually by a combination of the two. With many hole-nesting species, such as the collared flycatcher (Löhrl 1949, 1951) and redstart (Buxton 1950) the procedure conforms to a pattern which varies in detail. As an example, the pied flycatcher's procedure may be summarised. Having appropriated a suitable nest-site the male defends it, pops in and out from time to time, and sometimes lays the foundations of the nest. On the appearance of a potential mate he invites her to follow by flying ostentatiously to the cavity and displaying with quivering wings and high-pitched squeaks. He also utters a subdued or " stifled " song (Gilbert 1929; Haartman 1949, 1951; Owen 1943).

Among other species with a rather simpler form of nest-invitation consisting mainly of popping in and out of a hole, may be mentioned the great tit (Gibb 1950), starling and house sparrow (Daanje 1941). The male Tengmalm's owl carries prey to the hole he has selected and " sings " in front. When the female appears he flies in and out of it in similar fashion to the wren. She inspects the cavity and eats the food provided there (Kühk 1943, 1949).

The nest-invitation of a number of species of warbler, including the blackcap, garden warbler (Raines 1945), whitethroat and lesser whitethroat (Howard 1929) approximates to that of the wren.

After the male penduline tit has built a nest, or part of one, he perches, singing, close by or actually in it (Burckhardt 1948). It is noteworthy that birds so different as the European wren, the penduline tit and some of the weavers practise polygamy, multiple-nest-building and nest-invitation. Some weavers, such as the baya (Ali 1930) and mottle-backed weaver (Benson 1945) nest in colonies, each individual making a series of nests. From time to time the birds display together, each fluttering at the entrance to his nest.

Nest-Invitation of Other Organisms

The avian procedure of nest-invitation is paralleled among fish—an interesting illustration of convergent evolution. The three-spined stickleback (*Gasterosteus aculeatus*) builds a nest in his territory and performs a zig-zag dance when a female comes on the scene. This evokes display on the part of the female, which in turn elicits a new reaction from the male; and so forth until the eggs are fertilised (Tinbergen 1942; Tinbergen and Van Iersel 1947). The sequence of activities of bird and fish may be compared:

Courtship Sequence

Stickleback		Wren	
♂	♀	♂	♀
		Sings	
	Approaches		Approaches
Zig-zags		Displays	
	Displays		Acquiesces
Leads		Leads	
	Follows		Follows
Shows nest entrance		Shows nest entrance	
	Enters		Enters
Quivers		Quivers wings	
	Lays		Lines
Fertilises		Fertilises	
			Lays

The wren's series of reactions is less stereotyped than the stickleback's and, as we have noted, wide divergences occur.

By means of a dance in which the extravagantly developed claw is brandished fiddler crabs attract the females into burrows to copulate (Crane 1941), but, of course, these burrows are not equivalent to nests. Certain Australian spiders stridulate, apparently to attract females to their burrows. Little is known of their behaviour, but it seems to resemble the nest-invitation procedure of the wren more than that of the fiddler crab.

Courtship and Connubial Feeding

On rare occasions the male wren may bring food to his mate while she is incubating. This behaviour is best described as " connubial feeding " to distinguish it from " courtship feeding," which is the administration of food to the female before the eggs are laid and brooding has started. Courtship feeding in any species is never more than token feeding, but connubial feeding may extend to providing the whole nourishment of the female as she incubates and tends the young, as among hornbills.

Courtship feeding proper has not been definitely recorded of *T. troglodytes*, but it may, perhaps, occur on rare occasions. While Vigors's wrens are foraging together early in the year the female is fed by the male from time to time (Miller 1941). Courtship feeding also occurs among dippers (Nethersole-Thompson 1944b) and, of course, many other species (Armstrong 1947).

Mrs. R. E. Moreau noticed that on the eighth day after the laying of the last egg a cock twice took a caterpillar to his mate on the nest. On each occasion the female seized and ate it as she sat. On the day another brood hatched the female replied to the male's song with a chitter. Two days later he brought a small green caterpillar while his mate was brooding, sang and displayed, but she did not respond and he went away. Although frequent watch was kept he was never again seen to approach the nest (R. Gait, *in litt.*). Another male visited the nest twice with food when the chicks hatched but did not feed them until some days later (Whitehouse and Armstrong 1953). Mr. C. Newcomb noticed the mate of the bird shown in Plate v (p. 141) at the nest the day after hatching occurred, but never again. Mächler (1947) observed a wren visiting and feeding his mate, who was sitting on her second brood clutch, and Miss C. Stanwood writes that she saw an incubating winter wren emerge from the nest in response to the male's song, fly to him and be fed. A male eastern house wren carried food to both his mates incubating contemporaneously (Hempel 1919), and connubial feeding is also reported of the rufous-browed wren (*Troglodytes rufociliatus*) (Skutch 1940a), Bewick's wren (Laskey 1946a), Vigors's wren (Miller 1941), the rock wren (Bent 1948) and the northern cactus wren (Anderson 1948). It plays a prominent part in the behaviour of the Carolina wren, but apparently does not occur during late nestings (Wight 1934; Laskey 1946b, 1948; Nice and Thomas 1948). Laskey (1944) has noticed that the male cardinal feeds the female only during the early broods and suggests that this may also be true of the Carolina wren. Apparently when the male Carolina wren has fledglings to tend he does not feed the female. The long periods spent on the eggs by this species may contribute to the accentuation of connubial feeding (p. 181). A male has been seen bringing food 13 times in 55 hours (Nice and Thomas 1948). Dippers also tend to spend long periods incubating and in at least one race, the American dipper, the male may be very attentive to his mate. A bird brought food seven times during one incubation session (Hann 1950). However, Ryves (1938b) believes that the British dipper seldom feeds his mate on the nest and during lengthy watches at an Irish dipper's nest the male was not seen feeding the female (Rankin and Rankin 1940).

FEMALE SOLICITATION DISPLAY AND COITION

When performing the solicitation-display the female squats on a branch with wings partially expanded and spread horizontally, tail widely fanned, wings and tail quivering rapidly, uttering a rapid sequence of high-pitched squeaks or squeals (p. 95). I have known a bird display thus some twenty times in succession, with interludes varying from a few seconds to a minute or more, occasionally moving from one twig to another, without obtaining any sexual response from

the male. Such calls, though uttered somewhat feebly, may be heard on rare occasions when males are beginning their first nests about the third week of March. Perhaps they have a stimulating effect on them. When the female house wren utters the invitatory call the male approaches " singing softly, tail upturned, wings a-flutter" (Kendeigh 1941). The hen Carolina wren emits a trilling call to attract the cock to tread

FIG. 17. Female solicitation display, low intensity. In the high intensity display the wings are quivered in a more horizontal position and the tail is fanned.

her, and after the act, or attempted act, he sings. In his display he postures before her with outspread wings and utters a specific note (Nice and Thomas 1948). Crouching low the female rock wren (*Salpinctes o. obsoletus*) crawls mouse-like over a rock with her tail spread, uttering faint squeals. He flutters here and there around her, also keeping his tail fanned (Jaeger 1950).

> The wren goes to't and the small gilded fly
> Does lecher in my sight,

cried the distraught King Lear, but observation suggests that male wrens may not be continuously in condition to copulate throughout the breeding season and that there may be a close succession of states when the impulse to tread is inhibited and the nest-building impulse is strong. Certainty in this matter cannot be attained by field studies alone.

Prior to copulating the male may move his erected tail laterally and quite slowly (p. 99)—behaviour which contrasts very strangely with the excited, rapid movements which he makes at such times.

On one occasion copulation took place without my noticing any call from the female. The male came along, singing in flight, then uttering a long phrase of 23 seconds he alighted on a robinia branch where the female was squatting. He approached with a running movement, his wings flapping vigorously all the time. After coition the female made picking movements in the air as she perched on the branch; then she flew to a wall a few yards away, where the nest in which she later laid was situated, and over the house. There I found her feeding two young of her first brood. The scraping notes uttered during this, presumably successful, copulation, were subdued.

Consummation may be effected, apparently, during two to five seconds of contact, during which the male balances on the female's rump with rapidly fluttering wings. He does not hold her neck plumage with his beak. Although the male prairie marsh wren is usually more forward in his advances than the female one of these has been seen soliciting a male only 25 minutes after coition.

Female wrens will leave a male's territory if, after repeated efforts, they do not succeed in eliciting adequate response.

Sexual display is most commonly observed, and in most varied forms, in April, although chases may take place as early as February and copulation with a mount, during which semen was deposited, was observed on 8 March (p. 99). Before the initiation of the second brood display is less elaborate, though, as we have seen, pouncing is common. By August the impulses responsible for sexual display have usually almost disappeared. In September I have noted wing-quivering display on several occasions and the subsong heard in autumn, and even in winter, suggests that some sexual impulses are never far from expression (p. 90). Attempted copulation has been observed on 6 November and an apparently successful attempt on 23 November (Brown 1943). It is now well known that expressions of epigamic or sexual activity, usually incomplete, associated with the recrudescence of gonadal activity, are frequent in autumn among birds of temperate regions.

CHAPTER 9
NEST-BUILDING

This moss-lined shed, green, soft and dry,
Harboured a self-contented Wren,
Not shunning man's abode, though shy,
Almost as thought itself, of human ken.
WORDSWORTH. *The Contrast*

MATERIAL

MORE THAN four centuries ago William Turner described the nest of the wren. As he put on record observations made in Newnham I find it a pleasant fancy that he may have watched wrens and found their nests in the neighbourhood of my garden. He wrote:

> The nest is outwardly of moss and inwardly of feathers, wool or down, but mainly of feathers. The nest has the form of an upright egg standing on one of its ends, while in the middle of one side there is a little postern, as it were, by which the bird goes in and out. It sometimes builds its nest at the back of a house or in sheds thatched with straw or in woods.

Wordsworth more accurately described it as "moss-lined," for moss is by no means always the dominant material in the outer structure, though I have found nests of European, Shetland and St. Kilda wrens constructed almost exclusively of it. One nest of the European wren was built of withered cow parsley fronds; another was made of dry holly leaves. Others which I have come across were almost entirely composed of bracken. Mr. J. H. Owen observed a bird trying to build a nest of lawn clippings. In spite of the collapse of the structure as soon as it rose above the entrance hole the wren persisted for some time in his hopeless task. "Eel grass" or "wigeon grass" (*Zostera marina*) is used occasionally by wrens nesting on the seashore (Thompson 1849; Bolam 1912).

The extent to which the nest blends with its surroundings appears to be due merely to the wren's utilising the materials most readily available and therefore usually congruent with the site. Occasionally a bird builds a very conspicuous nest of white moss, brightly coloured leaves or other material (Walter 1888; Blakemore 1946). At Tring, where emus were kept in paddocks, some nests were composed mainly of feathers from these birds (Hartert 1910). Nevertheless, wrens exercise considerable discrimination in their choice of material, but apparently more on the basis of texture than tint. I have not succeeded in duping a bird into using coloured shreds of paper placed near where he was building. A wren seeking material will pick up and reject scraps until he finds a piece " to his mind." I have known a bird go fifty yards to fetch skeleton poplar leaves, but it is exceptional for materials to be sought so far away. Usually they are gathered within a radius of a few yards. Occasionally wet, bedraggled leaves attached to a nearby bush are plucked off. Green blades of grass are sometimes added to St. Kilda wrens' nests (Harrisson and Buchan 1936).

Individuals make successive nests of different types of vegetable débris according to what is available. Of three nests built in a small territory one was mainly of cow parsley, another of leaves and the third of dried grass. It is exceptional for a wren to use material from an old nest for another (Blakemore 1946) though reed warblers commonly do so (Brown and Davies 1949). A few instances are on record of a wren filching material from the nest of another species, such as a song thrush (Thompson 1849).

The house wren differs from the wren in being less particular about the choice of nest material. Usually twigs are used, but a bird may gather pieces of wire, nails or hairpins (Kendeigh, in litt.). As a feathered Autolycus this species is surpassed by the canyon wren (*Catherpes mexicanus*). The nest of one bird contained 1791 objects amongst which were paper clips, pen nibs, tacks, screws and toothpicks (Lofberg 1931).

Nesting Sites

The sites chosen vary greatly and include niches in ivy on trees and walls, crevices in thatch, ricks, walls and the roots of over-turned trees.

> These find, 'mid ivied abbey-walls,
>   A canopy in some still nook;
> Others are pent-housed by a brae
>   That overhangs a brook.
>   Wordsworth. *A Wren's Nest*

The wren shares with the robin, swallow and swift a partiality for niches inside buildings. When wrens breed in a shed or other large space to which they penetrate by means of a small hole the male remembers the way in for a considerable time after the nest is built, and the female, when she is guided to it, quickly learns how to get in and out. Only rarely do birds nesting in such places lose their way and their lives (Mylne 1952).

An ideal wren nesting site would provide: (1) suitable *points d'appui* for material; (2) a sheltered, snug situation; (3) concealment, and (4) a clear fly-way from the portal. Actual choices are usually compromises in which all or nearly all these desiderata have been attained to some extent. Although there is no European species of bird more adept in threading its way through dense cover the wren avoids situations where the aperture of the nest would be obstructed. Tangled thickets such as are beloved of the lesser whitethroat are seldom or never chosen, though I have seen a nest partly obscured by branches of jasmine. It was appropriated by a field-mouse. A clear space before the threshold not only facilitates nest-building, feeding the nestlings and escape from predators, but also provides a dais where the cock can display.

As each male builds a number of nests and one or two may not be well concealed the naturalist who does not realise how many remain undiscovered is apt to underestimate the difficulty of finding them. I have located three in little more than five minutes, but this is exceptional. Only by assiduous observation of the building bird may all, or nearly all, the nests be found. Sometimes a nest is so deep in a cranny of a wall or tree that it is invisible from outside.

Sites which intrigue newspaper correspondents by their incongruity are reported from time to time. Nests have been recorded in cabbages and broccoli, and in the hanging, desiccated carcasses of carrion and hooded crow, jay, sparrowhawk, brown owl and cat (Walpole-Bond 1909; Glegg 1935) as well as in a human skull (Stevenson and Gurney 1872); also in the pocket of a scarecrow's coat and inside an old bonnet displayed for the same purpose (Montagu 1831).

A wreath in a shed, a tramp's shirt left on a bush, a pair of trousers hung up to dry, and the fold of a church curtain are among the objects of man's fabrication chosen, and nests of the European and Shetland wren have been found in coils of rope. The ancient legend recording how St. Malo, returning from pruning the monastery vines, found that a wren had built a nest in his cloak and laid an egg in it, may well be founded on fact. Pious imagination may, perhaps, be forgiven for adding one egg so small.

A house wren built in a boy's bathing trunks shortly after they had been hung on the line to dry—and was allowed to rear the brood (Griscom 1945). Of 24 cow skulls lodged in trees on an island in Virginia all but one were occupied by house wrens (Forbush 1916).

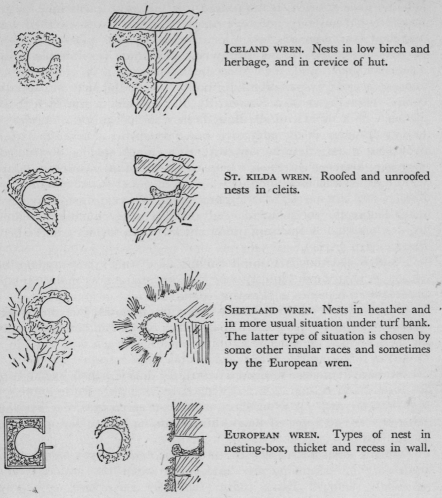

ICELAND WREN. Nests in low birch and herbage, and in crevice of hut.

ST. KILDA WREN. Roofed and unroofed nests in cleits.

SHETLAND WREN. Nests in heather and in more usual situation under turf bank. The latter type of situation is chosen by some other insular races and sometimes by the European wren.

EUROPEAN WREN. Types of nest in nesting-box, thicket and recess in wall.

FIG. 18. Cross sections of nests of different races of *Troglodytes troglodytes*.

A European wren failed to rear her nestlings in a vehicle in daily use (Twining 1949), but a Carolina wren succeeded (Stoddard 1948). So also, apparently, did sparrows nesting, not like Shakespeare's swallows " in Cleopatra's sails," but in those of a houseboat travelling on the Nile (Meinertzhagen 1949).

No nest is more frequently found touching that of another species than the nest of the wren because wrens' nests are often left unoccupied for a considerable time, and to a bird of another species the material lodged in the twigs is not recognised as a nest. Moreover, wrens sometimes use the nests of other birds for their own purposes. Fairly frequently old swallows' nests are occupied in this country and on the Continent, and nests of house martin, house sparrow and woodpecker (Hoertler 1934) may be requisitioned. The house wren occasionally (Fletcher 1944), and the Nicaraguan banded wren (*Thryothorus pleurostictus ravus*) apparently habitually, lay in the nest of another species (Dickey and Van Rossem 1938). I found a wren's nest in contact with a robin's, others have been recorded on top of a white-throat's (Dobson 1952), next to a house sparrow's (Makatsch 1935) and under a song thrush's nest with eggs (Black 1920). Sometimes these semi-detached dwellings are in occupation simultaneously; thus wrens have bred in association with robins, chaffinches, yellowhammers (Duve 1928) and blackbirds (Garling 1928) (Pl. VI, p. 148). One of my photographs, not included here, shows a wren entering her nest below a blackbird's nest containing chicks. Both species reared their young. Mr. J. H. Owen tells me that he has seen a young cuckoo in a hedge sparrow's nest built on top of a wren's nest containing young. A wren's nest built into the base of a magpie's, held nestlings when kestrels occupied it (Lancum 1953).

When a wren built at the base of a treecreeper's nest the latter deserted (Schmaus 1928), and a house wren which had laid three eggs left them because an American robin nested within ten feet, but when American robins nested on top of a box occupied by house wrens both species reared families (Kendeigh 1941). A prairie marsh wren's nest has been found on top of a red-winged blackbird's; both contained eggs (Welter 1935). A wren was flushed from seven eggs in a dipper's old nest. It had received an additional lining of feathers and hair (Bolam 1912).

When a wren has chosen a site for his nest he may show great pertinacity in continuing to build, even when the materials are repeatedly removed (Black 1920). Similarly a Bewick's wren may persist even when the unfinished nest is taken away (Beemer 1947). A Carolina wren filled two campers' hats with leaves in the early hours of a summer day. The owners, irritated by the noisy call-notes of the energetic bird, threw out the material, but before reveille they were filled again (Skutch 1940b). A wren which started building close to an Irish dipper's nest was chased repeatedly, but this treatment did not deter him from continuing (Rankin and Rankin 1940). Another ejected a robin's material from an old kettle and built in it himself (J. H. Owen, *in litt.*). A male began visiting a bedroom in spring and eventually built a nest on the curtain-rail, taking seven weeks to complete it. When it fell down he rebuilt it. The female who accompanied him on one visit did not approve of the nest and never returned.

RE-USE OF OLD NESTS

It is unusual for a wren's nest to be used twice in the same year for breeding, but a few instances have come to my notice. Possibly this occurs when the male's other nests have been destroyed or when, through some mischance, no other nest is available at the time the female is ready to lay. As a rule, she has an aversion to using the first nest for a second brood, but Beckmann (1926) states that in eastern Schleswig-Holstein the second brood is commonly in the old nest refurbished. This would seem to be an exaggeration, but I have known a first-brood nest to be re-upholstered after the chicks fledged in readiness for another clutch. In Iceland, Shetland (Saxby 1874) and North America (Bowles 1899) wrens are said to use a nest of the previous year, but probably birds of these races, like the European wren, recondition the nest. It has been noticed that the Alaska wren frequently builds on the ruins of the old nest (Heath 1920). Lowe (1934) remarks that St. Kilda wrens nested every year " under a particular bank." He found a nest in a niche from which one containing eggs had been taken earlier that season. Pale-bellied house wrens sometimes use the same nest for two successive broods (Haverschmidt 1952).

Congenial nesting sites may be used for many years. Mr. Owen tells me of a niche chosen nine years in succession. Even if statements made by bird-lovers recording the nesting of wrens annually for as long as sixty years in a favourite recess are not as fully substantiated as one could wish, they testify to the great popularity and regular use of certain sites. Dippers are also faithful to congenial nooks. One site is said to have been occupied by a pair annually for 123 years (Gladstone 1910).

Of course, it cannot be assumed that the same birds or their offspring are involved when sites are used in successive years. Indeed, when I have been able to check the identity of a wren building in a niche used the previous year a different individual was involved. Probably, however, a survivor sometimes returns to a site of the previous year as a ringed female Irish dipper has been known to do (Rankin and Rankin 1940). Favourite sites may be used by Bewick's wrens year after year (Miller 1941).

Height

Most wrens' nests are low enough to be reached from the ground, but sites considerably higher are chosen more often than is generally realised. There are records of nests at " about seven metres " in a Wellingtonia (Oury 1932), in a house martin's nest at 16 ft. 2 in. (Harting 1920), and in a woodpecker's hole 13 ft. from the ground (Hoertler 1934). The highest I have found were at 30 ft., 16 ft. 7 in. and 15 ft. Another at 14 ft. was in a cavity in a dead oak suitable for a blue tit; next year a treecreeper built in it. In the Balearic Islands Munn (1931) discovered a nest of *Troglodytes t. mülleri* on the ground and another at nearly 20 ft. In Tibet and Kashmir wrens (*T. t. nipalensis* and *neglectus*) build among cliffs or 12 to 15 ft. high in trees (Ludlow and Kinnear 1944; Bates and Lowther 1952). Northern cactus wrens usually build fairly low—I have seen a nest 4 ft. from the ground—but sometimes as high as 30 ft. (Jaeger 1950).

Nests of the European wren are occasionally constructed on the ground or within a few inches of the surface of a stream or pool (Harting 1920; Whitaker 1907), and examples may be found under overhanging banks in the kind of situation favoured by Shetland wrens. On the Blaskets a bird built an undomed nest at the end of a puffin burrow (Ussher 1912). A nest in my garden was actually in the ground —inside a cavity in a mound of earth behind an ivy-covered lath fence. The recess was thinly lined here and there with moss, and the threshold and entrance were neatly constructed. I collected a cupful of earth from the ivy leaves beneath the aperture. This soil had been dislodged by the wren and I could not but conclude that he had to some extent shaped and enlarged the cavity. A female took some feathers into this nest, but it was never occupied—possibly due to my trapping the male inside in order to ring him. Referring to the bank nests of the St. Kilda wren, Harrisson and Buchan (1936) state that " the entrance holes seem to have been burrowed in the earth as was a nest seen by Eagle Clarke," but this is not the sense of his comment (1915) and it is doubtful whether this bird ever enlarges a cavity in the ground. Lowe (1934) found a nest in a hole like a large rat hole—although there are no rats on St. Kilda. The nests of some subspecies, such as the Alaska wren, are placed in crevices between rocks (Heath 1920). I have seen a Shetland wren's nest in the latter type of situation and several under overhanging turf banks. Such sites are often chosen by Hebridean wrens. The rock wren (*Salpinctes obsoletus*) of western North America nests in rock crevices and makes a path of small stones to the nest (Ray 1904).

European wrens tend to build higher as the season advances; the highest nests are often constructed in mid-season or rather later. I have never known the highest to be the first built. Dr. B. Løppenthin informs me that in Denmark the earliest wrens' nests are generally built in ditches, banks and the roots of overturned trees; later they are commonly found in " witches' brooms " on beeches and oaks. Yellowhammers (Parkhurst and Lack 1946), and no doubt some other birds, build higher late in the season, adapting themselves to the increasing density of the growing vegetation, but most of the high wrens' nests I have seen were built in evergreens or other situations where concealment and shelter would have been as adequate early in the year as later. Probably the selection of higher sites is correlated with the extension of the male's range vertically as spring advances.

The only female wren which I have known to build actively recommenced work at a higher site when her brood came to grief (p. 156). Another female, having deserted her eggs through interference, laid her next clutch in a more elevated nest. I have noticed that in some species in which the nest is normally built by the female, such as the robin and willow warbler, replacement nests are sometimes constructed in a higher position. To what extent this is a general tendency is uncertain (Brackbill 1950).

NUMBER OF NESTS

It has long been known that wrens build a series of nests. Many of them are never used and are called " play-nests " by the Germans and " cock's-nests " in this country. They do not differ in construction from occupied nests except that, as the females tend to choose the cosiest nests, those badly built or incomplete are passed over. Similarly, unfavourably situated nesting-holes are rejected by female collared flycatchers even when the male displays vigorously at them (Löhrl 1951). Observers who have noticed such unoccupied nests have sometimes mistakenly referred to " cock's nests " as being recognisable by their careless construction.

It is difficult to determine the number of nests built by an individual wren because, no matter how frequent one's visits, a bird may construct part of a nest, or even a complete nest, in one's absence. Occasionally a wren may build for about ten minutes at a site and never return to work there. Nests may be abandoned in all stages. So, too, with the nests of northern cactus wrens (Woods 1948) and some species of weaver (Ali 1931). However, my observations of the activities of a few wrens were sufficiently frequent to ensure only a small margin of error.

TABLE V

NUMBER OF NESTS BUILT BY CERTAIN WRENS IN WREN WOOD

Year	Wren	Complete	Incomplete	Total
1944	Lob	4	2	6
,,	Tom	5	0	5
1945	Yellow-and-Black	3	3	6
1947	Cinnabar	5	3	8

Data for 1946 are omitted as no male wren spent the whole breeding season in Wren Wood, and in other years my surveillance was not sufficiently regular to preclude the possibility of missing the building of more than one nest. The nest-building activity of Yellow-and-Black is not completely indicated by the total given, as he repaired three nests built by his predecessors the previous year. Making allowance for the possibility that the building of a nest or two may have escaped me, and supposing that the data constitute a typical sample, as I have reason to believe they do, the number of nests built by Cambridge wrens during a season averages between six and seven. Incomplete observations of a large number of nests and their builders indicate that a male wren usually makes more than four nests.

At Stein the nest-building activities of the birds were recorded:

TABLE VI

NUMBER OF NESTS FOUND IN THE GARDEN AT STEIN, HOLLAND

Year	Number of Wrens	Number of nests	Average
1937	10	58	5.8
1938	7	57	8.1
1939	8	40	5.0

The average is 6.2 nests per bird. Dr. Kluijver tells me that a considerable number of the nests were left unfinished. The most vigorous builder, No. 42, constructed twelve nests in 1936 and in the succeeding years ten, nine and nine. The Dutch observers suggest that the provision of nesting-boxes and cans may have stimulated nest-building abnormally; this is not supported by my experience as my average approximates to theirs although only two of the nests included in the data were in nesting-boxes. However, where suitable nesting-sites are scarce nests may tend to be fewer than in favourable habitats.

Plate Va. Female wren bringing strand of lining material to nest.
(*C. P. Newcomb*)

b. Wren peeping out of nest in the folds of a man's coat in a greenhouse.
(*B. M. Nicholas*)

Analysis of the nesting activities of wrens at Stein in 1938 shows:

TABLE VII

NUMBER OF NESTS BUILT BY WRENS AT STEIN IN 1938

Number of Wrens	Number of nests per bird
1	2
3	4
2	5
2	7
2	8
1	10

The bird which built only two nests sang abnormally and was driven out of his territory.

Throughout its range the European wren tends to build several nests. In Switzerland, for example, four or five nests are recorded (Fatio and Studer 1907) and this is not a maximum. In some other races the nest-building impulse is less strong. The Iceland wren builds more than one nest, but apparently fewer than the European wren (Armstrong 1950a, c). In Shetland, St. Kilda, and probably the Outer Hebrides, wrens build few nests. Apparently more than two is unusual, and so far as *T. t. hirtensis* is concerned the males may not average as many as two (R. Atkinson, *in litt.*). " Cock's nests " are made by the wren in the Balearic Islands (Henrici 1926). Reduction in building activities is correlated with monogamy and relatively harsh habitats. The western winter wren apparently builds from four to eight nests (Bowles 1899), and the eastern race also makes several nests (Palmer 1949); so, too, does the Kashmir wren (Bates and Lowther 1952).

Multiple nest-building is recorded of many other species of wren. The desert wren (*Thryomanes bewickii eremophilus*) (Simmons 1925) and possibly other races related to Bewick's wren occasionally begin more than one nest (Miller 1941). The male prairie marsh wren averages about five nests during the rearing of the first brood and may make as many as ten, but the female lays in a nest of her own making. The function of the males' nests is not definitely known (Fig. 40, p. 274). Wheeler (1931) found four or five unoccupied nests of Marian's marsh wren (*Telmatodytes palustris marianae*) for every occupied nest, but Wheelock (1904) noted only one in thirty nests of the tule wren (*Telmatodytes palustris paludicola*) occupied, and Dawson and Bowles (1909) discovered 56 nests of this bird, only three of which were in use. Male short-billed sedge wrens (*Cistothorus platensis stellaris*) build several nests (Forbush 1929; Taverner 1934) as cactus wrens of various species also do (Welter 1935; Skutch 1940a). Northern cactus wrens (*Campylorhynchus brunneicapillus couesi*) build six or more (Anthony 1891), and the hooded or rufous-naped cactus wren (*C. rufinucha capistratus*) may " keep on building throughout the year," the proportion of occupied nests being about one in eight (Dickey and Van Rossem 1938). According to Todd and Carriker (1922) a Columbian race of wood wren (*Henicorhina leucophrys anachoreta*(?)) builds many " false nests " which are always set in conspicuous places, but the nest used for breeding is carefully hidden. Perhaps these are dormitory nests; Sclater's wood wren (*Henicorhina leucosticta prostheleuca*) builds roosting nests where they are exposed to view but conceals the breeding nest (Skutch 1940a) (Fig. 39, p. 273).

Multiple nest-building is recorded of birds in widely diverse families and may serve various functions, such as providing a stance where coition may occur or a roosting platform for the young, as with water-hens. It is characteristic of the polygamous penduline tit and reaches a high development among the weavers. The masked weaver, for example, may begin eleven nests in three months (Taylor 1946).

NEST-BUILDING TECHNIQUE

A wren usually begins the nest by placing material to form its base but, during the first series of visits, moss, leaves or other vegetable matter may be fixed where the sides will be constructed, especially if the site is among thorns or twigs to which material may readily be attached. A sketchy roof is often added while the walls are quite flimsy so that the shape of the structure may be discerned after a few hours' work, but it may continue bowl-shaped for some time. In enclosed sites the sides or roof may be omitted, and the interior of a nesting-box is simply packed with moss and leaves arranged to form a cavity. On rare occasions an unroofed nest has been found in an open situation.

According to Ussher and Warren (1900) the roof is sometimes the first part of the nest to be built, but I have not noticed instances of this. There is no evidence that some individuals are specially apt to choose, or more adept at building in, cavities where adaptation of technique is necessary. Any European wren may build a series of nests in different types of situation. The available evidence for the other subspecies indicates that they are also adaptable in these respects. I have seen a Shetland wren's nest built in an exposed tuft of heather on an open moor and another entirely concealed in a crevice between rocks. The Iceland wren, Kashmir wren (Bates and Lowther 1952) and the winter wren choose varied sites. A nest of the latter has even been found in a site suitable for a dipper—a mossy recess on a rock where water trickled over it (Piers 1898). The Alaska wren sometimes builds in wet situations. Heath (1920) found that a nest with which he experimented was perfectly dry inside after a night under a dripping tap.

If utilisation of a wide range of sites and materials be taken into consideration as well as other aspects of craftsmanship, the wren is the most accomplished building technician among British birds. No other combines great adaptability with efficient technique as does the wren. The flimsy materials are sometimes so strongly compacted that nests in relatively exposed situations may survive to be used as roosts eighteen months after being built. Sheltered nests endure even longer.

Nearly all wrens of the genus *Troglodytes* breed in roofed nests, and, indeed, this is true of the majority of wrens of all genera, but the rufous-browed wren of Central America (*Troglodytes rufociliatus*) is an exception; it builds an open cup of pine needles placed in a crevice (Skutch 1940a).

Upholstering by the Male

The extent to which the interior of the nest is coated with moss or other soft stuff varies. If the structure is such as to provide a smooth interior there may be little or no specific upholstering. When the nest is made of material which becomes stiff on drying, as for example, at Wicken Fen where withered fronds of the marsh fern (*Thelypteris palustris*) are used, the inner walls are faced with moss. Sometimes for weeks after a nest has apparently been completed a bird will visit, inspect and titivate it, carrying in withered leaves, fibres or strands of moss. In spite of all this attention to the structure twigs sometimes protrude through the floor. Such nests are usually rejected by the females.

Construction of the Entrance

The threshold is reinforced with withered grass or fibres skilfully woven into the framework. If it were not thus strengthened the entrance would be worn to a ragged hole and the whole structure would probably crumble. The entrances to nests of the Iceland, Shetland, Hebridean and winter wrens are similarly reinforced, but some St. Kilda wrens' nests built mainly of coiled grass stems lack this strengthening. Nests constructed by female prairie marsh wrens have a long sill which, with the roof, constitutes an interior tube, but those made by the males, which are not used for breeding, are without it (Fig. 40, p. 274).

Other passerines avoid attrition of the threshold by means of various devices. The dipper strengthens the " doorstep " with mud (Ryves 1943) and the paradise flycatcher " oversews " with cobwebs (Moreau 1949a). The nuthatch not only plasters the entrance with mud but, according to my observations at one nest, slips in with a movement such that the claws scratch the entrance very little. The red-breasted nuthatch, which smears resin at the nest entrance, flies directly into the hole without her feet touching the sill (Brewster 1938).

Wren and dipper often construct eaves over the portal, concealing it as well as providing an overhang from which rain may drip. The aperture is neatly fashioned and maintained in good order by the male on his visits before the nest is occupied. It is completed towards the end of the operations and much of the work is done from inside, the builder leaning forth prettily to fit fibres into place. At all stages of construction he will lift and lay scraps, sometimes elongating and twisting his neck as he adjusts material.

When a wren reconstructs a nest of the previous year he may orientate the entrance differently. Some woodpeckers and other birds tend to direct the opening towards a favoured point of the compass, but the direction in which the aperture of the wren's nest faces is determined by its situation and the bird's convenience (Timmermann 1931). In some districts northern cactus wrens prefer a south-westerly aspect, but different orientations preponderate in various marsh wren colonies (Trautman 1940).

Among the curious adaptations recorded of some wren species may be mentioned the reputed practice of the Cape Horn grass wren, which is said to surround the aperture of the nest with thorns (Paessler 1928). Perhaps the observer found an exceptional nest. The Balearic wren sometimes fixes the dry leaves of a very prickly thistle in the outer structure (Munn 1931).

The Nicaraguan or mountain house wren (*Troglodytes musculus oreopolus*) commonly builds a snake or lizard skin into the nest (Dickey and Van Rossem 1938). Scraps of snake skin are also frequently present in the lining of house wren nests. Kendeigh thinks that, in at least some instances, they deter predators.

EFFECT OF RAINFALL ON BUILDING

The materials of a wren's nest are often bonded so firmly that older writers suggested that the bird uses its saliva as glue (Montagu 1831). The siskin salivates on the material set in place for the nest's foundation

(K. Lorenz, *in litt.*), and various species of swift use saliva in the construction of the nest or to attach their eggs to it. But the compactness of the wren's nest is achieved by the use of wet material, which, as it dries, contracts and twists so that the scraps interlock.

Building activity is stimulated by rainfall and thus the finding of nests is simplified. I have often said to myself: " Here's a rainy day. I'll go and see where the wrens are building." Sometimes I found four or five birds at work. Fig. 19 (p. 147) shows the correlation between rainfall and building activity. Of course wrens do not confine their nest-building exclusively to wet weather; during a dry spell they may " make do " with what material they can find in damp places, and sometimes the building drive is so strong that dry materials are used; when this happens the scraps do not bond and the nest is not completed. In such circumstances I have known the structure disintegrate two or three days after it had been built. A male feeding young, or whose drive has slackened late in the season, may not respond to rain by building. A heavy downpour may, however, stimulate a male to build as late as 23 July (Kluijver *et al.* 1940) or even 30 July (J. H. Owen, *in litt.*). My latest date for building, 10 July, also coincided with heavy rain. Iceland and Kashmir wrens (Bates and Lowther 1952) sometimes build so late in the season that there is little likelihood of the nests being used for breeding.

In Shetland I discovered that a wren, which had been titivating a nest begun four days earlier in a cow-byre, was repeatedly bringing scraps of moss *Isothecium* (=*Eurhynchium*) *myurum* with, perhaps, some *Eurhynchium praelongum* forty-four yards from a stone overhung by another large, flat boulder in a roughly built wall. It was rainy weather and this was one of the very few places where dry moss for finishing the interior could be obtained.

Cinnabar's nest-building technique in 1947 was particularly interesting. During the first week of April he began his first nest (No. 1) in a can which I had provided. (A predecessor and a successor also nested in it.) It was in a damp, shaded corner of the wood. There was no rain between 9 and 18 April, but a shower on 19 April stimulated him to make a flimsy framework of moss in a nearby damp corner (No. 2). He built six more nests, finishing four of them (p. 164). One of the latter (No. 7), constructed almost entirely of moss, was placed only twenty-five feet from the earlier mossy nest and the material for both was collected from the same place. From 21 to 24 April there were showers and drying winds. On 22 April I found Cinnabar building in the roots of an overturned tree, carrying damp moss from the water's edge only two feet away (No. 3). He left this nest incomplete, but two days later began another in a similar situation, fetching material from where the boughs of a willow, like those from which Ophelia was reported to have fallen, lay in the water (No. 4). Work on this nest continued during these rainless days and, when it had been completed, analysis of the materials by Dr. H. L. K. Whitehouse showed it to be composed entirely of moss, ninety per cent being of the aquatic species *Leptodictyum* (=*Hypnum*) *riparium* and ten per cent of *Eurhynchium praelongum* and *Brachythecium rutabulum*. These two terrestrial species constituted the upper part of the nest. Thus, when there was little wet material on the ground this wren had recourse to the moss growing in the pond, having endeavoured fruit-lessly to build his previous nests, first of land moss from the dampest nooks available, and then of land moss moistened by pond water. Rainfall stimulated his building activity even when he did not avail himself of material softened by the showers. On 28 April, within half an hour of the beginning of a slight shower, he started work on a nest (No. 5) in a very overshadowed part of his territory, bringing material from moist places at the base of neighbouring willows and later on making excursions to a bed of damp leaves twenty-five yards away.

Observations of other individuals suggest that the tendency to resort to standing water for material during dry weather may not be unusual. Mrs. R. E. Moreau tells me of a conversation with an aged Welsh woman living in an isolated cottage who spontaneously pointed out a wren, which, she said, took moss to a pool close at hand to moisten it before taking it to the nest. Such information has to be accepted with reserve, but there is no apparent reason why the woman should have made up the story. Mrs. T. Silva, watching with binocu-lars, saw a mistle thrush repeatedly dipping beak-loads of material into water before going to the nest.

The prairie marsh wren builds with wet material (Welter 1935; Provost 1947), like the chiffchaff (Prenn 1936). The great reed warbler not only drags material from the water but dips dry leaves or stems and so renders them more flexible (ten Kate 1926; Kluijver 1949). Irish dippers moisten building material in the stream near the nest (Rankin and Rankin 1940), but reed warblers cease work when rain falls (Brown 1946), and a heavy shower put an end to the building activity of a Carolina wren (Laskey 1950). A brush turkey was seen to work in " feverish haste " when rain fell (Coles 1937).

FIG. 19. Histograms showing the correlation between rainfall and the nest-building activity of two male wrens: (Below) Yellow and Black, 1945; (Above) Cinnabar, 1947. (Nest No. 4, omitted, was begun on 24 April; Nests 6 and 8 on unknown dates.)

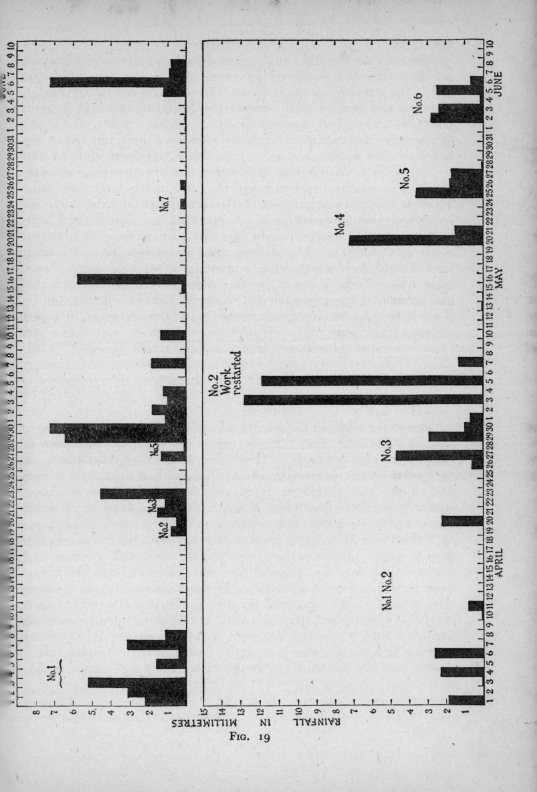

FIG. 19

Wren species adapted to arid regions tend to build in rock crevices or where the vegetation gives ample support to the structure. The nest of the northern cactus wren, as I have seen it in the Californian deserts, is a mass of material wedged deep among the spines of a cactus plant (Pl. VIII, p. 232), but in Mexico the Chiapas and rufous-naped cactus wrens are stimulated to build by rain at the beginning of the wet season (H. O. Wagner, *in litt.*), as, indeed, are many other birds.

The wren is not nearly so restricted to the neighbourhood of water by its nest-building requirements as the house martin and some hornbills (North 1942), but the moisture of a habitat seems to be an important factor in determining a wren's choice. Some regions, such as the fiords of Iceland, are so damp that suitable material is always available. In others, with a comparatively meagre rainfall, the birds tend to settle near where there is standing or running water. Some races, especially those which nest in crevices or near the ground, can make shift with comparatively dry material for nest-building, but in North Africa, where wrens may breed away from water (p. 16), nests are placed in bushes, on creeper-covered tree-trunks, in rock crevices, under overhanging banks or in the thatch of huts (Payn 1948; D. W. Snow, *in litt.*; Hartert 1910). Grasses, leaves, moss and *Lentiscus* foliage may be used.

BUILDING TEMPO

The wren, when actively building, gives an impression of almost frenzied diligence. Nests may be built very quickly: according to Kluijver, in one day early in the season and rather longer later. I have never known a nest to be entirely finished in a day, to the extent that no additions were made later. Sometimes on the first day nests appear to be, but are not quite, finished. It is difficult to decide when a nest should be considered complete as additions and adjustments are often made after the main structure has been built. Commonly there is some building activity on the third day, and often on the fourth or fifth day. Few other birds which make elaborate nests can finish them in a day. Kluijver records two instances of wrens building three nests in a week when rain fell after a drought. One of my birds (Cinnabar) began three nests in a week but finished only one of them. Another started a new nest less than five minutes after he had added material to a nest constructed earlier. Having set a few strands of moss in place he worked no more on it until three weeks later, when, in pouring rain, he completed it in three days. Not infrequently a wren will discontinue work on a nest, labour on another, and then return after some days to the first. I know of no instance of a wren

Eric Hosking

Plate VIa. Wren feeding young in nest built in a swallow's disused nest.

    b. Wren at nest below occupied robin's nest.

G. Hearn

working on two nests during the same building "stint"* although I have been informed of a doubtful instance, but a song thrush has been seen building at three sites some yards apart (Mees 1950), and Lack (1945) observed a female Galapagos finch working alternately in two of the male's display-nests.

The most rapid building tempo I have recorded was that of a wren fetching moss from a pool two feet below the nest-site. He averaged 11-12 seconds for the sum of the in-and-out movements during eight minutes. Two Texas wrens (*Thryomanes bewickii cryptus*) timed by Nice (1931) worked much more slowly, making only twenty trips in six minutes.

As the structure grows the tempo of activity tends to decrease. Fig. 20 shows the building activities of the wren Cinnabar during periods of observation on the first, second and seventh days of work on the nest, together with some comparable data for the wren Yellow-and-Black on the first and second days of building. In regard to each period of observation there are two points plotted, the average duration of the building spells and the average duration of the sorties. Thus by comparing the data one can see the extent to which reduction in tempo as the nest grew was due to increase in time spent in the nest and fetching material. Each period of observation, or "time transect," was sufficiently long to give a good average of the observations—half an hour to an hour—but pauses during the operations when the bird roamed his territory were omitted from the calculations.

It will be noted that as the day proceeds the tempo decreases and that Yellow-and-Black's rate of decrease on the second day approximated to Cinnabar's, although the periods of observation and the tempi of the birds differed. The duration of both sorties and building "spells" increase during the day, but the duration of the building "spells" increases more rapidly than the duration of the sorties. Towards 16.00 Cinnabar's tempo decreased markedly, mainly due to longer spells at the nest, but as these spells were so much longer than those required the next day, and the sorties were longer than earlier that day, it may be concluded that there was at this time a lessening of the building drive rather than that the manipulation of material required longer as the nest grew. At comparable times Cinnabar's rate of activity was less on the second day than on the first, and still less on the seventh day. The reduction was mainly due to the time spent building. This wren for whom we have data for

---

* "Stint" refers to the period during which a bird is continuously occupied in activity concerned with building. "Spell" is used of the periods occupied in fixing material in position.

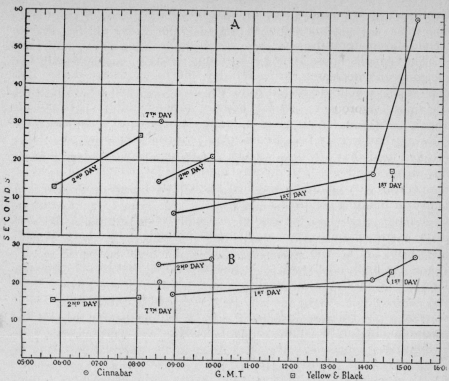

FIG. 20. Building tempo of two wrens. (A) Each point on the graph is the mean of the duration of the building spells during a period of observation at the time indicated. (B) Each point on the graph is the mean of the duration of the sorties during a period of observation at the time indicated.

approximately the same time on two successive days, took rather longer for his sorties on the second day than he did even when his tempo had decreased in the early afternoon of the first day. This might indicate a reduction of drive on the second day, though it could also be due to greater difficulty in finding suitable material close at hand. On the seventh day his sorties were nearer their duration on the first day—which is evidence against the longer sorties on the second day being due merely to having to search farther for materials. He had built very little during the intervening days; perhaps not at all on some of them.

Summing up, building tempo tends to decrease during the day and on successive days, partly due to increasing time taken arranging material in the growing nest and to a minor extent owing to material having to be fetched from greater distances, but the decrease as the day wears on is probably due to decreasing drive rather than fatigue and there is some suggestion of the drive being rather less on the second day than on the first.

The female house wren's nest-lining activity is greater in the morning and decreases during the day and on successive days. The trips of one female decreased from 165 to 133, 33 and 47. The male was most vigorous in nesting activity around midday (Kendeigh 1952). Erickson (1938) gives a graph of a wren-tit's working day showing that activity became less regular in the afternoon. Kuusisto (1941) found that a willow warbler's building ardour decreased from day to day and was not directly influenced by changes of light or temperature. A chaffinch watched by Barrett (1947a) was also less active in building on successive days.

I have referred to the pauses in building operations. When the drive is strong stints occur at intervals throughout the morning and afternoon, but a wren commonly spends some time singing before he begins building, and as we have noted, tends to become less diligent later in the day. Towards evening he usually does no more than pay a desultory visit, though Jourdain (1940) mentions a wren working between 07.00 and 19.00 and Neal (1950) refers to another seen building in the dusk. Very few birds continue working until twilight, but long-tailed tits, some weavers and woodpeckers will do so (Taylor 1946; Skutch 1948a).

An individual wren may vary the rhythm of his building activities. Cinnabar, starting at 08.38 on 24 April, worked two stints of 30 and 32 minutes respectively, with 61 minutes, respite. In the afternoon he worked 13 + minutes and 22 minutes, with 44 minutes off. Next day, from 08.20 to 10.49 his building stints were 20, 13, 7, 12, 16 and 8 minutes, his inattentive periods being 45, 17, 4, 2 and 5 minutes. Thus stints and interludes both decreased. Physiological state, weather, and the distraction caused by the presence of a female may influence a wren's assiduity, but perhaps the building impulse is subject to an innate rhythm comparable, though not identical, with that which governs the drive to feed nestlings (p. 196).

Many passerines build mainly or almost exclusively in the morning, but reed warblers are more active in the late afternoon. The goldfinch, like the wren, brings material more frequently during the early days of building (Conder 1948), and the song sparrow, like the wren, takes progressively longer in arranging material and becomes less energetic when the nest is nearing completion (Nice 1943).

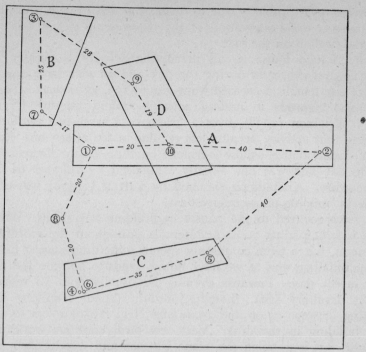

FIG. 21. Plan showing alignment and distance apart in metres of nests built by a male wren (No. 42) at Stein, Holland. The enclosed areas A, B, C and D indicate where the bird was deemed to concentrate his activities at certain periods. (After a plan in the notebooks of the Dutch observers.) The dates of beginning building were, in order: 17 and 22 March, 9, 19 and 29 April, 10, 12 and 16 May, 16 and 18 June

ALIGNMENT AND PROPINQUITY

The observers at Stein report that wrens concentrated their activities in particular sectors of their territories at different periods during the breeding season, as shown in their plan, In Wren Wood, as Fig. 22 shows, this was not apparent. It may well be, however, that in a territory containing several favourable areas, separated by others less congenial, the tendency to concentrate on different spots during the season is accentuated. In territories in two other areas three successive nests were built in a line. One series followed the course of a stream. Sometimes the observer can predict where a wren will make his next nest by noticing where he sings most, and as the season progresses a male having females or young in a part of his ground may restrict most of his activity to it. It is noticeable that, especially early in the season, when a wren has built a nest he tends to sing not far away.

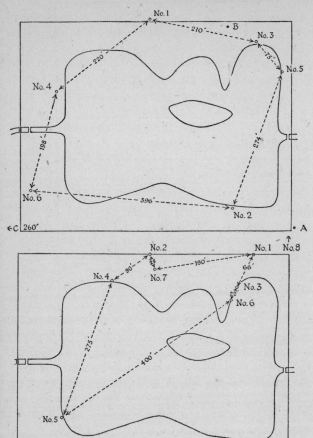

FIG. 22. Plans of Wren Wood, Cambridge, showing alignment of nests built by male wrens.

Yellow and Black, 1945

Cinnabar, 1947

The plans illustrate the alignment of nests in territories at Cambridge.

Wrens usually avoid placing their nests close to one another, but the Dutch observers found nests built by the same wren only twelve and fifteen feet apart. One nest was less than two feet above another, but it was impossible to ascertain when, or by what bird, one of them had been built. As a boy, I found a sketchy wren's nest in a ceanothus bush trained on a wall and within a few feet were the flimsy bases of two other nests. It seemed as if a wren had become confused as to the location of his nest and worked for a short time at several similar-looking niches among the twigs. Such confusion, where niches appear similar, has been recorded of a number of passerines. Nicols (1883) found four fresh wrens' nests within a few feet of one another on the trunk of an ivy-wreathed poplar, apparently built by one bird.

T.W.   L

As female wrens do not normally choose a nest close to another already occupied, natural selection would favour those males with large territories and widely dispersed nests.

Among house wrens nest-building seems to play a part in the establishment of territory second only to singing, but this is not so with wrens. I have not been able to detect any relationship between the location of nests and the delimitation of the territory. Some wrens placed their first two nests at opposite corners of the domain but others built their first nests in the same sector.

FEMALE BUILDING ACTIVITY

It is unusual for the female wren to participate in nest-building, though when she begins to line the nest she may carry in some beakfuls of dried grass or leaves. According to Weir (1837-52) a female wren, accompanied by a singing male, built a nest in one day, and the next day began lining. Marples (1940) and Jourdain (1940) also record supposed instances of female building activity. The former describes how the presumed male, a singing individual, harried the female, compelling her to work. Mr. M. D. England and Mrs. R. E. Moreau have each told me of two wrens bringing vegetable material to the nest together. Cox (1922) says that he saw both parents hastily constructing what he naïvely describes as a roosting nest for the fledglings. The Dutch students watched a female collaborating in work at the nest from the first day. As she was ringed her sex was certain; once she solicited the male unsuccessfully. Another female wren in the same garden watched the male working at the entrance to a nest for some time and then began to build energetically. As I have shown elsewhere (1951) the sight of a bird building may sometimes stimulate another to do likewise. While a Panama house wren was building in one corner of a cabin her mate built in another and occasionally added a scrap to her nest (Skutch 1940a). Heath (1920) refers to a female Alaska wren building but, as he mentions that the bird sang, he was undoubtedly mistaken.

Until 1948 I never observed consistent building by a female, as distinct from the portage of a few beak-loads of material before feather-lining began, but on 13 April I noticed a female take a dry, withered leaf into a nest built almost entirely of moss in a branch which had fallen into the pond. The male sang subsong and flipped his wings gently when he saw her near the nest. On the 16th I found both birds at work on another nest 25 yards away in an ivy-twined trunk. The male's bewilderment was ludicrous. On returning to find his mate methodically carrying in material he reacted by quivering his wings excitedly and uttering scraps of song. Usually he became so perturbed that he dropped his material. Burkitt (1919-20) also noted that when a female carried moss into the nest the cock dropped his loads and Conder observed that if a male goldfinch brought nesting material to the nest the female became confused and sometimes reached forward as if expecting food. Although both my birds were unringed there was no difficulty in distinguishing one from the other as the female never uttered a sound and crept up the tree-trunk unobtrusively, whereas the cock flew in an agitated way from twig to twig and sang frequently.

During four hours on 17 April I recorded every visit by the birds. Some inexactitude was inevitable, but the data are accurate to within six visits. Once or twice at the beginning of my watch, when both came together to the nest, the male sang, displayed and dropped material as on the previous day, but after fifteen minutes male and female tended to alternate their spells. The proportion of visits by the female increased, as Table VIII shows:

TABLE VIII

COLLABORATION OF MALE AND FEMALE WREN IN NEST-BUILDING

Time	Number of visits	
	♂	♀
11.00—12.00	52	39
12.00—13.00	12	54
14.03—15.03	40	53
15.03—16.00	13	60
	117	206

There being abundant damp leaves readily available the female maintained a rapidly increasing tempo—reaching fourteen visits in six minutes during one stint.

Both birds were building on 18 April at 08.15 during my watch of half an hour. The female did most of the work. In the early afternoon neither bird visited the nest during another half-hour period. Next day I found both wrens building in a nesting-box. The female was again the more diligent worker. I suspect that it was on the female's initiative that activities were transferred to the box as the male would hardly have abandoned work so readily on the tree-trunk nest if the female had been satisfied with it. On 22 April, while she was taking fibres, small leaves and feathers into the box the male was again working at the tree-trunk nest. It was as if they had agreed to differ. She lined the box-nest and laid the first egg on 26 April, but the nestlings disappeared unaccountably between the afternoon of 20 May and the morning of the 21st. On 25 May she was again building at the tree-trunk site, but more slowly than formerly. Almost certainly the fledglings which I found her tending in the first week of July were reared in this nest.

That this bird's impulse to build should be so strong is particularly interesting in view of the normality of her behaviour in other respects. She showed no other tendencies towards a " male " type of behaviour. When I placed the mount which had elicited song from the Girton wren near to her as she worked she evinced only a short-lived, mild curiosity. On the other hand, a female house wren which built a perfect nest unaided was evidently too " masculine " for successful breeding. She defended territory, even against other species, and laid twelve eggs which turned out to be sterile. No male was ever observed in the neighbourhood (Norton 1929). In some species the reverse situation may occur, and a male will undertake female responsibilities. The female willow warbler, pied wagtail, and song sparrow usually builds, but males have been known to do so (Brown 1927; Cullen 1947; Nice 1943). There are many other species in which the customary role of one sex may occasionally be undertaken to some extent by the other. Thus a drake mallard has been seen arranging nest material and settling as if brooding (Best 1939). In many species in which the substructure of the nest is built by the male, and the hollow fashioned by the female the latter is able to build the substructure should a male partner be lacking (Lorenz 1935). It is interesting that the female penduline tit sometimes co-operates with the male in nest-building as this species is also polygamous.

Experiments in which a form of male hormone was injected into month-old night herons elicited adult male patterns of behaviour—territorialism, nest-building, display and copulation (Noble and Wurm 1940) and research has shown that by means of appropriate injections female birds may be stimulated to act in various characteristically male ways (Armstrong 1947). One is tempted to infer from such experiments that patterns of behaviour associated with reproduction are correlated with one another in a series so that nest-building necessarily involves song and territorial activity, but, since this is not so, the relationship between physiological status and reproductive behaviour patterns may be more subtle than such experiments reveal. This is supported by the outcome of my experiment on fosterage

(p. 104), which indicates that the feeding of alien young may inhibit the female's desire for copulation and the impulses involved in nest-lining.

LINING

When a female has found a nest suitable for egg-laying she installs a mattress of feathers and other downy material. During this phase she may abandon the nest, or even the male's territory, if alarmed by people or animals. Nevertheless, the lining drive can be very insistent. When a wren was prevented from taking a load of feathers into a nest she carried the material to a neighbouring nest, and on the entrance to this being blocked, she flew off purposefully with the feathers as if to a third nest (R. Gait, *in litt.*).

The number of wrens' nests which are found lined but never contain eggs suggests that lining is not necessarily, nor even usually, a sequel to successful copulation, but often precedes it.

I have frequently had the impression that the male's excitement, expressed in song, subsong and posturing near to the busy female, stimulates her sexually and intensifies her nest-lining activity, and that in turn her activity stimulates him sexually. As he watches her, his tail sometimes moves in the slow side-to-side fashion which betokens erotic excitement. He pounces and attempts to copulate while his mate is working and may even tread her while she is holding feathers in her bill. The possibility that the male's song and movements may be stimulating to the female wren while she is lining the nest is supported by analogous evidence, for Kendeigh refers to the effect of the presence of a female house wren in stimulating the male to build and sing more actively, and Conder has shown that female goldfinches mated to the males which sing most frequently incubate most assiduously. He has also noticed (1950) that the male wheatear's song-and-dance incites the female to build more rapidly.

Lining may be completed in two days but may take as long as seven. Indeed, the impulse often persists to some extent after the laying of the first egg so that it is impossible to define the duration of the lining period exactly. One female took feathers inside when there were two eggs in the nest, four days after lining had apparently ceased. Another carried in feathers on the day she laid her first egg and again when she was incubating her clutch of six eggs. Yet another, which had been brooding the full clutch for some days, brought a feather to a perch beside the nest and let it float away. The wren (Silverband) whose activities at the nest are recorded in Table XX (p. 176) brought feathers on the day she laid her first egg and also three and six days later. The female depicted in Plate v (p. 141) is seen carrying a hair to the nest on the day the young fledged.

On two occasions when a Shetland wren was disturbed from eggs on which she had been sitting about a week she returned with a feather in her bill. Some days later this bird indulged in extensive sessions of displacement-preening when approaching the nest while I was in view close to it. Apparently, therefore, some of the instances just cited of wrens bringing lining material after the eggs have been laid, as well as the behaviour of this Shetland wren, should be regarded as displacement-lining due to conflicting impulses. Haverschmidt (1950) noticed similar displacement-lining by an alarmed cotton bird in Surinam and I have mentioned other examples elsewhere (1947, 1950b). An Orinocan banded wren (*Campylorhynchus nuchalis*) packed the entrance to the nest with silk-cotton and feathers while a collector sawed off the branch in which the nest was placed (Cherrie 1916). Probably this bird's action should be considered displacement-lining.

The winter wren sometimes brings lining material during the laying period (C. Stanwood, *in litt.*) and a Carolina wren carried in catkins and hairs during the first eight days of brooding (Nice and Thomas 1948). Birds as various as raptors and terns manifest this impulse to place lining material in the nest after the eggs have been laid.

As lining proceeds the female European wren tends to spend longer in the nest—at first only 6-15 seconds, later perhaps half a minute or more. Lining, like building, is conducted in stints. These vary from 10 minutes, or somewhat less, to about 25 minutes.

The interval between the beginning of lining and the laying of the first egg varies. I have records of 18, 9, 4 and 3 days after lining started.

The number of feathers used varies greatly, depending, among other factors, on the length of the period between the beginning of lining and the laying of the first egg and also on the availability of material. A nest in a poultry-yard was crammed with feathers, but in districts in the west of Scotland and in a remote Exmoor valley where feathers may have been difficult to obtain, nests have been found with eggs but no lining (Gray 1871; Pring 1927). St. Kilda wrens' nests may contain comparatively few feathers. Perhaps occasional birds lack the lining impulse. Willow warblers also sometimes omit the feather lining (Brown 1948b). Counts have shown 498 feathers in a wren's nest, 516 and 1199 in house sparrows' (Marples 1935a), and an average of 1,558 in six long-tailed tits' nests (Owen 1945), though for this species 2,500 appears to be the record (Corbet 1923). In Wren Wood feathers from sparrowhawks' kills and from hen-runs were used.

In the Lakes nests have been found lined with the feathers from the prey of peregrines. Kearton (n.d.) mentions seeing a wren picking up feathers dislodged from the plumage of fighting pheasants. I found ptarmigan feathers and duck down in an Iceland wren's nest, gulls' feathers in nests of the Shetland wren and fulmar feathers in a St. Kilda wren's nest. Probably white feathers are chosen by these races merely because they are conspicuous and readily available. St. Kilda wrens used to steal hair from snares set for puffins (Dixon 1888). In the Balearic Islands a wren lined her nest entirely with plumage from a dead barn owl lying close by (Munn 1931). A wood wren (*Henicorhina leucophrys*) gathered red feathers from a trogon's breast (Salvin and Godman 1879-1904). Eastern winter wrens may use fur as well as feathers and there is a record of hedgehog " fur " in a nest (Baird *et al.* 1874). The Alaska wren's nest may contain fur of arctic fox or reindeer in addition to feathers, such as those of the rosy finch (Allen 1887; Heath 1920). Hairs of the polar bear have been recorded but they probably came from a fox. Feathers of various hues may be found in European wrens' nests. In experiments made at my suggestion by Mr. R. Gait, a wren carried in feathers of various colours scattered near the nest in no particular order.

Male Lining Activity

Just as females may show some capacity as nest-builders so males sometimes manifest feeble lining impulses. Mrs. Moreau saw a male bringing a feather on the 7th day of building and a piece of wool on the 13th. At the top of a mass of material constituting a nest in a box I found a large hen's feather which had been brought there, presumably by the male. Once, as I watched a male displaying to a female, he picked up a feather after issuing from the nest but dropped it almost immediately. Another spent three minutes inspecting a nest the third day after lining had started; he brought out a feather, dropped it and failed to catch it as it fell. He displayed to the female and she proceeded to collect feathers. Yet another picked up and dropped a flower petal while the female was lining the nest (Whitehouse and Armstrong 1953).

On several occasions when I placed feathers on a partly-constructed nest or at the entrance to a completed nest the male carried them away. A Shetland wren with a nest in a cow-byre became so obsessed with removing feathers scattered near the nest that he had the appearance of building " in reverse." He even removed most of a large wad of wool wedged in the turf roof. The importance of the impulse to remove feathers from any nest which has not been chosen by a female

is evident when we consider that a female wren is likely to reject a
nest with feathers in or about it as one already selected by another
female, and therefore to be avoided. Otherwise, confusion and
altercations might result from two females choosing the same nest.
This has never been definitely recorded.

When feathers were placed near the nest which a female house
wren was building she took them away (Bent 1948). This behaviour
indicates that while the building impulse is dominant lining material
is not merely " neutral " in the sense of not arousing the bird's interest.
It is reacted to as alien material to be removed. A Hebridean wren,
annoyed by a large feather which projected over the entrance as she
brooded the young, carried it away when she went off for food, and a
pale-bellied house wren was seen removing feathers before laying in a
nest. Apparently the nest had been used for an earlier brood
(Haverschmidt 1952).

NESTING DATES

Although European wrens may begin to build, if the weather is
mild, early in March, or even, exceptionally, in the middle or towards
the end of February, the impulse is not usually thoroughly awakened
until after mid-March. Birds may, at first, merely pick up material
or place some in position and soon desist. General nest-building may
occur during an early warm spell. One would have expected survivors
of the severe conditions at the beginning of 1947 to be debilitated, but
building began within a week of the disappearance of the last patches
of snow.

Marshall (1949) found that in the robin, great tit and blue tit
development was arrested at the primary spermatocyte stage in this
cold spell and sudden tubular activity occurred with the onset of
milder conditions. The nest-building and egg-laying data for the wren
(p. 162) indicate some delay in breeding activity in 1947, unusually
early nesting in 1948 and late breeding in the retarded seasons of
1951 and 1953.

OUT-OF-SEASON BREEDING ACTIVITY

The unseasonable display activity to which reference has been
made (p. 131) sometimes culminates in an attempt to breed. I have
a record of a nest vacated by the young in the last week of October.
Walton (1925) found nests under construction in autumn and Kluijver
and his colleagues discovered three nests built after summer was over.
One is mentioned in the notebooks as a " winter nest." A nest which
was built in late October contained four eggs in November. Two eggs

hatched and the young fledged (Moir 1951). In November a wren was seen fashioning the outer shell of a nest, but he stopped when inclement weather occurred (Kelsall and Munn 1905). Forrest (1924) found nestlings being fed on 3 December and a nest being built on 30 December which contained eggs in January. Saunders (1927) also mentions a December nest and Bucknill (1900) a nest in the first week of January. Seven fresh eggs were found in a Hampshire nest on 13 January (Willmore 1881). In Middlesex a nest with two eggs was discovered on Christmas Day and another with two nestlings on 9 March (Glegg 1935). A February nest with eggs is recorded by Barrett-Hamilton (1900) and Mr. J. H. Owen has sent me particulars of a clutch laid early in March 1950. In Holland broods of wrens in winter have also been noted (Dijk 1904). Thus breeding has been recorded in every month of the year, as with the robin (Lack 1948a), song thrush (Glegg 1951) and barn owl (Wallace 1948). Nesting of our resident Columbidae and probably also of the blackbird may be reported throughout the year. Starlings have been found nesting in every month, except, perhaps, February (Bullough 1942). All these species are influenced to a considerable extent by man's activities as a builder and cultivator. As we shall see, nest-building out of the breeding season is normal among some species of wren (p. 274).

Earliest Records of Building and Egg-Laying

No attempt was made to secure specially early records and several dates of nest-building or egg-laying earlier than those in Table ix were omitted as the observations were made outside the immediate neighbourhood of Cambridge. Some birds, such as the Arctic terns on the lake in Reykjavik, nest earlier in towns or their suburbs than elsewhere, but there is no evidence that wrens do so. In order to make the records more complete data are also included from Montgomeryshire in Wales (J. H. Owen, *in litt.*) and Stein in Holland.

TABLE IX—EARLIEST RECORDS OF BUILDING AND EGG-LAYING BY THE
EUROPEAN WREN

Year	First nest-building observed	First egg
	MONTGOMERYSHIRE	
1911		28 March
1912	15 March	
1913	9 March (Complete)	
1914	2 March　　"	
1915	3 April　　"	
1916	15 March　　"	
1917	None observed in March after severe winter	
1918	2 April (Complete)	
1919	16 March　　"	
1920	None observed in March	
1921	18 March	
1922	23 February (Complete)	
1923	1 March	
1924	8 March	
1925	15 March	
1926	23 March	
	STEIN	
1934		21 April
1935		24 April
1936	2 March	7 April
1937	1 March	10 April
1938	5 March	7 April
1939		24 April
	CAMBRIDGE	
1944		28 April
1945	{ 1 March* { 26 March	25 April
1946	22 March	23 April
1947	28 March	3 May
1948	{ 8 March† { 13 March	15 April
1949	{ 24 February‡ { 25 March	24 April
1950	19 March	27 April
1951	4 April	8 May
1952	10 April	29 April
1953	17 April	2 May

*Carrying material to site but nest not completed.
†Refurbishing old nest built by predecessor.
‡Picking up leaves.

TABLE X

CHRONICLE OF NEST-BUILDING BY AN UNMATED WREN, YELLOW-AND-BLACK, DURING 1945

1	April	Visiting nest A
2	,,	,, ,, ,,
3	,,	,, ,, ,, with female
4	,,	,, nests A and B
6	,,	Courting female
7	,,	,, ,,
8	,,	,, ,,
9	,,	Female soliciting
12	,,	*Nest No. 1 begun*
13	,,	,, continued and *Nest No. 2 begun*
15	,,	Nest A tidied
16	,,	Female has left male
17	,,	Nest A further adjusted
18	,,	,, ,,
19	,,	,, ,,
22	,,	Nest No. 1 lined by a female who then deserted
23	,,	Nests A and B visited
25	,,	,, ,, ,,
27	,,	*Nest No. 3 begun*
28	,,	,, discontinued
29	,,	Nests A and B visited
30	,,	Nest A visited
1	May	,, ,,
2	,,	Nests A and B visited
4	,,	Building recommenced at Nest No. 2
5	,,	,, continued ,, ,,
6	,,	,, ,, ,, ,, Nest C refurbished
7	,,	Nests A and B and No. 1 visited
8	,,	,, A and B visited
9	,,	Nest C visited
10	,,	,, ,,
12	,,	Nests A, B, C and No. 2 visited
14	,,	Nest B repaired
15	,,	Nest No. 2 adjusted
16	,,	,, A visited
21	,,	,, .*No. 4 begun*
22	,,	,, ,, continued
23	,,	,, ,, discontinued; nests A, B, C and No. 2 visited
26	,,	,, *No. 5 begun*
27	,,	,, ,, discontinued; nests A, B, C and No. 2 visited

2 June   Nests A, C and No. 2 visited
3   „   *Nest No. 6 begun*
5   „   „   „   continued. Nest A and No. 2 visited
6   „   „   „   „
8   „   „   „   „
9   „   Nests A and No. 2 visited
10 „   Building recommenced at Nest C
13 „   Nests C and No. 2 visited
20 „   Yellow-and-Black found roosting in nest No. 6 at 19.40

Nests denoted by capital letters were built by Yellow-and-Black's predecessors and taken over by him; those denoted by numerals were nests
built by him. Evidence that nests were visited was obtained usually either
by placing a straw across the entrance or by attaching small pieces of
coloured wool near to it. The disappearance of these objects was regarded
as indicating that the wren had visited the nests in question. Probably he
adjusted the fabric of the nest to some extent on many of these occasions.
The correlation between these activities and rainfall is shown in Fig. 19
(p. 147).

TABLE XI

CHRONOLOGY OF BREEDING BEHAVIOUR OF THE BIGAMOUS WREN CINNABAR IN 1947

Date

±1   4 April   *Nest No. 1 begun*
    18   „   Courting Scarlet and Silverband
    19   „   *Nest No. 2 begun*   ⎧The dates of building
    22   „   *Nest No. 3 begun*   ⎨nests Nos. 6 and 8
    24   „   *Nest No. 4 begun*   ⎩are unknown
    28   „   *Nest No. 5 begun*
±1   8 May   First egg in Nest No. 6   (Scarlet)
    11   „   (Record of song during the morning, Fig. 11a)
    17   „   First egg in nest No. 5   (Silverband)
    24   „   *Nest No. 7 begun*
    26   „   (Record of activities throughout the day, Fig. 11b)
±1 29   „   Eggs hatched in nest No. 6
     4 June   (Record of activities throughout the day, Fig. 11c)
    5-6   „   Eggs hatched in nest No. 5
     7   „   Cinnabar pouncing on Silverband
     9   „   Cinnabar feeding young in nest No. 6
    15   „   Young fledged from nest No. 6
    16   „   Young perished in nest No. 5
±1 24   „   First egg in nest No. 8 (Scarlet)
    12 July   Scarlet's second brood hatched in nest No. 8
    28   „   Scarlet's second brood fledged.
     1 Aug.   Cinnabar feeding young more assiduously than Scarlet
              (Watch kept from before dawn until early afternoon)
     8   „   Scarlet still feeding young

CHAPTER 10

INCUBATION

Or in sequestered lanes they build
  Where, till the flitting bird's return,
Her eggs within the nest repose,
  Like relics in an urn.

WORDSWORTH. *A Wren's Nest*

EGGS AND EGG-LAYING

AMONG British breeding birds only the long-tailed tit and goldcrest
lay smaller eggs than the wren. Wrens' eggs average 16.66 × 12.77
mm. and are dull white with ruddy spots. Immaculate eggs occur
occasionally but more frequently among northern subspecies whose
eggs also tend to be somewhat larger (Armstrong 1950a). Egg-laying
usually occurs before 08.00 on successive days. Observation of one
bird suggests that the European wren, like the Carolina wren (Nice
and Thomas 1948) and unlike the great tit (Kluijver 1950) goes off
the nest soon after sunrise, and after a short interval returns to lay.[7]
The Carolina wren and the neotropical house wren lay within an
hour of sunrise (Skutch 1952). In the month of April a Vigors's wren
laid before 06.00 (Miller 1941) and prairie marsh wrens in May laid
before 08.00, but an Irish dipper, contrary to the practice of most
passerines, laid late in the morning (Rankin and Rankin 1940), and
an American dipper laid between 07.11 and 10.38 although she had
stayed twelve minutes in the nest at 06.31 without laying (Hann 1950).
Exceptionally there may be an intermission of a day during the laying
of the clutch—as recorded of the robin (Lack 1948a), blue, great, and
willow tits (Gibb 1950) and suspected of the song thrush (Silva 1949)
and reed warbler (Brown and Davies 1949). Dr. D. Lack tells me
that when such an intermission occurs during egg-laying by robins
it is usually towards the completion of the clutch, and when the
number of eggs is below normal. A wren has been known to lay two
successive eggs just outside the nest entrance (B.T.O. records) so it is
possible that occasionally when there is an egg-less day the bird may
have dropped the egg elsewhere.

A period of about 5-6 days elapses between copulation and the first egg—the same interval as has been recorded of song sparrows, white-crowned sparrows and pied flycatchers (Nice 1937; Blanchard 1941; Haartman 1951).

A wren does not lay fewer eggs if some are added to the nest while she is laying (Chappell 1948), but in two experiments in which I removed an egg daily, always leaving one, the bird ceased when six had been laid. Thus some individuals are determinate layers. On the other hand, a note on the wren in the *Statistical Survey of the County of Londonderry*, to which Mr. C. D. Deane calls my attention, comments: " Boys make this little bird lay eggs to a vast number, by taking them gradually from the nest." In temperate regions most small passerines on which observations have been made are indeterminate layers. Cole (1930) measured a long series of eggs obtained from a house wren and discovered that their length increased up to a certain point, then remained static, increased to a second maximum, and after this tended to decrease. Van Tyne (1950) found that the eggs of a Panama house wren's second laying were larger than those of the first clutch.

The clutch size of the European wren varies in different regions of the bird's range, in general increasing northwards.

TABLE XII

CLUTCH SIZE OF THE WREN IN BRITAIN, HOLLAND AND FINLAND

Region	No. of clutches consisting of c/2 c/3 c/4 c/5 c/6 c/7 c/8 c/9								Total clutches	Average no. of eggs in clutch	Source
Britain	—	5	7	30	50	12	1	—	105	5.6	B.T.O. records.
Holland (Stein)	1	1	5	27	45	11	—	—	90	5.6	Kluijver *et al.* 1940
Finland	—	—	—	3	3	6	3	1	16	6.7	Palmgren, *in litt.*

In Sicily 4 eggs are usual (Lynes 1912) and in the Balearic Islands 4-6 (Munn 1931). The Iceland wren lays 6-8 (Timmermann 1949), the Faeroe wren about 8 (Landt 1810), the Shetland wren 4-8, the St. Kilda wren 4-6 and very occasionally 7 (Witherby *et al.* 1938). The eastern winter wren lays 4-7 eggs, 5-6 being most usual (Bent 1948) but the Alaska wren's clutch is 6-7 (Heath 1920). Other data for Europe have been collected by Lack (1947a):

TABLE XIII

CLUTCH SIZE OF THE WREN IN EUROPE

Southern Spain	England	Central Europe (Saxony)	Eastern Galicia	Norway
(4) 5	5-6	7	6-7 (8)	6-8

A figure in brackets indicates a regular but less common clutch.

These data show that the wren's clutch-size conforms to the trends recognised as applying to those of the majority of passerine, and many other, birds in Europe—an increase northwards correlated with increasing day-length and the consequent prolongation of the time available for foraging, and also an increase from west to east (Lack 1947a). Possibly this latter trend may be partly due to a greater abundance of food in continental areas as compared with island habitats, for there is a tendency towards a smaller average clutch size on islands. Even within the British Isles there is evidence of an increase northward in the swallow's clutch (Boyd 1936). The clutch size of British birds is considerably larger than that of many related equatorial African species (Moreau 1944).

Late layings of many species tend to be small. Analysis of the B.T.O. records gives the following averages:

TABLE XIV

AVERAGE CLUTCH SIZE OF THE EUROPEAN WREN IN BRITAIN

April	May	June	July
5.4(14)	5.8(60)	5.2(10)	4.0(4)

The number in brackets indicates the number of clutches analysed.

Perhaps the average for July is too high. I have found several clutches of three in that month. The paucity of July records is due not only to the smaller number of wrens laying then, but to the nests being less sought and more difficult to find. There is some evidence that in Scotland and the Scillies late clutches are also small. Second brood clutches of the wren, house wren (Kendeigh 1934), prairie marsh wren (Aldrich 1935), redstart (Ruiter 1941) and numerous other birds are smaller than the first, but when robins have both their first and second clutches early the second layings tend to be larger than the first; if, however, the second are as late as June or July they are smaller than the first (Lack 1946b). This is consistent with food supply being ultimately the determining factor. Kendeigh (1934) sees a direct connection between the decrease in the clutch size of the house wren from c/7 in May to c/4 in July and rising temperature, and supporting evidence is available from a study of the extension southward of the breeding range. Odum and Johnston (1951) found that in Georgia high temperatures during the egg-laying period reduced the number of eggs laid and hatched. Of course correlations between clutch size and food supply, on the one hand, and temperature, on the other, are not necessarily mutually exclusive, for temperature is of major importance in determining the abundance of food for insectivorous birds. The expenditure of energy by the female wren in rearing her first brood may also have some bearing on the reduction in size of the second clutch. Kendeigh's observations (1952) indicate that house wrens feeding large families may be under considerable strain. An eastern tree sparrow may lose twenty per cent in weight during the period of feeding young (Heydweiler 1935), and if an inordinate number of young are added to a starling's brood, a parent may work to the point of exhaustion in feeding them (Carrick 1950).

Trustworthy evidence of the large clutches traditionally ascribed to the wren is scanty. Thompson (1849) was informed of two nests which contained fourteen eggs, but apparently did not see them himself. I know of an instance of boys trying to trick an ornithologist by placing the clutch from one wren's nest in another. Jourdain (1919) mentions clutches ranging from sixteen to nine eggs and Blomefield (1946) records seventeen in a letter-box in Norfolk, but the nature of the nesting-site and the fact that the wren is called " Tom-tit " in East Anglia suggest that confusion with one of the Paridae may have occurred. Probably the exigencies of rhyme have demanded " ten " to rhyme with " wren " in the well-known doggerel verse, and certainly this explains the immense clutch ascribed to the wren in the Scottish couplet:

> The big Cushie-doo, only lays two,
> The wee Cuddy-wran, lays twenty-wan.

Burkitt (1919-20) noted an unhatched egg in four out of five first-brood nests and Mr. P. Baldwin informs me that unhatched eggs are common in some seasons in first clutches, but are unusual in second broods. In Cambridge I have seldom found unhatched eggs after the young have flown, but, as we have noted, a late clutch laid by one of the mates of the polygamist White-leg was infertile. Kendeigh (1942) found that the percentage of house wren eggs which fails to hatch increases appreciably when temperatures rise above or fall below the optimum.

INCUBATION PERIOD

Treating the incubation period as the time between the laying of the last egg and the hatching of the first, the Dutch students obtained the following data:

TABLE XV

DURATION OF INCUBATION BY THE WREN IN DAYS AT STEIN, HOLLAND

Month in which incubation began	20	19	18	17	16	15	14	13	12
April	1	—	3	2	2	—	—	—	—
May	—	2	—	3	9	2	1	—	—
June	—	—	—	1	4	7	2	—	—
July	—	—	—	—	—	2	2	—	—

These data, relating to 43 broods, show average incubation periods of 17.5 days in April, 16.3 in May, 15.3 in June and 14.5 in July. Insufficient information is available in the record cards of the B.T.O. or elsewhere to make exact comparison possible. The majority of records refer to May and give the following figures, reckoning the incubation period, as is now customary, from the laying of the last egg to the hatching of the last young:

TABLE XVI

EUROPEAN WREN INCUBATION PERIODS IN DAYS DURING MAY IN BRITAIN

20	19	18	17	16	15	14	13	12
1	2	2	3	6	3	2	1	2

There are two records of 16 days in April and one of 14 days in June. These data are rather unsatisfactory, especially as it is not known exactly when incubation began. My most accurate record is of a wren in 1952; she began to sit in the afternoon of 8 May, the day before she laid her last egg. It hatched at 07.55 on 24 May. This incubation period was therefore about 15 days 4 hours. The penultimate egg had hatched by 19.00 on 23 May.

On the basis of the data obtained by the Dutch students and observations to the effect that wrens incubating their first-brood

T.W.   M clutches were found off the nest more frequently than birds incubating second-brood clutches, Kluijver suggested that as temperature rises, food becomes more plentiful, the eggs are more consistently incubated and consequently hatch sooner. Unfortunately direct comparison between the data for the different months is fallacious. Kluijver points out, that in his experience, incubation usually starts in April and May on the day the last egg is laid, or a day later, while in June and July it often begins before the clutch is complete. Beginning incubation before the clutch is complete appears to be fairly common among passerine birds. Thus Kluijver's first-brood data probably show a day or two more than the true incubation periods and his second-brood data a day or two less. His own data of the nesting activities of great tits, obtained with a recording instrument, show that it was not until the third day after the completion of the first clutch that regular incubation began, but in the second-brood incubation period there was an increasing amount of brooding while the last five eggs were being laid (Kluijver 1950). Without recording apparatus an observer might have supposed that the second laying took three days less than the first to hatch. Gibb (1950) found that great tits might begin to incubate any time from three days before until four days after the clutch is complete but, in a late season, incubation starts with the penultimate egg and in an early season with the last egg.

Kendeigh (1952), studying the house wren, noted that " each day as another egg in a five-egg set is laid, the female visits the nest more frequently and for a longer period. With six-egg sets this daily increase does not begin until the fourth egg is deposited." A Carolina wren which began to spend the night in the nest after the first egg of the second nesting-cycle had been laid was found on the eggs at 16.30 the day the third, and penultimate, egg was laid, but full-time incubation did not begin until the clutch was complete (Laskey 1950).

The European wren begins diurnal incubation by increasing the number of sessions on successive days, both morning and evening, until the full rhythm has developed.

If Kluijver and his colleagues had reckoned the incubation period from the laying of the last egg to the hatching of the last their results would not have suggested the shortening of the period, or, at least, not to the same extent. There is little evidence from any other species to suggest that the period varies in different months, but Ruiter (1941) studying the redstart, found that the two layings which hatched in the briefest time were begun as late as 7 and 12 June.

Kendeigh recorded an incubation period of 16 days for a house

wren, three days longer than normal, but his apparatus showed that
not until five days after the clutch was complete did the bird begin to
brood in earnest. According to Mr. M. D. England a wren in his
garden incubated for more than 20 days—probably another instance
of desultory brooding at the outset, for a song sparrow which at first
brooded irregularly took 2-3 days longer than normal to hatch the
eggs (Nice 1937). Prairie marsh wrens are said to begin incubation
before the clutch is complete, though not before the third egg is laid,
but Bowles (1909) mentions that the closely related tule wren broods
from the laying of the first egg. Probably there is some variation
according to season and environmental conditions.

NIGHT-BROODING AND ROOSTING

A further complication in assessing the incubation period is introduced by the birds' custom of spending the night in the nest before
diurnal incubation begins. My observations agree with Burkitt's
(1919-20) that the wren often sits in the nest during the laying period
and even roosts there before any eggs are laid (Owen 1919a). (I have
also known a bird to roost in one nest and lay in another.) Early in
the season a wren may roost on the eggs, not only during the laying
period but for a night or two after the clutch is complete, before
beginning diurnal incubation. This is probably uncommon.

The female Carolina wren sleeps in the nest after the first egg has
been laid (Nice and Thomas 1948; Laskey 1950). Kendeigh (*in litt.*)
noticed that the house wren's incubation temperature develops
gradually and, when she spends her nights in the nesting-box during
the egg-laying period, full heat is not applied to the eggs until, or
shortly before, the clutch is complete. Probably this is true of many
birds. Gibb (1950) finds that great tits tend to begin incubation by
extending sitting in the nest at night to occupying it also in the afternoon. Only after a day or two does the bird sit in the morning also.
The black-capped chickadee (Odum 1942a) and redstart (Ruiter 1941)
spend the night at the nest during the laying period but do not incubate. The nightjar incubates the first egg during the day, but not
during the two nights before the second egg is laid (Heinroth 1909).

Even when a bird seems to be settled for the night she may sally
forth. A house wren left her nesting-box at 20.50 and did not return
until 01.04 (Baldwin and Kendeigh 1927, 1932) and other house wrens
have been known to leave the nest for short periods. Automatic
recordings of the female house wren's behaviour show that she is often
active to some extent in the nesting-box all night (Baldwin and
Kendeigh 1932). Incubating willow warblers and a male great spotted

woodpecker have also been known to leave their nests during the night (Kuusisto 1941; Bussmann 1946).

EFFECT OF COLD WEATHER

Abnormally low temperature may affect the brooding rhythm. Early in May, after two nights with a minimum air temperature of 28° F. on the first and 34° F. on the second (19° F. and 30.9° F. grass temperature), a wren nesting in a yew tree deserted. Another instance of a wren forsaking after a severe frost in the second week of May has come to my notice. Such behaviour is not remarkable, except, perhaps, in so far as the wren incubates in a particularly cosy nest, for herons (Tinbergen 1931), doves (Whitman 1919) and other birds are apt to forsake their eggs in hard weather.

The incubation periods of some species vary according to the weather. Birds as different as the lapwing and the swallow (Waldeck 1932; Heinroth and Heinroth 1924-33) take longer to hatch the eggs during inclement conditions than when it is mild. The factors involved vary in different species; cold and stormy days interfere more with the swallow's foraging than with the lapwing's and tend to force it to spend a good deal of time off the eggs.

Perhaps a fall in temperature may inhibit the laying of the eggs after the nest has been lined. During periods of inclement weather periods of seven to nine days may elapse before the first egg is laid.

Any considerable reduction in the amount of warmth received by the eggs of the house wren during incubation, especially during the early stages, prolongs the incubation period or is fatal (Baldwin and Kendeigh 1932). Conversely, high temperature or more continuous warmth, within certain limits, tends to reduce the incubation period. Kluijver states that two wrens' eggs placed in a blue tit's nest hatched in eleven days after the bird had begun to sit, but I found that wrens' eggs under a blue tit sitting closely took fifteen days to hatch, and Groebbels (1932) remarks that a wren's egg hatched in sixteen days under a canary.

RETENTION OF VIABILITY

A wren which laid her first egg on 23 April roosted on the eggs for a night or two, incubated for a short time the morning after the sixth and last egg had been laid, and then deserted. The clutch did not receive regular incubation until I transferred it to a foster-parent's nest on 2 May, yet all but one of the eggs hatched. The eggs of some birds may retain their viability much longer (Manson-Bahr 1946).

With a few exceptions, such as the megapodes which bury their

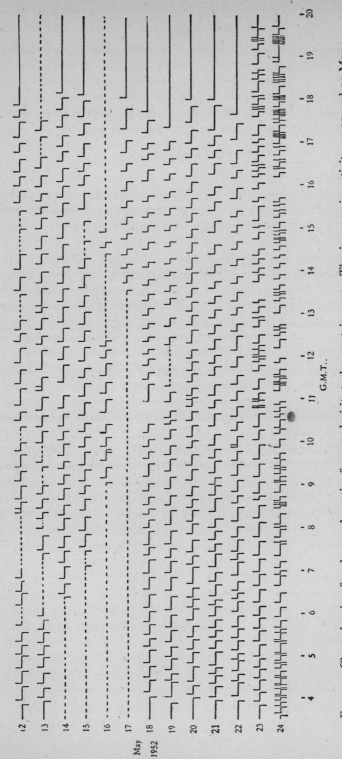

Fig. 23. Chart showing female wren's sorties from and visits to her nest in 1952. The increase in activity on 23 and 24 May was due to the hatching of the young. Note particularly long sessions after long recesses between 11.00 and 12.00 on 14 May, and between 10.30 and 11.30 on 18 May; also presumed visits by the male between 08.00 and 12.00 on 12, 13, 16, 20 and 22 May, indicated by double vertical strokes. (*After Whitehouse and Armstrong 1953*)

eggs in natural incubators, and species of swift which attach them to the nest, all birds turn their eggs at intervals. The house wren does so as she inserts and withdraws her feet. She does not use her bill (Kendeigh 1941). It is difficult to ascertain what method is employed by the wren but she may use her beak when she pokes into the bottom of the nest (p. 204) as well as move the eggs with her feet.

INCUBATION RHYTHM

Relevance of hunger and habit formation

The amount of incubation by birds varies from the maximum possible, achieved by such species as the golden pheasant, which remain on the eggs for the whole incubation period of 23 days (Goodwin 1948) to nil by the megapodes which utilise the warmth generated by decaying vegetation to hatch their eggs.

My observations on the brooding rhythm of the wren may be considered in relation to some of the theories regarding the factors regulating brooding rhythms in general. Nice (1943) believes that the song sparrow's rhythm is determined by the pangs of hunger, though her opinion is doubtfully consistent with the data showing that two-thirds of the female's departures from the nest are in response to the male's signal song (1937). Kendeigh (*in litt.*) expresses the opinion that, so far as the house wren's behaviour is concerned, hunger is primarily important but some habit formation may also be involved. On the other hand, Ruiter considers that the redstart's rhythm is not determined by hunger.

An experiment proved that factors besides hunger play a major part in determining the wren's incubation rhythm. For some time before it was made, the wren, which was nesting in a shed, emerged regularly by a chink under the door, although during a previous period of observation she used a hole in the wall. I barricaded the crevice under the door, expecting the bird to fly out by the hole only three feet distant. After incubating for 25 minutes, to my surprise, instead of going out by the hole she returned to the nest and remained brooding for another 25 minutes. She then flew out by the hole although the obstruction under the door had been removed. Thus when the impulse to feed was thwarted the impulse to brood reasserted itself and the rhythm was resumed as if the wren had made a sortie of the usual duration.

An experiment in which a wren was repeatedly forced to stay away from the nest for a few minutes when she returned from foraging showed that she tended to stay in longer than usual after such abnormally long recesses (Whitehouse and Armstrong 1953). Perhaps the temperature of the nest and eggs is important in this connection. As the anxious bird fed little or not at all during these enforced delays the experiment provides further evidence of the importance of other factors than hunger in determining the incubation rhythm.

Effect of physiological factors

Odum (1944) suggests that during the brooding spell congestion of the blood occurs which needs to be relieved by muscular exercise and he infers that response to this physiological condition determines the rhythm. The behaviour of the bird which returned to brood can hardly be reconciled with this theory. Before an incubating house wren leaves the nest her temperature usually rises by somewhat more than a degree, but it is not certain whether this is due to her restlessness after incubating for a while or to the effect of the warmed nest and eggs in conserving the bird's bodily heat (Baldwin and Kendeigh 1932). According to my observations, wrens brooding eggs or young fidget a great deal, as also do house wrens and various other passerines (Barrett 1947a; Conder 1948).

Temperature

Even superficial observation shows that birds' incubation rhythms tend to alter with rising temperature. Individuals nesting where the eggs are exposed to the sun's warmth, especially in the tropics, may brood them very little during daylight, and, indeed, sometimes shade them from the sun rather than incubate. On a hot August day I saw a wren emerge from the nest, preen for 11 minutes and then return to continue brooding. Apparently her behaviour was mainly due to discomfort caused by the heat.

Dr. Kendeigh writes that he has noted the following correlations between temperature and the incubation rhythm:

TABLE XVII

RELATIONSHIP BETWEEN TEMPERATURE AND INCUBATION RHYTHM
HOUSE WREN

Temperature ($^\circ$ F.)	53	68	79
Average duration of periods on (minutes)	14.0	12.3	8.4
Average duration of periods off (minutes)	10.6	8.8	8.7

He sums up the relationship between temperature and incubation rhythm thus (1952):

" As air temperature rises from daily averages of 48° F. to 88° F. there is an increase in the number of attentive periods per day and a decrease in the length of the attentive periods. This results in a decrease in total attentive time during the day and an increase in the total time of inattentiveness, even though there is no significant change in the average length of the inattentive periods." The percentage of time on the eggs varies from 61 at 48° F. to 47.6 at 88° F.

A similar trend towards reduction of brooding as temperature rises is characteristic of other species, as these Tables show:

TABLE XVIII

RELATIONSHIP BETWEEN TEMPERATURE AND INCUBATION RHYTHM
BEWICK WREN (Laskey 1946a)

Dates (June)	5th, 6th, 10th	3rd, 4th	11th, 14th
Temperature (° F.)	66-82	79-84	Max. 97
Percentage of time on nest	53	24	23

TABLE XIX

RELATIONSHIP BETWEEN TEMPERATURE AND INCUBATION RHYTHM
CAROLINA WREN (Nice and Thomas 1948)

Dates (May)	12th	7th	2nd
Temperature (° F.)	60	64	75
Percentage of time on nest	81.1	79.4	62.4

In warmer weather Carolina wrens shorten their sessions and increase their number. One of these birds spent 80 per cent of the daylight hours incubating when the temperature averaged 63.6° F. but only 64.5 per cent when it averaged 69° F. (Nice and Thomas 1948). Dr. Skutch tells me that none of six species of wren observed by him in Costa Rica spent less than 47 per cent nor more than 66 per cent of the daylight hours on the eggs.

With the help of Mrs. H. L. K. Whitehouse the following data were obtained during two whole days of observation:

TABLE XX

PERIODS ON AND OFF IN MINUTES OF A WREN (SILVERBAND)
ON 26 MAY 1947

Periods *on* 40 32 ? 49 26 26 ? 31 34 29 31 ? 40 31 24 34 41
Periods *off* 8 12 6 ? 10 12 14 ? 8 11 14 14 ? 11 11 11 12 14
Average periods on—33 minutes
Average periods off—11 minutes

Percentage time on—73.6*
Mean temperature during the wren's active day—65° F.
Mean temperature for the day—62° F.

PERIODS ON AND OFF OF A WREN (SILVERBAND)
ON 4 JUNE 1947

Periods *on*   22 26 21 16 23 ? 25 27 23 37 33 21 31 28 31 67
Periods *off* 10 13 13 12 13 13 ? 14 10 17† 14 11 14 15 11 20 19
Average duration of periods on—29 minutes
Average duration of periods off—14 minutes
Percentage time on—66.3
Mean temperature during the wren's active day—70° F.
Mean temperature for the day—69° F.

Thus on the warmer of the two days the sessions decreased in length
and the recesses increased.

More extensive data were obtained with a recording instrument
in 1952 (Whitehouse and Armstrong 1953) (Fig. 24).

The graph shows the close relationship between the time spent
brooding and air temperature. The correlation coefficient =—0.74.
During the ten days when data were obtained the total number of
sorties per day remained remarkably constant—about 40—in spite of
variable weather. The data cited above for Silverband indicate a
tendency to similar constancy at only 17 to 18 sorties per day. However, the mean number of sorties per hour for the 1952 wren shows
a steady decline from an average of 3.2 at dawn to 2.2 at the time
of retiring (Fig. 25).

The relationship between the duration of sessions and recesses is
shown in Figs. 23 and 26.

The influence of air temperature on the length of sessions and
recesses is apparent. Thus on 18 May when the temperature was
around 55° F. at the beginning of the wren's working day the average
durations of times on and off were approximately 6 and 14 minutes
respectively, whereas around 15.00 when the temperature was about
87° F. the corresponding figures were approximately 16 and 8 minutes
respectively. However, there is a remarkable tendency for the sum of
consecutive sessions and recesses to remain constant, apart from the
steady increase indicated by the figures above showing the reduction
in sorties per hour as the day advances. Thus sessions in the early
morning began at about 20-minute intervals, whereas, towards the

*The percentages are estimated on the basis of the recorded periods, not with
regard to the duration of daylight.
†This period would have been 13 minutes had not the commotion caused by
blackbirds and chaffinches mobbing a cat attracted the returning bird to the scene.

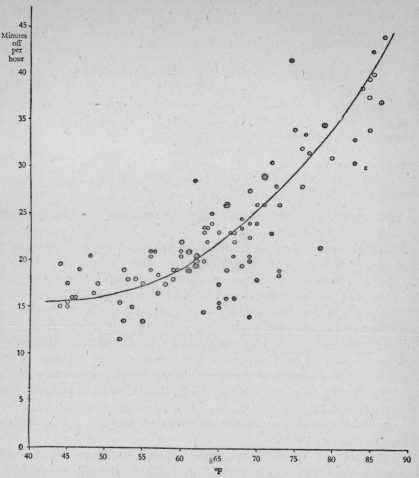

Fig. 24. Graph illustrating the correlation between air temperature and time spent off the eggs during the active day by an incubating wren in 1952. (*After Whitehouse and Armstrong 1953*)

time of retiring, they began about every 30 minutes. Comparison with the Silverband data indicates that this time-span of session-plus-recess varies for different individuals. Apparently there is some physiological mechanism which keeps the relationship between session and recess in equilibrium.

Kendeigh's investigations show that there is an inverse relationship between the house wren's sessions (or attentive periods) and temperature.

Table XXI, from data given by Kendeigh (1952), illustrates the

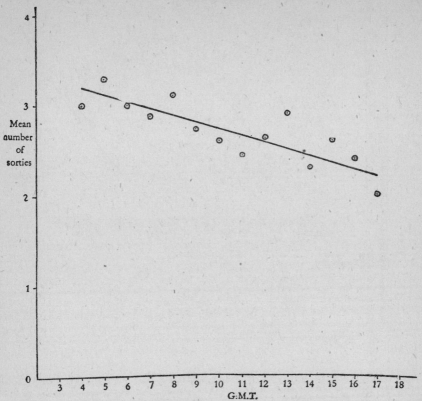

FIG. 25. Graph showing diurnal decline in number of sorties by an incubating wren in 1952. (*After Whitehouse and Armstrong 1953*)

decrease in the average length of the session which occurs in the early afternoon.

TABLE XXI

Time	06.00—09.00	13.00—14.00	19.00
Average duration of sessions (*minutes*)	12.5	10.4	15.0
Average duration of recesses (*minutes*)	6.7	9.0	8.1

Baldwin and Kendeigh's data (Fig. 27) show the changes in the temperature of a house wren's egg and the nest containing it according as the bird is incubating or not. In cool weather the temperature of the egg naturally falls more rapidly than during warm weather, but

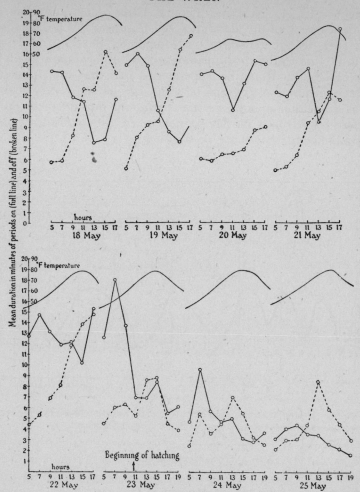

Fig. 26. Graphs illustrating the relationship of air temperature to duration of sessions and recesses of a wren in 1952. Note that the duration of sessions and recesses tends to vary inversely as temperature varies (*After Whitehouse and Armstrong 1953*)

the increased time spent on the eggs by the bird tends to compensate for this also.

It appears to be a general rule among passerines in temperate regions that with decreasing temperature the time spent incubating tends to increase and the duration of the recesses decreases, but there is variation between species as to whether this increase of time on the nest is attained by more frequent but shorter sorties or by longer sessions (Nice 1943; Nice and Thomas 1948; Allen and Nice 1952).

Probably some of the anomalies which appear when data for some species, such as the redstart, are compared (Buxton 1950) will be found to be due to the incompleteness of the information available.

It will be seen from the appended Table that the limits within which the incubation rhythm of some species may vary are wide. There is no reason to suppose that variations outside these limits do not occur. As length of day is not taken into consideration only approximate comparisons are possible:

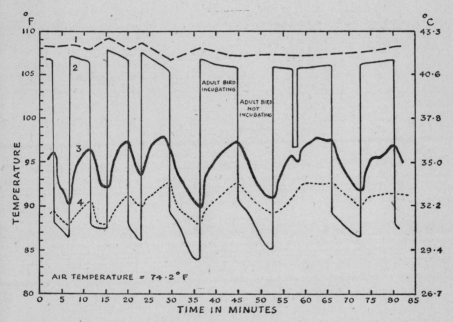

FIG. 27. Graph showing natural fluctuations in temperature of the eastern house wren's egg under normal conditions in the nest. 1—Body temperature of adult bird; 2—temperature at top of nest just above the eggs; 3—egg temperature; 4—temperature in bottom of nest beneath egg. (*After Baldwin and Kendeigh 1932*)

Table XXII

SORTIES FROM THE NEST DURING THE DAY BY INCUBATING PASSERINES

Species	Number of sorties	Authority
Wren	18–50	Armstrong
House wren	25–71	Kendeigh 1952
Carolina wren	6–7	Nice and Thomas 1948
Chiffchaff	17–34	Steinfatt 1938a

FIG. 28. Diagram illustrating temperature gradients in the nest of an eastern house wren during a recess (*above,*) and during a session (*below.*) (*After J. M. Valentine, in Baldwin and Kendeigh 1932*)

Redstart	23-32	Ruiter 1941
Swallow	46-79	De Braey 1946
Oven bird	5-13	Hann 1937
Song sparrow	14-39	Baldwin and Kendeigh 1937

The Carolina wren and oven bird have much slower rhythms than those of most small insectivorous birds for which data are available. The lowland wood wren (average 85 minutes on, 57 off) and riverside bay wren (average 68 minutes on, 35 off) (A. F. Skutch, *in litt.*) are also slow. So, too, are the dippers (Rankin and Rankin 1940; Hann 1950). A Bewick's wren, incubating in a metal box exposed to the sun, spent periods varying from 3 to 41 minutes on the nest and from 12 to 63 minutes away (Laskey 1946a).

Observations at nests of the Alaska wren show that the female spends 18 to 21 minutes on the eggs and 2 to 5 minutes foraging (Heath 1920). For two hours around midday a Shetland wren averaged 11½ minutes on and 10 off. A rock wren's sessions and recesses averaged 18 and 15 minutes respectively (Jones 1939).

The eggs of house wrens and Bewick's wrens fail to hatch if subjected to unwonted high temperatures (Baldwin and Kendeigh 1932; Kendeigh 1940; Laskey 1946a). During the middle of the day if a house wren's box becomes excessively warm the bird may not sit at all (Kendeigh 1934), and tule wrens may absent themselves from the eggs for two hours on a hot day (Wheelock 1904).

Some birds, such as the Irish dipper and chestnut-sided warbler (Lawrence 1948), may sit for longer periods towards the end of incubation than at the beginning, but this has not been recorded of any species of wren.

LENGTH OF ACTIVE DAY

At the end of May and beginning of June an incubating wren's active day may be surprisingly short. Often birds make their last sortie long before fading light would prevent foraging—indicating that hunger is but one of several factors influencing the brooding rhythm.

TABLE XXIII

LENGTH OF THE INCUBATING WREN'S ACTIVE DAY

Date	Sunrise	First departure	Sunset	Last Return	Duration of daylight	Active day
8/5/44	04.18	04.08	19.35	18.10	15 h. 17 min.	14 h. 02 min.
26/5/47	03.54	03.43	20.00	16.22	16 h. 06 min.	12 h. 39 min.
27/5/51	03.52	04.00	20.03	18.00	16 h. 11 min.	14 h. 08 min.
12/6/44	03.42	03.45	20.17	17.42	16 h. 35 min.	13 h. 57 min.

Another incubating wren, timed by a recording instrument, retired at just over 116 minutes before sunset. In the northern Isles of Shetland, a wren settled on her eggs for the night at 16.52 on 16 June although sunset (at Lerwick) was at 21.31. On the other hand, house wrens settle for the night a few minutes before sunset.

Comparable data are available for other species; an Irish dipper vacated the nest for only 12 minutes between 14.28 and nightfall and a hawfinch remained on the nest from 98 minutes before sunset. On several occasions a great tit on her second-brood clutch retired for the night 2 to 3 hours before sunset. She retired, on the average, 100 minutes before sunset (Kluijver 1950).

PSEUDO-INCUBATION

Occasionally a wren sits in an empty nest as if incubating. One female continued to brood for 6 days after her single egg had been taken (Bletchly 1938); another brooded assiduously for at least 15 days in a feather-lined nest (Whitaker, unpublished) and yet another for two months or more spent part of the day in a nest from which it would peep when anybody approached (Oldham 1937). Late in the breeding season an adult male white-bellied wren (*Uropsila leucogastra*) was flushed from a nest in mid-morning. He soon returned and when shot fell back into the nest. There were no eggs. It was well built with narrow entrance and deep recess, so it was probably not constructed for roosting. The bird's testes were inactive (Traylor 1949). I found a wren in an unoccupied robin's nest on the mornings of 4, 6 and 17 June though she was absent when I made two visits on 9 June. The bird need not have lacked a mate for there was a male singing freely close by. There was no reason to suppose that this bird had lost an earlier clutch, so it seems that broodiness may occur independently of egg-laying. Certainly it may develop before any eggs are laid for I have known a ptarmigan sit closely for a day or two before an egg appeared and similar behaviour has been recorded of a variety of species (Lack 1932; Owen 1940; Davis 1941). Reed warblers may come to the nest at sunrise the day before the first egg is deposited and go through the motions of laying, as if rehearsing for the event (Brown and Davies 1949). I have seen a blackbird with newly-fledged young go to a nest, built, probably, by the same bird earlier in the season, squatter and turn in it as if shaping a nest under construction, and then remain sitting for short periods—but she did not lay there. Brooding birds on egg-less nests usually maintain the customary incubation rhythm (Nice 1943).

There are very few instances of a bird brooding in the empty nest of another species as did the wren mentioned above, though this may occur now and then with some birds of prey which appropriate a disused nest. Occasionally a bird sits on another bird's eggs, as when a blackbird incubated a mallard's egg for 17 days (Henderson 1937).

A wren in Wren Wood sat for 26 days on infertile eggs and then deserted. Another incubated for 25 days until I removed the eggs. Mr. J. H. Owen informs me that he has known incubation of infertile eggs by a wren continue for 51 days. Other species have been observed to prolong incubation so long beyond the normal period that they suffered in health (Romanes 1883; Graham 1890).

RELATIONSHIP OF THE MALE TO THE INCUBATING FEMALE

There is no record of a male wren incubating except an unreliable account by Grunack (1879) concerning a pair which reared a brood in a small cage.

However neglectful male wrens may be of domestic duties, many, if not most of them, intermit patrolling, singing, feeding, nest-building and courting to visit their nests from time to time, sometimes singing or calling outside or, occasionally, peeping within. A cock will visit a nest where his mate is completing her clutch and copulate with her, or accost an incubating female when she returns from a sortie, attempting to tread her. He may peep into the nest on days when the eggs are being laid and at other times. Shortly after a nest had been deserted I found the male singing a loud, truncated song a few inches from the entrance as if inquiring how matters stood.

A nest in a gnarled stump could be watched from three feet away through a space in a wooden fence. The last of the three eggs to hatch had done so about 24 hours before I took my place at this peep-hole and there were still two unhatched eggs. I saw the female go off and then heard the male singing his way towards me. He perched spryly with tail erect on a thorn tree eight feet from the nest and uttered a loud, abbreviated song, then flirped to the fence and down to the stump. He came hopping in a tentative manner towards the entrance to the nest and perched on the threshold, looking in. Then he flew away, singing as he went. Perhaps his visit was due to his noticing the altered behaviour of his mate when the eggs hatched.

One evening while watching at another nest, I saw the female go off to find food for her chicks which were three days old. The male, who had been feeding the nestlings of his other mate across the wood, appeared at the nest at 20.00, four minutes after singing his last song. He entered, stayed inside 20 seconds, and then went off to roost. Somewhat similar behaviour is recorded of Irish dippers. A male was seen visiting his incubating mate on two evenings just before sunset.

Visits may be made at almost any time of the day, but are probably most usual in the morning (Whitehouse and Armstrong 1953). The cock may sing loudly or softly outside the nest and the female often responds with " chittering " or " chattering " notes. Only once have I known a female fly from the nest towards where her mate was singing. When a male banded cactus wren visits his incubating mate it is he who utters harsh calls; an unmated bird may also peep in now and

T.W.   N then, and later on, may help to feed the nestlings (Skutch 1935). The cock Carolina wren makes rasping notes as he approaches the nest but gives soft tweets when he looks in. The female arrives with soft twitters (Laskey 1948). After a Vigors's wren, carrying food, had entered a nest with eggs which had just been vacated by his mate he flew out and uttered a distinctive call (Miller 1941).

CHAPTER 11

CARE OF THE NESTLINGS

But now behold the greatest of this train
Of miracles, stupendously minute;
The numerous progeny, clamant for food
Supplied by two small bills, and feeble wings
Of narrow range; supplied—ay, duly fed—
Fed in the dark, and yet not one forgot.
                WILSON. *The Disconsolate Wren*

HATCHING

THE SIXTH and last egg in one wren's clutch hatched 21 hours and 8 minutes after the first (Whitehouse and Armstrong 1953). Often hatching is spread over two days and occasionally it may even take three days. The average hatching period of the house wren's clutch is over 26 hours (Kendeigh 1952). According to Welter (1935) the female prairie marsh wren begins to incubate before the clutch is complete so that " in most nests young of two or even three ages can be found." Apparently a protracted hatch is usually due to the gradual or intermittent beginning of incubation during egg-laying. Kluijver's data (1950) show that a great tit's first-brood clutch of ten eggs, which was not consistently brooded until after it was complete, hatched in two days, but the seven eggs of the second took four days to hatch, some of the eggs having been brooded a good deal by the time the last egg was laid. When I transferred five wren's eggs to the nest of a sitting blue tit—first three which had not been brooded and afterwards the others on successive days—three eggs hatched together and then the other two, again on successive days. Although my

numbering on the eggs was rubbed off during the course of incubation
the circumstances render it likely that the eggs hatched in the order
in which they were subjected to brooding. Thus probably the last egg
of the clutch hatches last, as is the rule with the house wren's and blue
tit's eggs (Gibb 1950).

In at least some species " spread " hatching is apparently an
adaptation correlated with food-supply. For example, morsels too
large for the youngest of a bittern brood may be eaten by the eldest,
and among raptors, whose food supply is sometimes precarious, it is
probably racially advantageous that in times of scarcity one or two
chicks should thrive at the expense of the younger nestlings. The most
backward chick may provide food for its brethren (Pickwell 1948), and
a harrier has even been seen feeding the body of a dead chick to the
surviving youngster (Breckenridge 1935).

For many small passerines in temperate regions the second brood's
food supply is apparently scantier or more precarious than the first
brood's, though Kluijver (1950) noticed that a second brood of great
tits received more food than the first. Thus a progressive increase in
the amount of incubation during the laying of the second clutch not
only involves an earlier hatch than if incubation began after the clutch
was complete, but by spacing births secures the survival of the sturdy
few in times of stringency rather than the rearing of a debilitated family
doomed to early death. On the other hand, a short spread of hatching
is advantageous for most species with nidifugous young because survival
is jeopardised if the parents have to divide their time between incubating
and leading chicks.

EGG-SHELL DISPOSAL

Nascent wrens and prairie marsh wrens bisect the egg with the
egg-tooth and shortly after hatching the female wren drops the half-
shells 10 to 25 yards from the nest—though occasionally the fragments
are let fall outside the nest (Whitehouse and Armstrong 1953). Prairie
marsh wrens and reed warblers (Brown and Davies 1949) carry shells
25 to 30 feet. A wren with hatching eggs carried strips of paper and
willow catkins placed in the nest to within a few feet of each other
25 yards away. A teat from a baby's bottle was not removed—
presumably because of its resemblance in some respects to a chick.
Two of three half-shells placed in a nest with young a week old were
dropped below the nest, indicating the waning of the impulse, although
fæces were being carried twenty yards. Wrens apparently carry the
droppings approximately as far as they do the egg-shells. Sometimes
in this matter there are differences in the behaviour of individuals or

even between the behaviour of the same individual at different times. A Carolina wren took one piece of shell out of sight, ate some fragments in the nest and carried a half-shell twenty yards to eat it (Laskey 1948).

Discarded egg-shells near a nest might betray it to a predator, but many birds remove shells farther than would seem necessary. I have seen a ringed plover carry a half-shell forty yards from the scrape.

BROODING THE NESTLINGS

When young wrens hatch the time spent brooding becomes shorter. On five successive days after the date of hatching—on which a wren brooded 53 per cent of the working day—she progressively reduced the time spent brooding and then maintained the same amount— about 25 per cent—for two more days. The average daily reduction in brooding is about 6 or 8 per cent (Fig. 29, p. 189). There is a marked drop in the time spent brooding during the afternoon when the temperature is usually highest. House wrens and wrens usually abandon brooding the young by day when they are about nine or ten days old, though occasionally a wren will spend a brief period over the young during daylight when they have reached that age. During a heavy shower a wren with young of ten days took refuge in the nest for twenty minutes. Mr. R. Atkinson tells me that both parents took a turn at brooding young St. Kilda wrens four to five days before they left the nest. That the male should act thus is remarkable. Winter wrens may brood nestlings of ten days for two or three minutes (C. Stanwood, *in litt.*) but in the warm climate of Surinam pale-bellied house wrens abandon brooding by day after the chicks are four days old (Haverschmidt 1952). Nocturnal brooding sometimes ceases when young European wrens are about ten days old, but I have known a female roost with the chicks until the night before they fledged. I flushed an adult after dark from outside the nesting niche four days before fledging occurred, but it is unusual for females with well-grown young to roost very near the nest.

Two-day old prairie marsh wrens are brooded only about 30 per cent of the time, but during the first three days after the eggs hatched a Carolina wren spent practically as much time at the nest as before (72-73 per cent) though she doubled the number of sorties. She roosted in the nest until the young were six to seven days old, missed at least one night, and again roosted with them when they were eleven to twelve days old (Nice and Thomas 1948). Another behaved differently. She brooded 68 per cent of the time on the day the eggs hatched and 65, 15, 10 and 11 per cent on successive days. Thereafter the young were not brooded, even at night, although temperatures

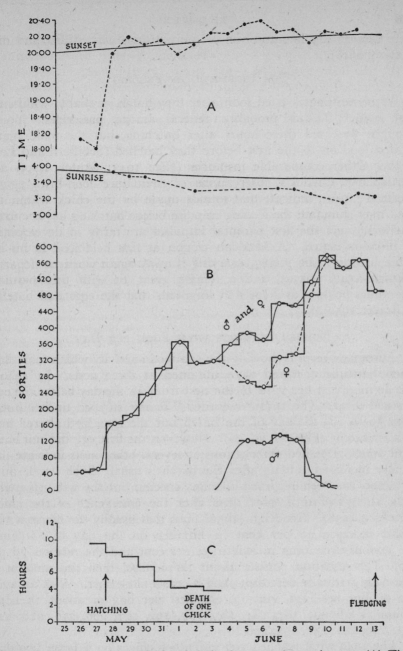

FIG. 29. Graph showing the activities of a pair of wrens at the nest in 1951. (A) Times of arising and retiring. (B) Number of trips per day. Sorties on 13 June by extrapolation. (C) Time spent brooding during the active day. (*After Whitehouse and Armstrong 1953*)

were abnormally low and one of the nestlings was chilled and died (Laskey 1948).

THE INCEPTION OF FEEDING

Wren nestlings are fed soon after they hatch, probably within the first hour.[8] This is probably general among passerines. Young choughs were fed three hours after hatching, but the male regurgitated food on to the nest before they hatched (Schifferli and Lang 1940). Other comparable instances (Nice 1943; Skutch 1953) and particularly Carrick's observations of premature food-bringing by starlings (1949), indicate that sounds made by the chick within the shell may stimulate the feeding impulse before hatching has occurred. But sometimes the first parental impulses are tardy in development or ill-co-ordinated. A Mexican trogon at first held food in his bill while brooding the young, carrying it away again when he departed (Skutch 1942, 1953a), and a female great tit with tiny nestlings sometimes behaves as if she had forgotten that the eggs had hatched (Kluijver 1950).

NUMBER OF VISITS WITH FOOD PER DAY

Automatic records showing the change in activity which took place when hatching occurred were obtained at three nests. In 1949 a female increased her visits to the nest from 42 the day before the eggs hatched to 91. The 1951 " recorded " female stepped up her sorties from 50 to 163 the day of the hatch but the 1952 bird altered from 39 sorties to 65 (Figs. 23, 29, 30). However, the first egg did not hatch until 10.48. Detailed observations at several other nests indicate that greatly increased activity after the hatch is usual. Such acceleration of tempo has been recorded of many species, but the wren-tit makes little alteration until some days after the emergence of the chicks (Erickson 1938). Kendeigh (1952) finds that usually the house wren's sorties increase 49 per cent in number on the day of hatching; the sessions decreasing in length 34 per cent and the recesses 29 per cent. This situation persists about three days, then the amount of brooding gradually decreases until it ceases altogether. With an average of four nestlings, visits to the nest per day of about 15 hours mount as follows: 184, 184, 185, 187, 192, 197, 206, 210, 218, 225, 233, 240, 246, 251, 255, 256.

The 1949 wren reached 397 visits to 6 chicks on 3 June, two days before they fledged. The 1951 female feeding 4 nestlings attained about 560 sorties two days before the day of fledging and the male contributed approximately 12 more (Fig. 29, p. 189). In 1952 the peak

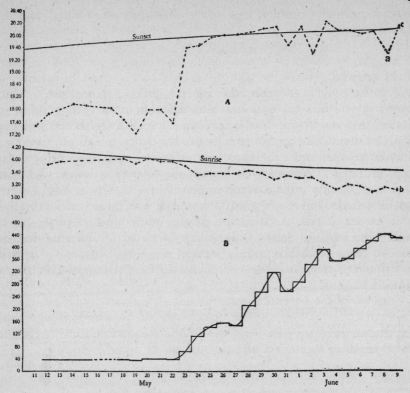

Fig. 30. Graph showing the activities of a female wren in 1952. (A) Times of arising and retiring; (a)—time of last visit on 8 June; (b)—time of first visit on 9 June; (c)—time of visit after nest was vacated on 9 June. (B) Number of trips per day. Sorties on 9 June by extrapolation. (*After Whitehouse and Armstrong 1953*)

attained by the female working alone to feed 6 young was 442 sorties. The graph shows that there was a tendency for the increase in the tempo of this bird to be interrupted every fourth day—for some unknown reason. On the other hand, the tempo at the 1951 nest tended to increase fairly regularly, apart from an interruption about the time when a chick died. This was remarkable, as during the middle of the nestling period when the female slackened her efforts the male compensated for her deficiencies until, after she began to work energetically again, he reduced his help and eventually, shortly before the young fledged, he desisted. When a blue tit was deserted by his mate he made a great effort to compensate for her defection, but greatly decreased his activity during the last few days, probably through exhaustion. One of the chicks died (Arnold 1952). A constant increase has been recorded in the activities of a pair of Carolina wrens although the efforts of the male and female varied (Nice and Thomas 1948). These observations support other evidence that the begging of the hungry chicks is important in determining the feeding tempo of the parents.

Fig. 29 may be compared with Kluijver's for a great tit's nest (1950) at which, with both parents active, a peak of 937 visits was reached five days before the ten first-brood chicks fledged. Gibb (1950), however, found that in this species the incidence of the peak varies in different seasons and may occur about the seventh day. Nice (1943) suggests that a " plateau " in the graph of feeding activity is typical of most passerines after a week or ten days. This is a very doubtful generalisation. There are many factors—size of brood, availability of food, extent of the participation of the sexes, and so forth—which modify the feeding tempo and routine of birds. A decrease towards the end of nest life has been recorded of a great variety of species, passerine and non-passerine. In some of these it is probably due to reduced begging by the chicks, but in others the fatigue or reduction of " drive " of the parents results in less feeding activity (Heinroth and Heinroth 1924-33, 1930; Nice 1943; Arnold 1952). It is significant that male great tits which neglect the nestlings before they fledge may feed them after they leave the nest (Kluijver 1950).

ROLES OF THE SEXES IN FEEDING NESTLINGS

The male European wren feeds the chicks at about 40 per cent of nests. As the breeding season advances and his nest-building and courtship activities decrease his co-operation at the nest tends to increase. In male birds of many species strong primary sex impulses tend, at first, to dominate " domestic " impulses. Of twelve male wrens watched by the Dutch observers in 1937, five fed the nestlings, but one of the two which helped during May remained unmated for the rest of the year and the other did not pair again when the second-brood nest was destroyed after the first egg had been laid. Probably all polygamous male wrens of various species interest themselves more in the young as their sexual concern with the females declines. Some male winter wrens do not feed the nestlings and male short-billed sedge wrens only occasionally tend the chicks (Walkinshaw 1935). Welter (1935) did not note young prairie marsh wrens being fed by the male before they fledged, but in their second week out of the nest the cocks became very assiduous.

I have never known a male European wren feed the nestlings before they were some days old, though, perhaps, he may occasionally do so. It was only after the chicks in a Shetland wren's nest had been hatched two or three days that the male began to feed them. Cock house sparrows and chiffchaffs also do not feed the nestlings until they are some days out of the egg (Dewar 1928; Treuenfels 1940), though this is probably not invariable. On the other hand, the male great tit feeds the young when they hatch, but the female does not do so regularly until the third or fourth day (Kluijver 1950).

The male wren, as we have noted, learns of the hatching of the young either by observing the foraging activities of his mate or by peeping into the nest. Male Carolina wrens may receive a more direct intimation. When the first egg in a nest hatched a female began to call and her mate, who had been bringing food to her as she incubated, almost immediately nearly doubled the frequency of his visits per hour (Nice and Thomas 1948). In other species in which the male provides much, or most, of the food for his incubating mate, such as the Montagu harrier and sparrowhawk, he increases the feeding tempo when he finds the young have hatched (Vincent 1910; Buxton 1946; Tinbergen 1946).

At a wren's nest where the male was, at times, more diligent in feeding the young than his mate, he chased her back to the nest when she had become disquieted by my presence. Although such episodes are not unusual at the nests of many small passerines, only on this occasion have I noticed the cock wren thus concerned by the female's neglect of her domestic responsibilities. The male corn bunting often chevies his mates back to their nests (Ryves 1934a, b). Thus even in a species with a strong tendency to polygamy such impulses, characteristic of birds with a monogamous pair-bond, may be retained.

It is unusual for male wrens to be more active than their mates in feeding the nestlings. They are apt to make trips without any food, or carrying only one morsel, and may break off after a few visits to go singing elsewhere. A female concentrates on feeding the family from the beginning of her day, but a male sings around his territory before starting work. Polygamy is so integrated with other adaptations of the species that broods do not come to grief for lack of the male's help, though probably, when he co-operates, some of the weaker nestlings fledge with greater stamina than they would otherwise possess, or even survive when they might have died.

Male Shetland and St. Kilda wrens sometimes work as hard as their mates, but a Hebridean male at a nest I watched was irregular in his visits.

Table XXIV enables some comparisons to be made between the foraging rhythms of different species and subspecies of wren.

TABLE XXIV

NUMBER OF FEEDING VISITS PER HOUR BY DIFFERENT SPECIES AND SUBSPECIES OF WREN

Species or subspecies	Visits per hour.	Time of beginning count	Date	Number of Young	Date of fledging or approximate age	Authority
European wren ♀	19 11 16	03.38 09.13 18.09	31/5/44	5 5 5	4/6/44	Armstrong „ „
European wren ♂ & ♀	♂26 ♀18 ♂36 ♀17	03.27 04.12	17/6/44 9/6/47	5 6	19/6/44 15/6/47	Armstrong „
Shetland wren ♂ & ♀	12 ♂10 ♀11 ♂ 9 ♀ 8 20	16.26 02.42 19.12 14.13	7/6/50 11/6/50 „ 20/6/50	6 6 6 6	22/6/50	Armstrong „ „ „
Hebridean wren ♂ & ♀	12 9 17 8	12.47 13.48 08.45 10.43	7/6/51 7/6/51 8/6/51 10/6/51	5 5 5 6	6 days 6 „ 7 „ 5 „	Armstrong „ „ „
St. Kilda wren ♂ & ♀	12 10 13	13.00 14.00 18.00		c. 4	Week of hatching	Harrisson and Buchan 1936
Iceland wren ♂ & ♀	c. 20			7	Nearly fledged	Holmes and Keith 1936
Eastern winter wren ♀	33	05.15	15/6/13	6	20/6/13	Stanwood, in litt. 1949
Western winter wren ♀	c. 12					Grinnell and Storer 1924
Eastern house wren ♂ & ♀	14.5			4	Average from hatching to fledging	Kendeigh, in litt.

Species or subspecies	Visits per hour	Time of beginning count	Date	Number of young	Date of fledging or approximate age	Authority
Pale-bellied house wren ♂ & ♀	15 25 21	13.03 06.15 09.55	28/2/32 29/2/32 22/5/49	c. 4 „ 4	c. 6/3/32 „ 29/5/49	Armstrong „ Haverschmidt 1952
Short-billed sedge wren ♀	9 5	11.30 6 hours' watch	16/7/34 15/7/33	6	27/7/33 20/7/33	Walkinshaw 1935 Mousley 1934
Tule wren ♀	4	Most of the day			Two days later	Wheelock 1904
Prairie marsh wren ♀	10			c. 6		Welter 1935
Bewick's wren ♂ & ♀	13 24 19 23	Three successive days		4		Skaggs 1934
Carolina wren ♂ & ♀	5.1 12.8 5.0 6.4		12-18/5/46 19-25/5/46 4-11/8/46 12-15/8/46	5 „ 3 2	26/5/46 „ 16/8/46 „	Nice and Thomas 1948 Laskey 1948

The maximum number of visits by a female European wren in an hour which I have noted is 43 to four nestlings, a tempo greater than has been recorded of a pair of wrens of any of the other races. A pair of European wrens may reach a total of 53 visits per hour. Thus a single parent may make nearly 11 visits per nestling per hour. This suggests that two parents may surpass the highest figure I have recorded of nearly 9 visits per hour. The highest tempo recorded of any of the northern insular races in relatively bleak habitats does not reach the average of between four and five visits per nestling per hour which Nice (1943) shows to be a common tempo among passerines of north temperate regions. The maximum she quotes is 8.4 for the wire-tailed swallow (Moreau 1939)—a tropical species—and the minimum .8 for the oven bird (Hann 1937). A male house wren who had lost his mate made the astonishing number of 1,217 visits with food to

the seven nestlings during a 15¾ hour day (Bayliss 1917). The maximum
number of visits in a day recorded by Kendeigh is 491. On the basis
of a 15-hour day this tempo would be about 32 visits per hour. A
great tit and a blue tit, when their mates had ceased to help, brought
food from nearby feeding tables at a great pace, the great tit 83 times
in an hour, the blue tit 49 times in half an hour (Kluijver 1950;
Arnold 1952).

It will be noted that the Carolina wren's tempo is slow. Over the
whole nestling period the average number of hourly trips per chick
at one nest was 2.2 (Laskey 1948) and 1.8 at another (Nice and
Thomas 1948). A pair of Guatemala spotted-breasted wrens (*Thryothorus rutilus umbrinus*) fed two nestlings only thrice in 75 minutes
(Tashian 1952). The number of meals given to young chaffinches is
of a somewhat similar order—2.3 per hour (Barrett 1947a)—but birds
which regurgitate food to their young visit the nest comparatively
infrequently.

VARIATION OF FEEDING RHYTHM DURING THE DAY

The European wren's daily feeding rhythm at the nest during the
first week tends to be highest in the early morning and lowest about
noon and the early afternoon. There is a rise in rate in the evening,
but not to the morning level. However, as we shall see presently, a
concave curve by no means represents the situation. Kendeigh (1952)
found that on their first day young house wrens probably were fed
more often in the afternoon than the morning, but on the 5th and 10th
days there was usually more feeding in the morning. The graph for
the 5th day shows morning and evening peaks and an afternoon trough.
On the 15th day, when the parents are strained to their full capacity,
the curve is irregular, but it generally remains high throughout the
day. Many bird activities, including the feeding of young by insectivorous birds, are accentuated in the morning and evening, with a
reduction in the afternoon (Steinfatt 1938a, b; Palmgren 1949). The
morning feeding peak, when it occurs, may be due to one or more of
such factors as the vigorous begging of the hungry chicks, the
accentuated energy of the parents, or the abundance of some forms
of prey in the morning, but probably the parents' internal rhythm is
most important. Treuenfels (1940) thought that the afternoon lull at
a chiffchaff's nest was due to the sleepiness of the chicks. As a female
wren spends less time in the nest during the early afternoon than in
the morning or evening, alike when incubating and feeding young up
to a week old, the begging of the chicks can be only one of the factors
determining the rhythm. It may be related to temperature to some

extent, but is probably determined in the main innately (Whitehouse and Armstrong 1953). Kluijver suggests that the afternoon decline in the feeding tempo of tits may be due mainly to the internal rhythm of the adults.

The most remarkable fact emerging from an analysis of the data for the nestling periods of two broods is that the daily feeding rhythm tends to show four peaks at about four- to five-hourly intervals. During the period when the male helped his mate this rhythm was more pronounced, showing that both birds tended to accentuate and relax their efforts simultaneously although the male was compensating for the flagging efforts of the female (Whitehouse and Armstrong 1953). It may be merely coincidence that a patrolling male made his round

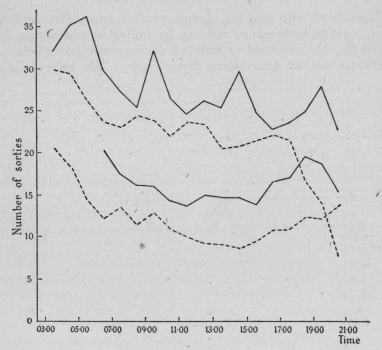

FIG. 31. Graphs showing diurnal rhythms of wrens feeding nestlings.

Full line—1951   { *Below—first half of nestling period 28 May—4 June*
                  { *Above—second half of nestling period 5-13 June*

Broken line—1952 { *Below—first half of nestling period 23-31 May*
                  { *Above—second half of nestling period 1-9 June*

No data are available before 07.00 from 28 May—4 June 1951. (*After Whitehouse and Armstrong 1953*)

at approximately similar intervals (p. 45). Kuusisto (1941) found that a pair of willow warblers tended to maintain a rhythm of two to three hours and that a male feeding a brood unaided also conformed to this tempo. Perhaps future research will show that these " shortwave rhythms " are typical of many species.

It may be remarked that evidence of such rhythms contributes to an explanation of the navigation of migrating birds, for orientation by the sun implies some " time-sense " and there is much to suggest that on the migratory journey a bird is able to act as its own chronometer and sextant. This problem is being studied by Dr. G. Kramer and Dr. G. V. T. Matthews.

FEEDING TEMPO AND POLYGAMY

Experiments with coal tits, during which I found that the feeding tempo could be increased or reduced by adding or subtracting chicks, showed that the increased or reduced demonstrativeness of the party of nestlings was the determining factor (1951). The effect of adding

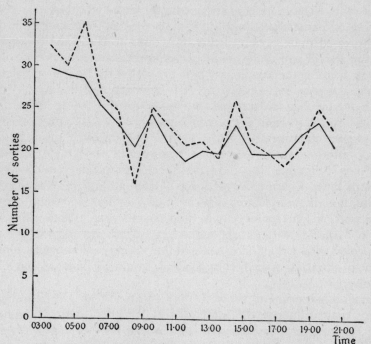

FIG. 32. Graph showing diurnal rhythms of wrens feeding nestlings in 1951. Full line—Whole nestling period 28 May—13 June. Broken line—Period when male assisted most actively (5-8 June.) (*After Whitehouse and Armstrong 1953*)

nestlings did not consist merely in augmenting the number of gaping mouths; rather the begging tempo of the whole nestful was quickened. However, increased demand does not invariably increase supply. Moreau (1944, 1947) and Gibb (1950) found that, as a rule, the more numerous the nestlings the more frequent the parents' visits, but not in proportion to the increase in the number of the young. Kendeigh (1952) noticed that broods of six house wrens were fed about half as often per bird as when there was only one present. He estimates that with families of more than six the curve of the number of daily visits reaches an upper limit. Kluijver did not find that individual members of large great tit families received less food than the nestlings of smaller broods. He suggests that such reduction occurs only when the task is beyond the working capacity of the parents.

Either directly by inspecting the brood, or indirectly by observing his mate's increased activity, a male wren may be stimulated to help. Actually his response is due to a subtle interplay of physiological and psychological factors, and the adjustment of labour-force to the necessities of the situation may fail. Kluijver's colleagues, for instance, noted a male wren helping quite needlessly with two successive broods consisting of a single nestling, but a male may not collaborate to help a hard-pressed mate or may leave the young to die if she disappears. None the less, if the males of a species constitute a reserve available to aid in feeding the nestlings when necessary the species possesses a valuable emergency adaptation. In experiments similar to mine Carrick (1949) has shown that the male starling co-operates if the family is large, but when the family is reduced by removing youngsters he may cease to bring food, start to clean out another nesting cavity and woo another mate. Male starlings outnumber females by about two to one (Bullough 1942). In this species polyandry and polygamy have both been occasionally recorded (Grabham 1895; Kessel 1950). The situation is complicated by the fact that females usually breed when a year old, but males only in their second year. If polygamy may occur in a species with a preponderance of males it is probable that in a species with a balanced sex ratio or a preponderance of females the type of situation described by Carrick would be likely to encourage polygamy.

Carrick's experiment showed that reduction in the number of nestlings may influence the male to seek another mate through not having his energies fully engaged. Eygenraam's experience with great tits (Kluijver 1950) suggests that an abundance of food may have the effect of reducing the male's parental activity and thus increasing his sexual activity. Where an abundant supply of food was provided the male began courting and courtship-feeding his mate, leaving the care of the nestlings to her.

This kind of situation may be compared with the behaviour of house wrens. When a female leaves her nestlings in order to begin another brood the male almost ceases singing and has no time for polygamous activities as he concentrates on feeding the family. That parental and sexual activities tend to inhibit one another is shown by observations establishing that if a male house wren, after feeding the nestlings, does not immediately concern himself with them when they fledge, he may begin soliciting another female. Sometimes, however, parental and sexual activities tend to balance one another and, like the male European wren, he may divide his time between seeking another mate and tending the family; if so, he may try to keep the youngsters within his territory.

Usually a male house wren can support the brood unaided after they are a week old; before then they are apt to perish as the male never broods.[4] A female banded cactus wren almost abandoned feeding the young, but the male, assisted by another male, undertook the task (Skutch 1935). When an American dipper's mate disappeared three days before the young fledged he took entire charge (Hann 1950). In passerines the rearing of young by one parent has been recorded of red-backed shrike, redstart and paradise flycatcher (Owen 1948; Buxton 1950; Moreau 1949a) and failure in the case of male willow warbler and snow bunting (Kuusisto 1941; Tinbergen 1939).

Williams' study (1952) of Brewer's blackbirds indicates that in some species polygamy may jeopardise nesting success. He found that polygamous males tended to be less assiduous in feeding the nestlings and that the death-rate of their young was appreciably higher than that of the nestlings of monogamous males.

I have no record of a male wren trying to feed two contemporaneous broods of nestlings as bigamous house wrens (Taylor 1905; Bridge 1911; Hempel 1919), sedge warblers (Brown 1951) and chaffinches (Van Beneden 1935) have been known to do, but I have seen a male feed fledged young of two different broods within an hour, and Kluijver records that a bird fed alternately two families which fledged on the same day. Bigamous Montagu and hen harriers will also bring prey to two nests within a short period (Dent 1939; Hosking 1943; Stals and Kiggen 1945).

It will be noted that the facts in regard to the tempo of wrens feeding nestlings in different types of environment reinforce the view set forth earlier, that so far as the holarctic wren *Troglodytes troglodytes* is concerned there is a correlation between food supply and polygamy (p. 219).

Of course, to say that polygamy among wrens is an adaptation correlated with a relatively abundant and readily available food supply merely summarises a complex situation. Adequate discussion would require consideration of the relationship between size of territory, length of the working day, competition within the species and with other species, the distance food has to be carried to the nest, and other factors.

NEST SANITATION

Usually the wren does not carry away the fæcal sacs until about the fourth day, and the practice is not regular until the fifth, but individuals vary. Mr. C. P. Newcomb tells me that he saw excrement removed several times the day after hatching. When some nestlings were four days old only once during two and a half hours' watch did I notice anything removed. In the course of three hours' observation at another nest containing young aged four days no fæces were carried away. Undoubtedly the female eats the fæces while nest-probing.

During their first two days Carolina wren nestlings void the droppings into the nest and the female consumes them; for three more days the fæces are picked up and swallowed by one or other of the parents while standing on the rim of the nest; thereafter the sacs are carried away (Laskey 1948). A similar transition from eating the capsules to removing them is characteristic of most other passerines (Blair and Tucker 1941). This is correlated with the transition from nearly always settling to brood after delivering the food when the chicks are very small, to spending less time covering them as they grow older. The procedure is not always consistent; prairie marsh wrens and other passerines sometimes eat and sometimes remove the sacs, song sparrows swallow some and fly off with others, and I have seen an Iceland redwing during one visit swallow two sacs and carry off a third. A chough laid several sacs on the nest rim and took them away with her when she left the nest (Schifferli and Lang 1940). Although pale-bellied house wrens cease eating the fæces when the young are three days old a bird was seen to stop nest-probing when a chick defecated, swallow the sac, and resume probing (Haverschmidt 1952). It is noteworthy that among passerines there is comparable variability in regard to the disposal of fæces and of egg-shells.

When young wrens are about a week old food is administered from outside, the parent perching on, or clinging to, the threshold. Later, when the growing young crowd the aperture one can observe that after a chick has been fed it turns round, and mutes the sac to the waiting female or male; then it retires and another takes its place. This routine is customary in a wide range of species with domed nests. When Carolina wrens were aged ten and twelve days sacs were removed on 18 per cent of the visits, the female taking more than her mate (Nice and Thomas 1948), but I have not noticed that the male wren removes fewer fæces than the female in proportion to the number of his visits. According to Yeates (1948) a female Shetland wren performed nearly all the nest sanitation when the young were nearly fledged, but the male of a pair which I had under observation through-out the whole of the nestling period was not noticeably less assiduous than his mate in performing this office.

During a five-hour watch at a house wren's nest the male never attended to the sanitation (Common 1948). When neglect occurs it tends to be just before the young fledge. A great tit, hard pressed because feeding the young unaided, may not remove the fæces. At two European wrens' nests with young five and six days old respectively the sacs were removed on 33.3 per cent and 34 per cent of visits. With some species the number of sacs voided decreases proportionately as the nestlings grow, presumably due to more complete digestion. This may well be true of European wrens. The day before a brood fledged the fæces were removed on only 20 per cent of the visits during 2½ hours.

Fewer sacs are extruded during the first hour of feeding than during a corresponding period in the evening. On two mornings five days apart the first sac was taken at the fourth visit. The bird took away four sacs in succession before her final eight visits in the evening, though previously there had been sixteen visits with only one sac removal. The voiding of sacs on four successive visits to a nest with five young probably indicates that the chicks were being fed in a fairly regular rota, confirming direct observations at other nests.

During the last day or two a few droppings may be found on the threshold, and if the chicks climb on the outside of the nest, as they sometimes do, some droppings fall to the ground. Occasionally the parent will fly down and carry away such sacs. The statement by Blair and Tucker that if fæces fall clear they are left where they drop is thus not quite accurate, though there may be some carelessness shortly before the young leave the nest. Nestling eastern winter wrens were observed to defecate over the edge of the nest and the female carried off a sac which fell into a pool (C. Stanwood, in litt.). Young western winter wrens voided the sac on the sill of the nest to be picked up by the parents. These took the excrement 50 feet and when a sac fell into a stream the bird snatched at it several times, eventually retrieving it and disposing of it as usual (Grinnell and Storer 1924). Irish and American dippers carry off sacs which drop below the nest (Rankin and Rankin 1940; Cordier 1927). A British dipper picked sacs from the stream and carried them away (Blair and Tucker 1941), and an American dipper took sacs from the chicks beneath her and dropped them over the edge of the nest (Hann 1950). Cordier speaks of young American dippers expelling the fæces vigorously out of the nest.

A Shetland wren was scrupulous about carrying off fæces which fell from the nest. On one occasion when she fumbled and lost a white pebble which I had placed below the nest to simulate a dropping she acted as if bewildered and eventually picked up and carried off another pebble. A Carolina wren behaved in a somewhat similar way. As she hopped up a brick wall after feeding the young she came on a withered leaf lodged in a crevice. She picked it up and carried it away as if she were disposing of a sac of excrement (Laskey 1948). Similarly Irish dippers pick up leaves and twigs from beneath the nest and carry them off. A British dipper, alarmed at my presence, began to take fæcal sacs from below the nest to the stream and then disposed of other objects from crevices in the same way. I have suggested that such behaviour in which an incongruous object rather than an incongruous action is involved should be distinguished from definite displacement activities and termed a " transference activity " (1952). A male European dipper went through the motions of taking a dropping to the water and wiping his bill, but left the nest sanitation to his mate (Eggebrecht 1937).

Wrens nesting in sheds carry the fæces outside. Some St. Kilda wrens were seen to remove the capsules to the boundary of the territory and drop them; others wiped the sacs off on clothes lines (Harrisson and Buchan 1936). Shetland wrens decorated a dozen yards of barbed wire thirty feet from the nest with white daubs at frequent intervals. European and Hebridean wrens sometimes wipe off the fæces on a branch. In winter, when wrens roost together in an old nest they defecate on the threshold, betraying their dormitory, so that on finding such clues it is possible to trap them, but Bewick's wrens do not leave droppings below the roost (Williams 1941).

Young prairie marsh wrens after ceasing to defecate into the nest do so on the rim, and, if Welter's observations were accurate, the female accelerates her return if there are sacs to be removed. At a later stage excrement is ejected from the nest. As one-third of the nests are destroyed, many by small mammals, their location may sometimes be betrayed by the droppings.

In 1948 two correspondents, Mrs. G. Morris and Mrs. T. Silva, independently sent me particulars of wren chicks apparently picking up the fæcal sacs in their bills and passing them to the parent after feeding. These observations are not easily interpreted (Armstrong and Thorpe 1952).

" CASTING "

During the last day spent in the nest by a brood of Shetland wrens I found morsels of a reddish-brown paste on a boulder 15 inches below the nest. Microscopic examination revealed that it was composed of arthropod remains, including fragments of insect cuticle. These had obviously been voided orally (Armstrong and Thorpe 1952). The presence of mineral grains in the castings suggested that the wrens might have brought grit to the chicks as great tits do (Kluijver 1950).

The ejection of " castings " is recorded of some young and many adult passerines (Evetts 1932; Tucker 1944), and probably the practice is commoner than references in the literature suggest. The Heinroths (1924-33) were surprised that young dippers did not eject insect remains.

NEST PROBING

When the chicks are tiny the female frequently pokes into the bottom of the nest. One bird on the day her third and last youngster emerged spent between half and one minute after returning with food in feeding and tending the young, usually clinging to the inside rim and bending over, making vigorous jerky movements. She up-ended so that from outside I could see her bare brooding patch. Mr. C. P. Newcomb informs me that he noticed this procedure the day after the young hatched and that the wren appeared to be tugging at the bottom of the nest. Another wren in an observation nest constantly scrabbled in it, poking her head downwards to the floor, quivering her wings and apparently working with her feet. Once or twice she picked up feathers and laid them on one side. Occasionally she preened a little. Now and then she quivered her mandibles after an excursion to the bottom of the nest, and once, when she raised her head, tiny shreds of down were in her bill. Probably she swallowed these, but it was difficult to be quite certain of what happened in the dimly lighted cavity. I believe that she tidied the nest and ate fæces and other extraneous matter on these occasions. Haverschmidt (1952) noticed that a pale-bellied house wren dived head first amidst the nestlings, wriggling with her wings. On emerging the bird made swallowing movements.

Nest-probing is performed by many birds (cf. *Brit. Birds*, 1945, 1946; Schifferli and Lang 1940; Schüz 1942; Barrett 1947a; Chisholm 1948a; Conder 1948; Haverschmidt 1949). It is essentially a means of keeping the nest tidy, but the procedure and function vary according to the type of nest. A probing wren, like a tit, probably presses the cup into shape as well as tidying the feathers and other small objects which are out of place. As a young blue tit and a greenfinch chick have been found entangled in the lining of their nests (Ryves 1946) the necessity for maintaining the nest in good condition is evident. Mr. J. H. Owen tells me that a wren he startled from the nest flew out and hanged herself in a loop of hair from the lining.

REMOVING EGGS, MAULING AND REMOVING NESTLINGS

The house wren is notorious for its tendency to break the eggs of other birds or even carry them from the nest. The prairie marsh wren and long-billed marsh wren (Allen 1914; Forbush 1929) also sometimes destroy other birds' eggs. The former removes infertile eggs from its own nest. So greatly is the Chiapas cactus wren (*Campylorhynchus rufinucha chiapensis*) addicted to sucking eggs that poultry keepers find it a nuisance (Brodkorp 1939). The European wren neither molests the eggs of other birds nor removes its own addled eggs.

Two nestlings four days old which I found dead had been mauled. The head of one was wounded, the lower mandible being broken and an eye eliminated, the other had an injury to its side. The nest entrance and interior were not disarranged. The only predators which might have been responsible are the long-tailed field mouse or, perhaps, a shrew, but one would have expected the animal to have carried off a chick or to have broken an unhatched egg still in the nest. The alternative, that one of the wrens did the damage, is hardly more probable. The male had inspected the nest soon after the young hatched and the female had been behaving normally. Kendeigh mentions an incident in which an agitated male house wren broke his mate's eggs. Many instances of " distracted " birds destroying their own nest, eggs or young have been recorded and several have been known to remove eggs or living young (Armstrong 1947, 1949b).

Mr. G. R. Vlies tells me that while a wren was making a great commotion at the nest he heard a splash in a pool under it and going to the spot he found a dead squab in the water. It had the appearance of having died otherwise than by drowning, and on its body were several small reddish parasites. Apparently it had been thrown out by one of the parents. I have only twice found the corpse of a chick in a wren's nest after the brood had fledged—during the inclement spring of 1951—but St. Kilda wrens sometimes leave dead young in the nest (I. J. Ferguson-Lees, *in litt.*). Many birds, however, remove dead young. A white stork has been known to eat a dead chick (Schüz 1942).

FOOD BROUGHT TO NESTLINGS

At various nests during the first 24 hours after hatching I have seen small caterpillars and mosquitoes given to the young. A single morsel may be brought, but even at the start of feeding, there may be two or three objects in the female's bill when she comes to the nest. Bigger loads are commoner during the later period, but even then sometimes only one victim is carried. At the nest which I adapted for interior observation the female brought a plump, dark green caterpillar half an inch in length to chicks three to four days old. It looked rather a large mouthful for a small bird. She offered it to them three or four times. Thrice she made as if to go out of the aperture and then returned, uttering fragments of the " swallow song " for about ten seconds on each occasion. Eventually she discarded the morsel. Other birds have been seen to bring unsuitable food to small young. The first meal brought by a male catbird to the nestling was a grub much bigger than the food his mate was bringing (Skutch 1953). A great crested grebe tried to induce a newly-hatched chick to accept a fish too large for it to swallow (Rankin 1947).

Awkward prey such as daddy-long-legs and spiders are not brought to European wren chicks during the first few days, though they are often tendered to large nestlings. When the young have fledged the parents macerate large caterpillars by flogging them against a branch. I have not noticed such preparation of prey during the nestling stage of European wrens, but Hebridean wrens maul moths in order to stuff them into the mouths of the nestlings, and house wrens frequently bring moths, bluebottles and other insects after removing wings or legs (Herrick 1935). Prairie marsh wrens, which usually graduate the size of prey according to the size of the chicks, tear a spider to pieces if the nestlings find difficulty in swallowing it. I have seen a male Shetland wren pecking and flogging what appeared to be a small mollusc against the rocks, but such food was never brought to the nest during many hours' observation.

Common (1948) noticed that a male house wren brought larger prey than his mate, but such behaviour has not been recorded of *T. troglodytes*. Male song sparrows and various American warblers also bring larger insects, or bigger portions, than females (Nice 1943).

Treuenfels (1940) observed that a male and female chiffchaff brought different kinds of food.

Among items brought to wrens' nests I have observed caterpillars of large and small white butterflies (*Pieris brassicae* and *P. rapae*), the winter moth (*Operophtera brumata*) and other geometrids and noctuids, a few adult moths, among them a brimstone (*Ophistographis luteolata*), none of them highly cryptic species, daddy-long-legs, mosquitoes, including *Theobaldia zebrina*, aphides, spiders and what may have been their egg cocoons. On two occasions small earthworms were brought. I once saw a privet hawk moth (*Sphinx ligustri*) carried away by a wren from where it had perched near the wren's nest. Brown (1937) noticed a common wainscot moth (*Leucania pallens*) and a silver Y moth (*Plusia gamma*) given to nestlings and Marples (1940) recorded a slug, flying ants, ant pupæ and small flies. Other items identified include a neuropteron (Kluijver, *in litt.*), cuckoo-spit larvæ (*Aphrophora spumaria*), a female spider (*Meta reticulata*) and a harvestman (*Phalangium opilio*(?)) (Hosking and Smith 1949). Reference has already been made to the feeding of young wrens on small fish (p. 25). Nestling St. Kilda wrens are given diptera, caterpillars, occasional moths, daddy-long-legs, spiders, centipedes and rarely, an earthworm (Lowe 1934). The diet of Shetland and Hebridean wrens is similar though, of course, it varies somewhat according to the locality. Most of the moths captured are cryptic in coloration. Some hymenoptera and, perhaps, plecoptera are eaten by Shetland wren nestlings (Armstrong and Thorpe 1952). I have seen a nestling Hebridean wren given a damsel fly (*Pyrrhosoma nymphula*). On the whole, the items of prey brought to the young by these insular races are probably somewhat larger than those brought by European wrens, but they may be less nutritious, weight for weight. Iceland wren nestlings receive diptera, caterpillars and spiders.

Experiments by Carrick (1936) with a wren feeding young showed that cryptic larvæ, such as those of the early thorn moth (*Selenia bilunaria*) were seized and carried to the nest if they were exposed in a conspicuous position. In normal surroundings, clinging to twigs, they escaped detection if they remained still, but if a caterpillar moved it was liable to be seized. I have never seen any twig-mimicking caterpillars brought to a wren's nest.

METHODS OF FORAGING

When a particular kind of prey is plentiful in some spot a wren will forage there again and again, bringing bundles of larvæ or whatever food is available, often a "mixed bag." One wren brought mainly caterpillars from some distance away in the morning and diptera from nearby in the evening. When both male and female are feeding nestlings they show no tendency to exploit any small area together and often go in different directions for food. Harrisson and Buchan (1934) recorded separate male and female " feeding territories " on St. Kilda, but their observations were wrongly interpreted (Armstrong 1953b). Male and female Shetland wren seek food for the young independently and each bird tends to return several times to a fruitful area, although occasionally they may both be seen seeking food only a few yards apart. These foraging areas are not defended and are therefore not territories.

DURATION OF SORTIES WHILE FEEDING NESTLINGS

A wren's sorties tend to become of shorter duration as the chicks grow. Observations on the 4th, 11th, and 18th days after the hatch showed that the proportions of sorties lasting one to two minutes during the three watches were 1/13, 1/3 and 1/2, respectively. The same trend was recorded of other wrens. When a bird is at full stretch feeding young she returns to the nest after finding one or two larvae and seldom collects a beakful. She appears to be using her energy uneconomically; but to conclude that this is so would be rash in view of our scanty knowledge of how the wren finds prey and other aspects of the situation. The feeding of goldfinch nestlings follows the opposite trend, absences becoming longer as the chicks grow (Conder 1948). However, since goldfinches regurgitate food they are able to accumulate a greater supply than birds which do not store food in their crops.

Many observers have commented on the fairly regular intermissions which interrupt the routine of many passerines feeding young, but these are not prominent in the European wren's procedure. At a nest to which recording apparatus was attached for the whole nestling period no absence of as long as fifteen minutes was recorded and absences of ten minutes or longer were very rare. During 22 hours' watching at a winter wren's nest containing chicks the female never absented herself for more than fifteen minutes (C. Stanwood, *in litt.*). Pale-bellied house wrens which I kept under observation for two hours in the early afternoon only once took a respite of as long as ten minutes. I have noted intermissions of 31 and 22 minutes during 90 minutes' observation at a Hebridean wren's nest and similar pauses have been recorded at the nests of St. Kilda and Shetland wrens (Harrisson and Buchan 1936; Yeates 1948). American dippers absent themselves for fifteen to twenty minutes from time to time (Hann 1950). So, also, do black-bellied dippers (Armstrong 1954). In some species such intermissions may be due to the prey containing a high proportion of indigestible material, such as chitin. If, as is probable, chicks after swallowing food of this kind beg feebly or not at all for some time the stimulus for the parents to forage for the family would be reduced and the tempo of effort slackened. In considering the theory that the nature of the pair-bond is influenced by the availability of food it is, of course, necessary to bear in mind the food-value of the chicks' meals as well as the time spent by the parents in obtaining their own food.

CHAPTER 12

DEVELOPMENT OF THE NESTLINGS AND THE SPREAD OF NESTING

Coo-oo, coo-oo,
It's as much as a pigeon can do
To maintain two;
But the little wren can maintain ten
And bring them all up like gentlemen.

COUNTRY RHYME

THE DETAILED STUDY of the development of nestling wrens in their domed nest presents special difficulties, but I was able to overcome most of them by transferring clutches to the nests of a great tit and a blue tit, both in boxes with removable lids. The growth of these nestlings was normal, as I ascertained by control observations of other broods.

APPEARANCE OF THE SQUABS

Newly-hatched wrens lie like squirming maggots with their relatively huge heads resting on the feather mattress at the bottom of the nest. They can move about to some extent, propelling themselves with their already fairly adequate legs while their stubby apologies for wings move like ill-co-ordinated front legs as they feebly struggle against, and to some extent, over one another. Vibration or a touch prompts them to open their bills. The spindly neck looks unequal to the task of raising the head, but on its first day out of the egg a chick can hold up its head for several seconds.

When the nestlings are a few days old their lemon-yellow mouths waver on the craning necks like wan alpine blossoms stirred by a sudden breeze. The gape coloration becomes slightly more vivid as the days pass, and the bill flanges remain pale yellow until after the young leave the nest, providing guide-marks additional to the yellow beacons of the buccal cavity and thus enabling, and even stimulating, the parent to introduce food without error or delay.

REACTION TO SOUND AND DEVELOPMENT OF UTTERANCE

From the 1st day until about the 10th day the chicks responded by begging when I made a chirruping noise by sucking in breath. Whistled notes had the same effect. When the eyes have opened it becomes difficult to ascertain whether there is a definite response to such sounds. Noises of a lower pitch, such as clearing the throat and speaking in a normal voice, do not stimulate the young to beg. Presumably the range of hearing of wrens, young and old, is, like that of starlings and house sparrows (Brand and Kellogg 1939), more restricted than man's, although it may be higher in the upper register.

On the second day faint squeaking was audible from a chick or chicks in one nest. During the first few days the squeaking of the young when visited by the parent is not normally perceptible to an observer near the nest, but towards the end of the nestling period it becomes a high-pitched chorus which may be heard by the attentive listener in favourable circumstances at a distance of about forty yards. The cheeping of young Hebridean and Shetland wrens is audible at about the same distance, but is apt to be more noticeable in the absence of rustling foliage. Young snow buntings reared in rock crannies secure from their only enemy, the arctic fox, are audible at a distance of 150 yards (Nicholson 1930). As a rule, those passerine nestlings are noisiest which are least exposed to predation, but although the European wren must be in greater jeopardy from predators than some insular races the nestlings call equally loudly.

MATURATION OF COWERING REACTION AND OPENING OF THE EYES

About the 10th day it becomes difficult or impossible to induce the young to beg by scratching the nesting-box, tapping or chirruping. At one nest tapping the rim of the box on the 4th day caused the young to cower, but the chicks in the other experimental nest did not react in this way until about the 7th day. Prairie marsh wrens cower about the 5th day. Cowering is commonly regarded as indicating "fear" (Nice 1943), but we must not suppose that this term has the connotation of normal usage.

It is difficult to determine exactly when young wrens first open their eyes or see effectively. Exposing them to the light on opening up the nest or nesting-box may cause them so to close the eyelids that the birds seem to be blind when they can already see to some extent. My observations show that the eyes of young wrens begin to open about the 7th day, perhaps in some instances, somewhat later—in contrast with the 3rd and 5th day for Carolina wrens (Laskey 1946b) and about the 4th day for tule wrens (Wheelock 1904).

Young woodpeckers beg when the light is cut off (Sherman 1910; Heinroth and Heinroth 1924-33). In order to ascertain whether nestling wrens would do so I covered the entrance to the great tit's nesting-box in which were the youngsters and, at the same time, simulated the arrival of the parent by making a faint scratching. There was no responsive squeaking. However, at a normal wren's nest the chicks begged when I placed my fingers on the entrance rim and slightly over the aperture. In experiments with young birds, such as I have described, one cannot readily determine when the difference between reactions is to be attributed to individual peculiarities or unknown factors in the situation. Thus, although one brood of Shetland wren nestlings continued to beg while my finger was exploring the interior of the nest the chicks of another brood at about the same stage of development were silent when I tried to feel the number of the young. These and other observations suggest that there may be variability in the reactions of nestling wrens and that discrepancies are sometimes to be ascribed to this cause and not to environmental conditions.

Before the eyes of wren nestlings open the stimuli causing them to beg are undoubtedly auditory and tactile—the sounds made by the parent, whether vocal or in the course of moving about, and vibration of the nest or actual touching of the chick. The importance of visual stimuli increases, but it becomes difficult to decide to what extent the chicks' response is to visual, auditory or tactile stimuli as examining them may condition their behaviour.

So far as I could ascertain, a brood of Shetland wrens begged before the food-bringing parent became visible and certainly before he or she reached the nest. Their calling began a fraction of a second before the parent alighted beneath the nest, apparently out of their field of vision. It seemed that the stimulus was the slight noise made by the incoming bird's wings, and possibly also by the, to me imperceptible, impact of the feet on alighting. Moreau (1949b) noted that young African mountain wagtails begged before the parent came into view or landed, and Skutch (1945b) noticed that an incubating allied woodhewer could discriminate the sound of its mate alighting on a tree-trunk from the sound made by other species alighting on it.

GROWTH OF PLUMAGE, PREENING AND INCREASE IN ACTIVITY

At first the squabs are naked, but for a thin tuft of down on the front of the crown and a few almost imperceptible strands on the back. The skin is flesh-coloured with a slight yellowish tinge and becomes rather more yellow and wizened in appearance after a day or two. When four days old the feather tracts are apparent; at five days the wing-quills are sprouting and there is sooty fluff all over the head. By the ninth day the youngsters look clothed but the flanks and belly are bare. Well-grown nestlings preen actively.

When chicks are ringed on the eleventh day they use their legs and feet vigorously and flap their quilly wings, but are unable to make any show of flying. Infertile eggs at the bottom of the nest are not perforated by the youngsters' claws. Chicks a fortnight old may leave the nest if disturbed and are sufficiently mature to survive.

DEVELOPMENT OF TEMPERATURE CONTROL

Passerine birds change from a cold-blooded or poikilothermic condition to a warm-blooded or homoiothermic state in the nest; nidifugous birds make the transition while in the shell. The foetus in mammals, including man, is poikilothermic; thus in this respect the ontogeny of birds and mammals recapitulates their phylogeny and is a relic of their reptilian ancestry.* It is not until nine days after the hatching of a young house wren that the temperature-regulating mechanism is fully functional, though it is in operation to some extent by the fifth day (Kendeigh and Baldwin 1928; Baldwin and Kendeigh 1932; Kendeigh 1934). Species vary in this respect. Oven birds have a fairly well-developed temperature-control at three days (Hann 1937), and pigeons on the 15th to 16th day. There is a correlation between, on the one hand, the coming into operation of the temperature-regulating system and other aspects of the physiological development and, on the other, the house wren's cessation of brooding, except at night, about the tenth day, as shown in Fig. 33.

This age also marks an important transition-phase for nestling European wrens. Rapid growth of plumage, effective functioning of temperature control and cessation of brooding tend to coincide.

Co-ordinated muscle tremors, which are important in connection with temperature-regulation and are inversely proportional to tem-

*Ontogeny—the development of the individual.
Phylogeny—the evolution of the race.

perature, begin in house wrens three days after hatching, but on the ninth day of incubation in the eggs of pheasants (Odum 1942b). This is in conformity with the principle that nidifugous birds undergo in the egg much of the development characteristic of nidicolous young in the nest.

Although their lack of temperature control during the first few days renders young house wrens particularly vulnerable to any prolonged interruption in brooding by the parent it is compensated by their great tenacity of life. A chick four days old deserted by its parents was able to open its bill feebly 70 hours later and a neglected newly-hatched house wren survived more than three days and nights alone in the nest (Kendeigh and Baldwin 1928). One of a deserted five-day-old brood of wrens begged weakly for food after 27 hours' neglect.

INCREASE IN WEIGHT

A wren's egg weighs some $1\frac{1}{2}$ gm. so that a clutch of 6 to 7 weighs 90 per cent. of the mother. The newly-hatched chick turns the scale at about 1 gm. and puts on weight at the rate of about 1 gm. per day (Heinroth and Heinroth 1924-33). A newly-hatched prairie marsh wren weighs 0.87 gm. and gains from 1 to 1.7 gm. per day so that by the twelfth day it weighs on the average 11.08 gm.

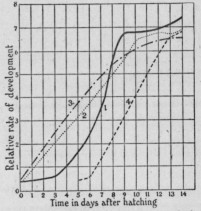

FIG. 33. Graphs showing correlation of (1) Development of temperature control in the nestling eastern house wren with (2) development of body weight, (3) body size, and (4) feathers. *(After Baldwin and Kendeigh 1932)*

Coinciding with the period of greatest feather growth the gain in weight tends to fall off about the tenth day. The weight of nestling house wrens increases rapidly during the first week and after ten days their weight is five-sixths of that of the adult (Kendeigh and Baldwin 1928). A slight reduction may occur just before the time of leaving (Stoner 1930). So, too, with pale-bellied house wrens about the eleventh day (Haverschmidt 1952). It is normal in many species for a slackening of the rate of increase in weight, or an actual reduction, to occur before the young leave the nest. Reduction in the rate of increase in weight is correlated with the decrease in feeding visits which we have already noted to be recorded of many species of bird (p. 192).

DURATION OF NESTLING PERIOD

The Dutch observers obtained the following data from 43 nests:

TABLE XXV

DURATION OF NESTLING PERIOD IN DAYS AT STEIN

14	15	16	17	18	19	20
1	3	9	11	14	4	1

The nestling period of 20 days was abnormal, for on the 19th day the single chick was seen to pop out of the nest to be fed and then return to it. The 14-day period also cannot be considered normal, for the young were disturbed from the nest—as they were also in some other instances, namely two 15-day broods, one 16-day brood and two 17-day broods. The average nestling period of undisturbed broods is 17.3 days.

The number of nestling periods of 18 days appears to be exceptionally high and is probably due to the reckoning of the period from the hatching of the first egg to the departure of the last nestling. The B.T.O. records, with the nestling period reckoned from the hatching of the last egg to the departure of the last nestling, are as follows:

TABLE XXVI

DURATION OF NESTLING PERIOD IN DAYS IN BRITAIN

12	13	14	15	16	17
1	3	3	5	4	3

Unfortunately, it is not mentioned whether any of these broods left the nest prematurely owing to disturbance. One observer noticed that some young emerged when he approached on three successive days although the complete family flew out on the third occasion. He states that this is the second nest to which he had known young return. Such peculiarities render it difficult to estimate precisely the nestling period of wrens, but probably the average of the above data, 14.9 days, is too low. With a recording instrument more exact data were obtained. From the hatching of the first egg to fledging was 16 days 23 hours at one nest and 16 days 5 hours at another. At the first-mentioned nest 16 days 2 hours elapsed between the hatching of the last egg and the departure of the last chick.

Lack (1948c) has estimated the average nestling period of mid-European passerines, excluding the crow family, and shows it to be

17.3 days for hole-nesters, 15.9 for birds with roofed nests and 14.9 and 13.2 respectively for those making niche and open nests. The shorter nestling period of species in the more exposed types of nest is correlated with the greater danger to which they are exposed.

The meagre information available in regard to the nestling period of other races of wren is quoted below:

Table XXVII

NESTLING PERIODS OF RACES OF T. troglodytes

Race	Nestling period in days	Authority
Hebridean wren	20 ($\pm$1?)	Armstrong
Shetland wren	16 ($\pm$1?)	Armstrong
Western winter wren	17-21	Wheelock 1904
Alaska wren	22	Heath 1920

The period quoted for the Alaska wren is surprisingly long. The Shetland wren figure is based on observation of a single nest; so also is the figure for the Hebridean wren. Too much importance should not be attached to these data. They suggest, but are insufficient to establish, a somewhat longer nestling period in northerly regions. It should be noted, however, that some species in the arctic rear broods more quickly than birds of the same species in temperate regions (Armstrong 1954).

The young wren's sojourn in the nest is longer than that of the young Bewick's, Carolina and prairie marsh wren, all of which spend about 13 to 14 days in the nest, though prairie marsh wrens may emerge on the 12th day if frightened. The usual nestling period for the Panama and Costa Rica house wrens (*Troglodytes musculus inquietus* and *T. m. intermedius*) and the Mexican banded wren (*Campylorhynchus z. zonatus*) is 18 days, and for the tawny-bellied spotted-throated wren (*Thryothorus rutilus hyperythrus*) 16 days. The highland wood wren (*Henicorhina leucophrys collina*) has an incubation period of 19 to 20 days, and may have a nestling period of 14 to 18 days (Skutch 1945a).

NESTLING PERIOD AND FOOD SUPPLY

It is remarkable that Panama, Costa Rica and pale-bellied house wrens with four young in a brood, should bring them to the point of fledging later than eastern house wrens with four to six young, which average 16.6 days (Kendeigh 1952). (Broods of two to three nestlings fledge in 15.3 days). Unless the unlikely assumption be made that birds do not rear as many young as they can, without undue physiological strain, it would seem that food for house wrens is not as readily available in the tropics as in temperate regions. The prime factors regulating the duration of the nestling period are availability of food and danger from predators. One would expect young house wrens to spend a shorter time in the nest in the tropics, where the incidence of predation is heavier than in northerly regions. For example, in the forest of Panama Skutch (1940b) noticed that 86 per cent of the nests he found were destroyed. Where predation-pressure renders a short period in the nest highly advantageous to the species only the difficulty of procuring food can account for a long nestling period. The crucial factor may be the shorter day in the tropics.

Danger from predators may be reduced by nesting where they are few or in inaccessible situations. Thus in the Pribilof islands, where the arctic fox is the only ground predator, Alaska wrens spend 22 days in the nest—if Heath's data are accepted. As house wrens nest in approximately similar sites all over their vast range the longer nestling period in the tropics is not correlated with any nesting technique which secures greater immunity from predation but, it would seem, with food for the young being less readily available than in temperate regions.

In such areas there is a plethora of resurgent life in spring, species being fewer but individuals more numerous than in the tropics. In higher latitudes most passerines rear larger broods than related species in tropical regions, with the consequence that whole populations of some species must migrate in autumn when food becomes scarce. In the tropics there is not the striking rapid seasonal waxing and waning of bird populations characteristic of temperate regions although, of course, seasonal rainfall has a direct bearing on food-supply and breeding. The contrast in conditions is illustrated by comparing the behaviour of the hive bee in different latitudes. In the north there are comparatively short periods of abundant honey flow, and for bee-keepers the control of swarming is a major problem. Farther south honey-flows are longer and less intense, while in some parts of the tropics the honey-flow, though less abundant, is practically continuous and stocks are not so prone to swarm (Phillips 1947). Extensive stands of vegetation of a few species are more characteristic of temperate regions than the humid tropics. For honey bees and wrens alike this probably involves seeking food in greater variety, and also, in many instances, with more trouble and delay, as less search and scrutiny are required if a bird's food is mainly of one type. During caterpillar plagues in temperate woodlands or in the Icelandic birch scrub it is

Plate VIIa. (above, left) Robin feeding wren nestlings.
(*G. R. Duval*)

b. (above, right) House wren feeding young cowbird.
(*A. A. Allen*)

c. (below, left) Willow warbler disconcerted by young wren perched at entrance to its nest.
(*A. M. C. Nicholl*)

d. (below right) Wren bringing food to nest containing willow warbler and wren families.
(*A. M. C. Nicholl*)

probably easier for wrens to secure food for their young expeditiously than it is for Central American wrens in rain-forest. The naturalist, on his first acquaintance with tropical jungle, may easily be deceived by the varied and luxuriant growth around him into supposing that insectivorous birds are more readily able to obtain food for their young than comparable species in temperate woodlands.

SPREAD NESTING

Where food sufficient for brood-rearing is available over a prolonged period there are various adaptations whereby birds spread their breeding. Egg-laying may be spread so that in a brood the young may vary considerably in age*, pairs may begin breeding at different dates over a prolonged period or they may have a series of broods. Any two of these procedures may be combined. In Europe one might cite the short-eared owl, the greenfinch and the blackbird as representative of these three types, but the climate does not permit perennial breeding, except, within certain limitations, in the Columbidæ, which have special feeding adaptations, notably the secretion of " pigeon's milk." In rain-forest and other humid tropical areas, although the inception of breeding by some species may occur very close to the same date each year, it is possible for some species to breed at any time. Thus Belcher and Smooker (1936) remark that in Trinidad the pale-bellied house wren is the only bird known to breed throughout the year. In Surinam it also nests all the year round (Haverschmidt 1952). Skutch (1940b) records that a pair of neotropical house wrens in Costa Rica laid four clutches of four eggs between December and June, successfully rearing at least one chick of each brood. The Panama house wren also nests throughout the year (Van Tyne 1950). In tropical waters shoaling among fish and consequent food-peaks are not on such a scale as in temperate regions, and consequently pairs of some marine birds are found breeding all through the year. Nesting may also be spread to some extent by means of non-monogamous types of pair-bond, although this tends to involve the responsibility for the brood falling on one parent. Thus although oropendolas nest annually very close to the same date they practise successive polygamy (Chapman 1928), and the prolonged " lek " performances of some tropical birds enable females coming into condition at different times to secure fertilisation when they are ready for it.

Although information in regard to many subspecies is not as complete as one would like, it appears that in *Troglodytes troglodytes* both spread nesting and successive polygamy occur, the former being

*This adaptation occurs when the food supply is meagre or erratic.

more characteristic of the insular races inhabiting comparatively bleak
areas and the latter of *T. t. troglodytes* in habitats where food is more
readily available.

It is usual for there to be an interval of some days, or even as long
as a week or two, between the inception of the broods by different
females mated to one male European wren. The intervals are not so
great as to prevent the breeding season being divisible into the periods
of the first and second broods, but the effect is to spread nesting so
that one may find nestlings being reared over a considerable period.

In contrast, the wrens of St. Kilda and Shetland, and probably the

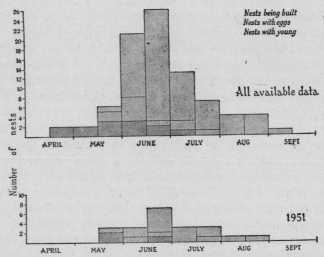

FIG. 34. Histograms showing the Shetland wren's seasonal spread of breeding
activities. Data supplied mainly by Mr. L. S. V. Venables.

Hebrides, as we have already noted, are mainly monogamous, build
comparatively few nests and do not regularly rear second broods.
Moreover, the inception of egg-laying by different females seems to
synchronise less. Within ten days in June I saw in the Hebrides a
fledged brood, two nearly half-fledged broods and a male inviting a
female to an unoccupied nest, while in the same period in Shetland
I found a wren nest-building, another enticing a female, a bird incubating, three nests with chicks at different stages and an already
vacated nest.

Thus although the Shetland wren's period of maximum breeding
activity is in June nesting is diffused. The prolongation of breeding
activity might be attributed to the starting of second broods and, to a
minor extent, re-nesting after disaster, but, if second broods were

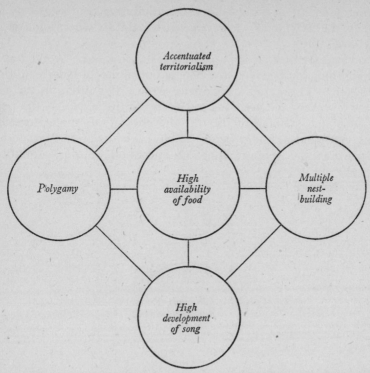

Fig. 35. Diagram illustrating the integration of the European wren's activities.

regular, one would expect a second peak in July-August comparable with the second peak of egg-laying indicated by Kluijver's data for the wren in Holland. We know that during the spring in garden-woodland areas such as those favoured by the European wren there is a steady and relatively rapid increase in insect life, particularly of caterpillars (Gibb 1950) whereas the number of arthropod species inhabiting such islands as St. Kilda is less than in these more fertile areas and there is no increase of individual organisms with a relatively high nutritional value comparable with a caterpillar plague in wood-land. We have already noted that one European wren may maintain a more rapid tempo at the nest than two Shetland wrens (p. 194). Spread nesting in North Atlantic islands may be adapted to a con-tinuous, relatively stable food supply or conditions in which one of several successive minor food peaks may fail. It is significant that, during a cold spring when insectivorous food is not so readily available as in a mild season, the breeding of great and blue tits is more spread than in a normal year, and that in their northerly range these species

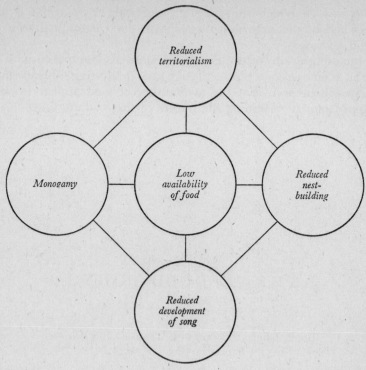

Fig. 36. Diagram illustrating the integration of the St. Kilda wren's activities

are single-brooded (Lack 1950). Moreover, it has been shown that in years when first broods of great tits are late, second broods tend to be fewer; also that the influence of climate on breeding season in this species is probably direct and not determined by food supply (Kluijver 1951). Thus the breeding span of insular races of *T. troglodytes* apparently conforms to principles which may be found to be of general application. It may be that the divergences of behaviour of the insular races are not genetically fixed to the extent that individuals introduced to woodland habitats would not approximate to the behaviour of the European wren, but the adaptations to bleak surroundings which they show are so closely integrated that, if in any species with such a series of adaptations they went beyond a certain point, individual adaptation to different conditions would be precluded. Such a set of integrated behaviour adaptations might serve as an isolating mechanism so that ultimately, if the range of two organisms which had diverged in this manner were to overlap their different habitat preferences and mating procedures might prevent inter-breeding (Armstrong 1952).

The way in which the adaptations of wrens are related to one another and to the environment is shown diagrammatically on pages 219 and 220.

If the adaptations of the European wren are compared with those of the St. Kilda wren, a representative race inhabiting a bleak environment, it will be seen that the availability of food appears to be the principal factor determining the nature of these adaptations.

CHAPTER 13

THE FLEDGED YOUNG

Look, where the youngest wren of nine comes.
SHAKESPEARE. *Twelfth Night*, III. ii. 70

VACATING THE NEST

IF WELL-GROWN nestling wrens are disturbed by interference with the nest or too close an approach they will fly out before they would normally fledge. Sometimes a single nestling bursts forth, but often all, or nearly all, the young issue abruptly together as if an explosion had occurred. Even if a predator were not sufficiently bewildered by this abrupt exodus to muff his pounce he is unlikely to capture more than one of the dispersing chicks.

On emerging from the nest wrens, unless unusually prematurely fledged, can make short flights and are able to keep out of harm's way. They proclaim their emancipation from the nest with a chittering alarm-call which I have never known to be uttered by them while still in the nest, though the same, or a very similar, call has been recorded of nestling winter wrens (C. Stanwood, *in litt.*), and I have heard a faint, incipient version of it from well-grown Shetland wren nestlings.

The normal departure usually takes place in the forenoon—not often very early. Occasionally a brood leaves in the afternoon. At one nest a chick fledged at 08.50, but the other five emerged between 09.42 and 09.52. The female continued actively feeding them until they began to flutter out, one by one, but twice she came to the nest without food and once I heard the "swallow" song. The male "ticked" excitedly but did not help (Whitehouse and Armstrong 1953). The brood in the Girton nest (p. 90) were fluttering around the shed by 07.00. The female fed them as usual and in ones and twos they followed her out of the hole in the wall. Once she flew out holding a caterpillar with a youngster flying after her, but it could hardly be said that she used food to entice the fledgling.

A male Carolina wren's enticement behaviour was more definite. After an hour spent assiduously feeding the chicks he attracted them forth by visiting them without food and by loud singing. At first the female sought to lure them back, but she later helped to entice them out by uttering coaxing notes and by refusing to deliver the food she carried (Nice and Thomas 1948). Luring the young by holding food out of reach is recorded of a wide variety of species, though it is more usual for chicks to leave the nest without such enticement.

At 08.00 I was watching a female, Bunty, feeding young in a nest amidst ivy on an inclined bough six feet above my head. The male, White-leg, who had assumed a proprietary interest in the female and her nest after the disappearance of her mate (p. 105), was dancing attendance on Pinkie with her foster-young at the other side of the wood. He had been around not long before and came again. Whether his arrival had any connection with what now occurred is doubtful, but probably not. The female hopped towards the nest and in a few seconds appeared, creeping along the branch in a peculiar way with half-spread wings drooped and quivering. She kept uttering a subdued single note resembling a swallow's flight call, heard at a distance, rather similar to, but louder than, the succession of calls or whisper song uttered in the nest when feeding tiny chicks. At first I thought she must be soliciting the male, but she did not utter the appropriate call nor did he pounce upon her. Suddenly the six youngsters came into view in a queer, uneven little procession, squeaking as they hopped up the sloping branch to some twigs a couple of feet away. Filing jerkily upwards the little group of brown figures reminded me of the Seven Dwarfs in Walt Disney's film. The female, who had hitherto been rather shy, busied herself feeding the family above my head while the male sang excited strophes, interested in her rather than the fledglings. Now and then he chased her abortively.

Wrens also may perch, calling, close to the nest entrance with tail erected (Plate IV, p. 116). Male house sparrows sometimes lure the young out of the nest with notes and postures similar to those used to attract the mate to the nest-hole for the second brood (Daanje 1941). However, it is not unusual for the nestlings of some nidicolous species to leave in the absence of their parents, as chiffchaffs (Treuenfels 1940), nuthatches and a young hoopoe (Dewar 1928) have been seen to do.

BEHAVIOUR OF THE MALE WHEN THE YOUNG FLEDGE

If the departure of young European wrens from the nest is due to disturbance the female promptly appears, attracted by the fledglings' chittering alarm-notes. The male may also approach, especially if he has been helping to feed them. When the brood issues normally he is nearly always early on the scene, manifesting his excitement with churrs, abbreviated songs and staccato movements, now and then chasing and pouncing at his mate. In his excitement he may cling to a twig upside-down (G. Boyle, *in litt.*) or even precipitate himself on one of the young by mistake and endeavour to tread it (R. Gait, *in litt.*) as an American robin also has been seen to do (Brackbill 1947a). Sometimes when the female gives the alarm-note he responds by dashing to her as if he had mistaken the call for an invitation to coition. His interest is predominantly in the female. He may never feed the fledglings at all, and in many cases, so far as the first-brood young are concerned, he only gives a morsel to one of them at infrequent intervals.

BEHAVIOUR OF THE FLEDGLINGS

If the young are not unduly disturbed they keep together during the first day or two; indeed, like many other small passerines, they tend to form quaint little huddles on twigs as if regretting the warm contiguity of the nest. Occasionally there is some changing of places, and chicks inconveniently situated for receiving food come forward at intervals, so that the system economises the parents' efforts and enables meals to be dispensed expeditiously. This procedure would be dysgenic if adopted by fledglings unable to perch where predators cannot readily seize them. Thus young snow buntings and wheatears disperse on leaving the nest (Tinbergen 1939) and short-eared owlets, perhaps lured by their parents, make their way to tussocks some distance from where they were hatched (Armstrong and Phillips 1925).

FEEDING PROCEDURE

A wren does not memorise which chick has been fed. Where both parents help it is impossible for one to note the order in which the chicks are fed by the other. A fledgling wren may be fed four times in succession if it happens to be near the returning forager, but insistent birds are apt to get priority, and as hunger determines the frequency and vehemence of the begging calls an equitable distribution is usually achieved. At first the young may make little attempt to approach the laden parent. He or she tends to return to where a chick was last fed; sound and sight serve for more precise location. The high-pitched squeaking note acts not only as a signal to the parent and a means of locating straying fledglings, but also as a call whereby the young are able to keep in touch with one another and reassemble if dispersed. It is often difficult for the observer to determine from which direction the squeak proceeds. Possibly predatory mammals have similar difficulty.

Females may feed fledged chicks for as little as 9 days, perhaps sometimes less, and for as much as 17 to 18 days; males may feed fledged young for 15 to 16 days and, exceptionally, for even longer. One male fed a youngster 28 and 31 days after his brood had fledged. As I was unable to see whether this young bird was ringed I could not be certain that it belonged to this brood but there was no reason to think otherwise. The unlikely alternative is that the male responded to the begging of a stray bird reared outside the wood. When a young American dipper strayed into the territory of a neighbouring pair it was fed (Hann 1950). The Dutch observers noted a male wren accompanying young for 18 days. Thus wrens receive parental care for about 30 days, which is longer than most passerine chicks are tended. Nice (1943) tabulates the ages of attainment of independence by the young of 21 passerine families, showing that it ranges from 24 days among warblers to 40 for dippers. Of these, apart from the dippers, only the crow family, with 36 days, and possibly also the shrikes, have a longer period of parental supervision than wrens. With lyre birds an extreme is reached; a female may still be accompanied by her offspring of the previous year while being courted by a male (Campbell 1941).

For the first few days the young are entirely, or almost entirely, dependent on the parent or parents for food, but soon after leaving the nest they peck tentatively at tiny specks on leaves, and a day or two later make feeble attempts to snatch at small objects which attract their attention. After four or five days they may find a certain amount of food for themselves. The female is assiduous in bringing food at short intervals and the fledglings become more enterprising and scatter over a wide area, but usually two or three tend to keep contact in a loose group, and sometimes the family becomes separated temporarily into two groups with the male interested in one party and the female in the other, but such division of labour appears to be fortuitous. Similar sharing of duties may occur among house wrens.

At first the young tend to fly with a rather blind intentness and an appearance of effort reminiscent of a small boy trying to reach the other side of the swimming bath. They are agile among the twigs and soon become competent. A youngster nine days out of the nest can hover momentarily, though it is seldom that one attempts to do so.

THE TRAVELS OF THE FAMILY

Although the male European wren may give little or no food to the fledged young he usually joins the party when the nest is vacated. He expresses his excitement with frequent churrs, and if danger threatens he sounds the alarm. By means of his calls, songs and movements, he leads the group, though sometimes the youngsters seem rather slow to respond. When the male is absent, and possibly sometimes when he is in the neighbourhood, the female takes the lead and the fledglings follow her warning chitters as she retreats from danger. Often, however, the old birds appear to acquiesce for a time in the general drift of the young, though I do not think they ever entirely relinquish the pilotage of the family during their wanderings. In contrast, young chiffchaffs go their own way and their parents follow out of the territory (Treuenfels 1940). Young house wrens are usually conducted beyond the confines of the territory not long after fledging, but wrens show stronger attachment to the breeding area.

A family of wrens under female guidance does not always confine itself to the male's territory, and indeed this is not to be expected, as, like the female house wren, the female wren disregards, or is unaware of, its extent; but she tends to keep to the area familiar to her and, so far as my observations go, does not trespass much on ground belonging to other males. When she accompanies the young outside the territory she seldom goes far beyond its borders and normally leads the family back to the dormitory within it. In my experience, when the male leads he usually keeps the party within his domain, but Kluijver found that females frequently transgress territorial boundaries and that males accompanying such families are not attacked. No doubt the situation varies according to the type of habitat, the density of the wren population and the size of territories. In conversation with Dr. Kluijver he agreed with me that if males do not sing when escorting families outside their territories they would not be identified as such and therefore would not be attacked. In August when territorial reactions are weak and boundaries are in a state of flux (p. 36) non-singing males with young would not elicit protest. On the only occasions when I have watched a family party accompanied by a male move into the corner of a neighbouring territory, the male sang excitedly, but I found that this intruder had already so dominated the owner that he made no protest. Probably the latter had already disappeared as I never saw him again.

OVERLAPPING BROODS

As we might expect from the attention given to the nestlings by males of the North Atlantic insular races they usually accompany the broods of fledged young. Male Shetland wrens, and probably male St. Kilda wrens, assiduously feed the young at this stage. Male Iceland wrens also accompany the young, but Mr. Venables saw a male nest-building after the chicks had fledged.

The European wren usually rears two broods and has been recorded doing so as far north as Kuopio in Finland (P. Palmgren, *in litt.*). It seems that in the Outer Hebrides, Shetland and St. Kilda a certain number of second broods are reared, but in these races the situation is complicated, as we have noted, by the tendency to spread nesting.

If the second brood of species nesting in temperate regions can be started before the chicks of the first brood are independent time is saved and the chances of the second brood's success are augmented. Adaptations to this end are common and the males of many species, such as some of the finches, the blackbird, robin, reed warbler, song sparrow, cardinal, nightjar and waterhen, may undertake charge of the fledged young while the female begins the second nesting cycle. Whether this occurs in some individual instances appears to depend on a number of factors, one of which may be the availability of food. In different species the procedure varies greatly. Cedar waxwings, stock doves and goldcrests will lay in the second-brood nest before the first-brood young have fledged, and house wrens, chaffinches and willow warblers may build the second nest before the departure of the first brood (Barrett 1947a; May 1947a).

In view of the European wren's polygamy and the meagre help vouchsafed by the male it is remarkable that he sometimes takes over the care of the fledglings from his mate. How frequently this occurs I am unable to say, for I have known only one certain instance. A female started lining the nest for the second brood nine days after the emergence of the first brood. Thenceforward the male took charge and fed them until they were independent. Heath (1920) records that an Alaska wren laid a second clutch within a week of the young fledging. If this is correct it seems that the male must have made himself responsible for the young of the first brood, for fledglings left to themselves so soon could hardly have survived.

If female house wrens are disturbed during the feeding of the first brood they may start the second nesting, leaving the task of rearing the young to the male. An episode has been recorded in which a male house wren was seen tending a cowbird from an earlier brood while the female was looking after newly-hatched young (Hamerstrom 1947). Bent (1948) thinks that the male prairie marsh wren takes over the first brood while the female is busy with her second nesting. Carolina wrens may raise three broods in a season, the cock assuming responsibility for the young of each of the first two in turn after the female has started the next brood (McIlwraith 1894).

The Inception of the Second Brood and the Relationship to one another of the Phases of the Breeding Cycle

The appearance of a female with newly-fledged young stimulates the male sexually. His susceptibility at this time is an adaptation eliminating delay in beginning the second brood. As the first egg of a second laying after the destruction of the nest appears 5 to 8 days later and the first egg of a second-brood clutch 10 to 14 days after the emergence of the young (Kluijver *et al.* 1940) it is evident that care of fledglings restrains inception of the second nesting cycle. That this is not governed exclusively or predominantly by physiological factors is demonstrated by the episode in which a female who was being courted by a male, and behaving as if the breeding cycle were about to begin, took over the care of a brood of wrens reared by great tits and did not proceed with her own breeding cycle until more than a fortnight later, after she had reared her foster-family to independence (p. 104). This episode shows that we should be on our guard against underestimating the influence of psychological factors on physiological development, and thus, indirectly, on behaviour.

Observations on some species suggest that the state appropriate to one phase of the nesting cycle may inhibit another phase. Thus a female snow bunting apparently took a new mate because, when she and her partner were both feeding young, he did not respond to her sexual advances (Tinbergen 1939). When tri-coloured redwing nestlings are placed in a nest under construction the adults pile material on them, though during egg-laying and incubation they will feed nestlings placed in the nest, and while building the second nest continue feeding the young of the first brood (Emlen 1941). As noted earlier, a male Carolina wren, dominating the male of a breeding pair, placed nesting material on their young without attempting to feed them (Laskey 1950).

Among European wrens, as we have seen, the male's parental and domestic activities tend to increase as the building, singing and coitional impulses decline. On the other hand, females with the masculine impulses of song and nest-building are not deficient in feminine characteristics. As the male's sex drive decreases he acts in a more " feminine " way, but although it is tempting to think of his reproductive drives being organised in a hierarchy corresponding to the order of their seasonal appearance this is but a specious simplification.

The majority of female house wrens begin preparations for the second brood 7 to 13 days after the first-brood of young leave the nest and there is about a fortnight between nestings of the prairie marsh wren.

LEADING YOUNG TO ROOST

In the afternoon or evening the young are led by one or other, or both, parents to some recess or cavity in which to spend the night and which may be used on successive nights if the chicks are undisturbed. Often this is one of the male's unoccupied nests, but old nests of other species, such as the song thrush, greenfinch, robin, spotted flycatcher or hedge sparrow may be appropriated. House wrens also sometimes guide their young to abandoned nests of other species, such as the catbird (Merritt 1916; Gross 1948).

During the first night or two out of the nest the chicks may roost where they are unduly exposed to predators. Perhaps this is due to the parental impulse to lead not having sufficiently matured, or to the young not following the lead, through sluggishness or fatigue, or to a combination of both. Perhaps a comparable delay in maturation of behaviour is exemplified by the neglect of the dabchick to cover her first egg with nest-material (Finn 1907). Wrens on their first day or two out in the world have such nostalgia for a snug recess that any sheltered nook where they can cuddle close together may lure them in. Like newly-fledged goldfinches which huddle on top of one another (Conder 1948) they seek the natal environment, as the Freudians tell us we " unconsciously " seek the womb. Fledglings which happen upon an old nest, or even a thick clump of foliage, early in the afternoon, may establish themselves there until the following morning, unresponsive to their parents' call-notes. However we may seek to explain the situation this lack of co-ordination between old and young is puzzling, for it jeopardises the family at a critical time. Perhaps further observation will show that ill-co-ordinated behaviour is not uncommon when chicks leave the nest and old and young have to orientate themselves to a sudden change in the situation. Skutch

(1944) watched a pair of prong-billed barbets so concerned with leading one of their offspring to the roost that they forgot about the other. A Carolina wren brought food to the nest after the young had fledged (Laskey 1948) and reference has already been made to the lack of co-ordination between a pair when the chicks were leaving the nest (p. 222).

The most blatant instance of inadequate roosting behaviour noticed by me was when five youngsters which had fledged earlier in the day settled in a compact covey on the threshold of a pigsty where they would have been at the mercy of any nocturnal marauder. Towards nightfall, their mother, who alone tended them, had called frequently as she moved about, but she gave them their last meals on the ground and then flew right away. The next night they roosted in a much more secure nook six feet high in thick ivy only a few yards off.

As the days pass the efficiency of the procedure increases and the chicks' bedtime becomes later. The family may be escorted to roost for about a fortnight. Second-brood families receive this attention rather longer than first broods owing to the parents being undistracted by reproductive impulses, but leading to the roost may come to an end, apparently, as much because of the fledglings' disinclination to follow as through the parents ceasing to pilot them. Moreover, the family tends to disperse as the chicks attain independence and seek separate roosts. Thus a family of four western winter wrens were led to the dormitory by the female for 14 evenings, but on the 15th there were only three, on the 16th only one, and on the 17th this youngster was led to the roost, but would not enter (Merritt 1916).

Watching a family being guided to the roost is a delightful experience. As the sun nears the horizon and long shadows slant across the wood the male is heard calling and, when we draw near, the squeaks of the fledglings are heard here and there. Often before we realise what is toward, the little party has drifted away and we may then be hard put to it to rediscover the birds before they have disappeared into the dormitory. If the male is leading he moves towards the roost with staccato flights, calling and singing. He indicates the chosen recess by singing outside and, perhaps, creeping in and out as he did earlier in the year when showing his nests to prospecting females. When the female leads, as she does less often than her mate, she may attract the family's attention by flying repeatedly from where they are assembling to the roosting-place. I have seen a wren fly eleven times across a road before she succeeded in inducing the young to follow; and when they did so they crossed, not at the place indicated, but farther on where overhanging trees shortened the journey. When the roosting nest or niche is attained the mother may sing the dainty whisper or " swallow " song as she puts the chicks to bed and after they are ensconced. If they are disturbed she will return and lead them to another dormitory, and yet another, if they are again alarmed, but a point is reached—probably due to the increase of darkness—when she departs and leaves them to fend for themselves. This is true of the male also.

Fairly frequently the young are fed in the roosting nest after they are ensconced, as if they had never left the breeding nest. This is most noticeable, of course, when they take refuge there some considerable time before sunset. In such circumstances I have never known the male to help, but Bentham (1925) found five young in a neighbouring nest the evening they had vacated the breeding nest, and there they stayed, fed by the parents, for three days. Thereafter they used it as a dormitory for a fortnight.

Females may roost with the chicks up to, and even after, fledging. One has even been known to allow the fledglings of her first brood into the nest where she was incubating her second clutch (Mächler 1947). Similar behaviour has been recorded of the neotropical house wren (A. F. Skutch, *in litt.*). Young equatorial wrens (*Troglodytes solstitialis ochraceus*) may be led to the pendant sleeping-nest and left there, or they may sleep with one of the parents (Skutch 1940a).

In the roosting nest wren chicks squat low, as they do in the breeding nest when frightened. Occasionally the young return to roost in the nest where they were reared, but this is exceptional among wrens and, indeed, among passerine birds in general, though bearded tits may be led back to the breeding nest for five nights after fledging (Watson 1946). This species, like the wren, is apparently of tropical origin. Barn swallows, spotted flycatchers (Swaine 1945), willow warblers and whitethroats (Southern 1949) occasionally use the nest where they were reared as a dormitory and young waterhens sometimes sleep on one of the additional nests built by the male early in the year.

Broods of wrens prematurely frightened from the nest may return to it to complete their development for another day or two. Perhaps when they leave again normally they tend to return to roost in the same nest. A family of Shetland wrens which I disturbed went back in the evening to spend the night in the nest. This tendency may be greater among wrens building few auxiliary nests and inhabiting areas with few small mammalian predators. One would suppose it to be advantageous for birds to sleep away from recently-occupied nests which harbour parasites.

There are remarkable similarities between the roosting habits of wrens and woodpeckers. Olivaceous piculets pilot the young back to the nest and sleep with them. At the entrance the male utters a clear monosyllabic call, apparently corresponding to the churrs of the male wren on such occasions. Like young cactus wrens the fledglings are sometimes clumsy in manœuvring into the orifice. Juvenile golden-naped woodpeckers sleep with their parents until shortly before the next breeding season (Skutch 1948a, b).

Observation of how such birds as whitethroats behave in regard to their young at dusk shows from what simple elements the wren's " leading to roost " procedure may have evolved. There are somewhat similar " tick " notes and soft, grating calls as the birds move along a hedgerow in a loose group, one of the parents bringing food from time to time. As the light fades they are left to themselves, huddled, two or three together, on a branch some feet above the ground.

Although our lack of knowledge on these matters makes generalisa-tion precarious a definite procedure whereby the young are guided to a dormitory appears to be more characteristic of tropical species than of those nesting in temperate regions. This may be correlated with the tendency for tropical birds to build roofed nests and the abundance of arboreal mammals in the tropics. Greater survival value attaches to a safe roosting place. Probably, therefore, the wren's behaviour in this respect may be regarded as an adaptation acquired before the wren's ancestors left the New World. Many of the tropical American species of wren roost communally. Lawrence's song wrens (*Leucolepis phaeocephala lawrencii*) spend the night in family parties (Skutch 1940a). Male and female northern cactus wrens escort their family nightly to one of the auxiliary nests which are built during the incubation period, or even to the nest in which they were reared (Ayer 1937). The parents occupy a nest near at hand (Antevs 1947). The young birds soon begin to build nests of their own in which to roost (Woods 1948). Banded wrens (*Campylorhynchus zonatus*) are among the species in which a supernumerary or auxiliary helper—sometimes more than one— assists a pair with their domestic responsibilities. Parents, assistants and fledged brood sleep together in one of the nests. Sometimes it is the assistant who guides the young to it and induces them to enter by popping in and out. Parties may remain faithful to the roost for months or they may seek a different sleeping-place from time to time. When eggs are due to be laid the female deposits them in one of the dormitory nests. A male whose roost had apparently been destroyed spent the night with his incubating mate. A cock highland wood wren (*Heni-corhina leucophrys collina*) slept with the hen while she was incubating and brooding chicks. The fledglings of this species are led to the roost, as also are rufous-browed wrens (*Troglodytes r. rufociliatus*). Female riverside bay wrens (*Thryophilus nigricapillus semibadius*), equatorial wrens (*Troglodytes solstitialis ochraceus*), and neotropical house wrens (*Troglodytes musculus*) also sleep with the chicks, though not invariably (Skutch 1935, 1940a). The three *Troglodytes* species mentioned by Skutch commonly roost in natural crannies and cavities, but the eleven other species of wren studied by him sleep in nests of their own construction (p. 272).

Roosting in Occupied Nests of Other Species

Wren fledglings' predilection for investigating and roosting in attractive nooks sometimes leads to their invading the occupied nest of another species. Two days after a spotted flycatcher laid her third egg the nest was found crowded with newly-fledged wrens: only one egg remained intact and the flycatchers had disappeared (Thompson 1849). Evidently the wrens made themselves at home while the flycatcher was off the eggs. A grotesque situation arose when a brood of young wrens settled into a hedge sparrow's nest in which a cuckoo was being reared. On at least six evenings the wren fledglings were found sheltering under the half-fledged cuckoo's wings. In a letter to me Mr. C. H. Lewis describes how, after hearing that the young wrens had been " in and out all day," he inspected the nest about 20.30 and found four young wrens' heads poking out from under the cuckoo, and two more fledglings hopping around while the mother wren and hedge sparrow called close by. The wren's nest was not far from the hedge sparrow's. As the young cuckoo's impulse to evict nest-mates disappears after about six days (Armstrong 1929) the interloper tolerated the wrens as bed-fellows.

The three species involved in this episode reached a *modus vivendi*, but when a family of wrens occupied a willow warbler's nest it was not without protest from the owners. One day at least four fully-fledged wrens were found inside the nest resting on the bodies of the young willow warblers. A wren chick peeped out of the entrance and the young willow warblers, on whose backs he perched, tried every now and then to heave him overboard. The parent wren brought food only to her own young, but the willow warblers fed both broods without discrimination. In spite of this, they resented the presence of their lodgers. Once they came to the nest and the female entered, leaving only her tail protruding. There was a great commotion inside for some three or four minutes, but the warbler emerged unsuccessful, and the two birds perched side by side as if nonplussed by the situation. One of the young wrens now came to the entrance, standing on a young

b. Cactus wren at nest, Arizona.

Plate VIIIa. Bewick's wren at nest in gourd. West Virginia.

willow warbler's back, and the female willow warbler hopped forward, thrusting her head between the wren's legs and heaving upwards and backwards with all her strength; but she was unable to dislodge the fledgling. The adult wren and one of the willow warblers sometimes approached together, but they were not seen to go to the nest simultaneously. The willow warblers fledged three days after the young wrens departed (Nicholl 1923) (Plate VII, p. 217).

We may assume that the willow warbler's perturbation was due rather to the changed situation caused by the invasion of the nest by chicks more advanced than her own than " recognition " of the wrens as alien intruders. When a willow warbler's eggs were placed in a wren's nest the wren hatched and reared the young in addition to her own brood (Gladstone 1910). That birds of a variety of species will feed a fledged cuckoo which they have not reared indicates how irrelevant the appearance of an importunate young bird may be and how strong the impulse to feed it.

Eckermann, in his *Conversations with Goethe*, describes picking up two newly-fledged wrens and wrapping them in his handkerchief to take home. As he was passing through a wood they escaped. Three days later he found them in a robin's nest being fed together with the robin's own young. Evidently the young wrens, as they looked for a snug resting-place, came on the robin's nest, insinuated themselves and were accepted by the robins.

FOSTERING

We have already noted that great tits successfully reared a brood of wrens, and the sequel, that a female wren being courted by a male took over the task of feeding them, helped occasionally by her follower (p. 105). Probably a single wren chick reared by blue tits was also taken over by neighbouring wrens, but I could not be certain of this as the fledgling managed to get rid of its ring. As the photograph shows, a robin may feed nestling wrens (Pl. VII, p. 217) (Duval 1953).

Not only may a situation arise naturally in which wrens are tended by a bird of another species, but the reverse also has been recorded. A wren fed two spotted flycatchers after they had left their nest close to that of the wrens (Heaven 1948), and a male busied himself with nestling great tits while his mate was sitting, bringing food approximately every five minutes while the pair of tits averaged a visit only once in nine minutes. This behaviour was observed for four days (H. M. Heybroek, *in litt.*). Significantly, the episode occurred late in the season, in July, when the male's parental impulses tend to dominate the sexual. Another wren, after entering a hide and perching

T.W.

on the camera with which Pike (1932) was photographing a young willow warbler, went away and soon returned with some food for the chick. A pair of wrens fed in turn their own young and linnet chicks in a nest six yards away (Steiniger 1950). Mr. J. H. Owen observed the desertion by a male wren of his mate in order to devote his energies to feeding a young cuckoo in a nest three yards away.

Mrs. B. Mainwaring has given me details of a curious relationship between a blue tit and wrens. During the last five days of the wren chicks' stay in the nest the female was accompanied on her visits with food by a blue tit. The tit was never observed to bring food. On one occasion when the male wren approached he was driven away by the interloper.

Both types of fostering have been recorded of other species of wren. A house wren brought food to a pair of black-headed grosbeaks at the nest, passing it to one or other so that they could feed the young. Like the wren mentioned above this bird made more visits to the nest than the sum of the parents' efforts. When the young grosbeaks left the nest the house wren was found feeding a family of house sparrows, (Hills 1924). A cock bluebird busied himself feeding a brood of young house wrens, disconcerting the parents of the latter, until his own young hatched and he transferred his attention to them (Forbush 1935). A male junco was seen supplying young Bewick's wrens with food (Williams 1943), and a Carolina wren, not content with feeding his incubating mate, also fed the nestlings of a crested flycatcher in a nest close by (Wight 1934).

So many instances of the feeding of chicks of one species by a bird of another species have been put on record that such behaviour cannot be regarded as surprising. The drive to feed young sometimes matures before it can be expressed in the normal way. In such circumstances a bird, catching sight of a gaping chick, may feed it and so satisfy itself psychologically and the chick physiologically. It is well known that the threshold of release of many behaviour-patterns may become so low that they are activated by an inadequate object, and are manifested as " overflow activities " (Armstrong 1947, 1950b). The signals releasing the impulse to administer food are usually rather simple, being constituted by the begging call and the bright gape of the chick. As many passerines have yellow gapes it must occasionally happen that a chance glimpse of an importunate chick of another species initiates the impulse to feed it. Thus Pike (1930) noticed that when a grey wagtail flew over a brood of young thrushes they begged as it passed. The wagtail faltered in flight, turned, alighted and fed them.

The feeding of alien young also sometimes occurs when the offspring of a pair of birds have come to grief. The drive to feed young may persist after they have been destroyed. I have seen a song thrush, goldfinch and kingfisher bring food to the nest after the young had perished. In such circumstances a bird may satisfy its parental impulses by feeding young in a neighbouring nest or newly-fledged chicks. When an auxiliary neotropical wren is noted helping feed chicks it is, at least sometimes, a youngster of an earlier brood which has roosted with the nestlings (Skutch 1935, 1953b).

CHAPTER 14

PREDATION, VICTIMISATION BY THE CUCKOO, AND MORTALITY

Cold, cold!
Cold to-night is the broad plain of Lurg,
Higher the snow than the mountain-range,
The deer cannot get their food.

The hounds of Cuan-wood find not
Rest nor sleep in the dwelling of hounds,
The little wren cannot find
Shelter in her nest on Lon-slope.

On the little company of the birds had broken forth
Keen wind and cold ice,
The blackbird cannot get a lee to her liking,
Shelter at the side in Cuan-woods.

From the early Irish. Tr. KUNO MEYER

THE WREN is so small that it cannot effectively defend itself, its nest or young from marauders. Moreover, its fondness for feeding and nesting near to the ground brings it and its offspring into special jeopardy, but like many other species of temperate and tropical regions which feed in the lowest zone of woodland it is protected to some extent by its cryptic coloration and also by its alertness and swift, adroit movements in dense cover. The Shetland wren, affectionately called " Wee Brown Button " by the islanders, is less readily disturbed by the approach of human beings and quadrupeds than the European wren, owing, no doubt, to never having been persecuted.

WINGED PREDATORS

The merlin has been known to take wrens (Jourdain 1939a), but this must be a rare occurrence as meadow pipits are so much more easily caught by a falcon accustomed to hunt over the open moorland. Wrens in Scottish glens sing vigorously regardless of merlins nesting on the hillside a short distance away. When I was watching a golden eagle's eyrie a wren sang close by at frequent intervals and a chaffinch perched a few feet above the eaglet. Of course these birds never have any cause to regard the eagle as an enemy. Wrens are said to utter short, sharp, high-pitched notes when a peregrine passes over and sometimes—though this may be coincidence—when it " barks " (H. St. John Hart, personal communication), but Bolam (1912) states that wrens sing as usual when a falcon is overhead. Seebohm (1884) was mistaken in regarding the darkening of the upper parts of the St. Kilda wren as an adaptation to conceal the birds from " hungry hawks." Preble and McAtee (1923) state that at one time the Alaska wrens on St. George Island were almost exterminated by gyrfalcons, but this must be an exaggeration. An indication that the larger falcons may, perhaps, take wrens is the finding of the remains of a rock wren below a peregrine's eyrie (Dixon and Bond 1937).[9]

Among the British Falconidae the sparrowhawk is the chief destroyer of woodland birds. Its victims are obtained by surprise rather than by flying them down. Research into the sparrowhawk's diet shows that an adult destroys some 64 birds each month throughout the year and each eyas is given an average of 2.1 birds per day while in the nest. During Tinbergen's investigation (1946) only two wren carcasses were found at sparrowhawks' nests—a small number in comparison with 921 sparrows, 263 great tits and 76 robins. Uttendörfer (1930) found 13 wrens and 1419 sparrows. The proportion of the stock of a number of species captured by the sparrowhawk during the month of May has been estimated by Tinbergen. The largest percentages are of the house sparrow (8.4) and tree pipit (6.9); the lowest the goldcrest (1.8), icterine warbler (1.1) and wren (0.3). In the observation area of North Veluwe in Holland the wren constituted only $\frac{1}{16}$ per cent of the summer food of the sparrowhawk.

There is a close correlation between conspicuousness and vulnerability. Although the goldcrest is smaller than the wren it suffers more severely owing to its characteristic way of feeding in the tops of conifers, but the icterine warbler—a larger bird—is protected by its secretive habits.

A pair of sparrowhawks bred in Wren Wood for three years of my period of investigation, but I never found any wren remains at the tree stumps and other places where prey was plucked. The presence of the hawks made no appreciable difference to the activities of the wrens, but they were alarmed when a hawk flew near. A male and female were feeding by the pond's edge when a sparrowhawk shot from behind a bush and swerved almost overhead some fifteen feet away. One of the wrens, apparently the male, jerked out a short grating call which reminded me of a familiar, harsh sedge warbler note, as they flew into the vegetation. It was quite distinct from the reeling note uttered when a ground predator approaches. Thus the European wren, like many other birds, such as the great, blue and long-tailed tits and the house sparrow, as well as some mammals, utters different types of alarm according to whether the menacing object is in the air or on the ground. The rock wren's warning of the approach of a bird of prey is also distinctive. When a falcon appears the parent gives a clear, urgent call and the young immediately take cover (Jaeger 1950). Usually the note signalling airborne danger is shorter and sharper than that announcing the approach of a slower-moving ground predator.

Only a few minutes before the sparrowhawk appeared several low-flying bombers roared past without disturbing the wrens. During the war aircraft were so frequently overhead that most birds became indifferent to them unless they passed over very low. On two or three such occasions I noticed wrens flying into cover. Once when two rooks flapped low over two newly-fledged wrens perched on a fence they dived precipitately into cover. This *sauve qui peut* reaction seems to be associated with no precise enemy configuration, but with the sudden appearance of a large aerial object. It may also occur, apparently " in error," when a bird unexpectedly flies very close overhead. Birds get accustomed to, and cease to take evasive action on the appearance of, objects which at first frighten them. As a boy in Ireland, I remember watching a hen hurriedly lead her chicks to cover when an aeroplane appeared at a considerable height overhead, but nowadays aircraft do not perturb our sophisticated poultry.

Brown owls call forth indignant remonstrances from wrens, but I have observed no other evidence of the supposed enmity between the wren and the owl so prominent in folklore, noted by Aristotle (*H.A.* ix. 608a 12) and mentioned by Shakespeare:

> The poor wren,
> The most diminutive of birds, will fight,
> Her young ones in her nest, against the owl.
>
> *Macbeth*, IV. ii. 9

An unfledged brown owl about four weeks old, kept as a pet, swallowed the body of a full-grown wren (M. Tulloch, *in litt.*). I know of no record of an owl of any species raiding a wren's nest, though owls will snatch sleeping birds from their perches and—strange coincidence—as I write I hear the screams of a blackbird caught by an owl while roosting in the ivy of my house. If an owl were to tear open a wren's nest it would have difficulty in extricating the chicks from the tangled ruins or in catching them as they flew out. Moreover, Shakespeare was unaware that by the time the youngsters are somewhat more than a week old the parent sometimes roosts elsewhere and is not at hand to retaliate if an owl were to attack the young. His birds are more often creatures of folklore than denizens of the woods and fields (Armstrong 1946b). However, as owls occasionally take house wrens (Fisher 1893; Errington *et al.* 1941) and rip up the nests of cactus wrens (Jaeger 1950) it is possible that an owl may capture a wren now and then.

Two incidents out of many may be chosen to illustrate the behaviour of wrens when owls are about. One August evening, after Pinkie had led her family to roost, a brown owl alighted a few yards away. I found the wren on a willow branch uttering machine-gun volleys of " chirp churrs," with a chitter or two interspersed. At times she stretched up as if on tiptoe, showing her pink socks, and twice she bent over with her beak to her breast, apparently displacement-preening.

Male wrens sometimes express their dislike of owls even more forcibly. Hearing a hubbub one May morning, I was attracted to a Scots pine on an upper branch of which sat a brown owl. Blackbirds and chaffinches were clinking around him, and a goldcrest, like an urchin at a cup-tie, was adding his high-pitched outcry to the chorus. A wren came along, rattling out ticking notes, and went bouncing up the pine, a diminutive ballet-dancer standing on tiptoe on each branch, constantly flipping his wings. Poised on stiff, straight legs a few feet from the owl he stood for some seconds flipping and cursing; then he bounced downstairs again. The owl endured without comment, waited until the rabble had desisted and then floated off across the pond. At his going the wren, now deep among the bushes, uttered an imprecatory churr and a few other curse notes.

For some weeks an owl roosted fairly regularly in an ivy-covered tree in Wren Wood. Six feet below was a nest used as sleeping quarters by a wren. Almost certainly the two roosts were sometimes used contemporaneously, one bird arriving about the time the other was departing.

I was constantly on the alert to ascertain, if possible, whether or not the wren reacts to the utterance of owl, hawk, jay, cuckoo or any four-footed predator, but I never succeeded in gaining evidence that it does, though on one occasion I thought the abrupt return of a wren to its nest might be due to hearing the loud hoot of an owl nearby. Miss Stanwood tells me of a winter wren which went to the top of a tree to scold a screaming broad-winged hawk, but the wren may have been attracted by the sight of the hawk rather than its calls. Although song sparrows manifest alarm when they perceive owls a hand-reared bird gave no response to imitations of the hoots of various species (Nice and Pelkwyk 1941). On the other hand, Hartley (1950) and Miller (1952) report birds reacting to owl calls, and some Australian species take to cover when a man or a spotted bower bird imitates the call of a bird of prey (Chisholm 1948b). The wren is so little harried by raptors that it would be rather surprising if it were to react to their calls. However, although the willow warbler is not much victimised by the cuckoo in this country, Smith (1946) found that an imitation of the call elicited threat display by these birds.

Jays sometimes tear the roof off a wren's nest (Sluiters 1947) and magpies occasionally rob wrens. In Finland, where the wren is sparsely distributed, a magpie plundered a nest (P. Palmgren, *in litt.*). Although magpies were nearly always resident in Wren Wood during the breeding season and jays were present for two seasons the wrens were not molested by either species. California jays rob northern cactus wrens in spite of the secure position among cactus spines in which they often build their nests (Woods 1948).

Youngsters disappeared from two nests in boxes at both of which I had seen a great tit showing much interest while building was in progress, but in spite of these suspicious coincidences I have no evidence that great tits take the chicks of small birds, though a neighbour tells me that the eggs of a song thrush in a nest built on top of a box occupied by tits were found punctured. The circumstances suggested that one of the tits was responsible. The sight of a wren emerging from a hole stimulates great tits to enter and inspect it—behaviour closely linked with their nest-invitation display. Occasionally tits breed in wrens' nests (Hinde 1952).

Adult wrens, and, no doubt, newly-fledged young, are occasionally killed by red-backed shrikes, and a bittern has been known to swallow a wren (Schreurs 1941; Jourdain 1938c, 1939b). Mr. I. J. Ferguson-Lees tells me that he saw a St. Kilda wren enter a burrow occupied by an adult puffin and emerge safely twenty seconds later.

House sparrows sometimes show an aversion for wrens. Indeed, they have been observed to throw the eggs out of a wren's nest and take feathers from the lining (I. Rainier, *in litt.*). I have seen sparrows fly petulantly at a singing wren. When a wren flew up to the eaves of a cottage and clung upside down near his nest a sparrow darted at him. The wren flew down a few feet and perched with tail expanded and wings slightly drooped in mild sexual or displacement display. On another occasion when two wrens were squabbling, while a female looked on, a sparrow dashed at one of the males. However, Mr. R. Gait informs me that he has observed a male wren drive inquisitive house sparrows away from where his mate was incubating. Where house wrens and house sparrows come into competition the house wrens dominate (Bread 1945). A wren will evict a hedge sparrow from a favourite song-post (R. E. Moreau, *in litt.*) or defy in turn the threats of one of these birds and a pair of chaffinches (Thompson 1849). I once saw a Shetland starling chase a wren from where he was singing —perhaps a transference-activity occasioned by my presence near the starling's nest. After a wren had displayed to a presumed female he drove off a cock blackcap (Nicholson 1951).

Bent (1948) and others mention instances of the persecution or slaughter of various wrens by other birds, but, so far as is known, no species suffers seriously from the depredations of winged predators, though the cuckoo can be a menace to the European wren in some areas.

VICTIMISATION BY THE CUCKOO

In Britain wrens' nests seem to be chosen by the cuckoo for her egg only when the nests of other fosterers at the appropriate stage are not available. Correspondents tell me of four instances of cuckoos being seen in wrens' nests and another is mentioned by Blezard *et al.* (1943). Only five victimisations of wrens have been noted in Holland (Helle-brekers 1949, 1951), but there are numerous records from other regions of the continent (Labitte 1940; Géroudet 1951). In some parts of Germany the species has at times been so persecuted by cuckoos as to have its numbers greatly reduced (Jäckel 1891). In one week Walter (1893) found two wrens' nests each containing three cuckoos' eggs. He attributed this multiple victimisation to the reduction in numbers of wrens and the increase of cuckoos due to cumulative parasitisation in previous years. It would be difficult to believe that the popularity of the wren with the cuckoo as a fosterer had not been exaggerated did not the evidence of so many authorities concur (Rey 1892; Bidwell 1896; Jourdain 1925; Makatsch 1937).

According to Poulton (1926) the percentage of instances in which the wren has been known to reject the cuckoo's egg is very high. He bases this opinion on a paper in which Jourdain (1925) quotes observations by Walker indicating that wrens deserted in 21 instances out of 44 (47 per cent) in which a cuckoo's egg was placed in the nest; but in five experiments in which a strange egg was added to a wren's clutch the bird accepted it on every occasion (Link 1903). I suspect that desertions may have been due to interference with the birds or their nests rather than the presence of an alien egg. Cuckoos' eggs found in wrens' nests do not resemble those of the foster-parent in colour, but so dark is the interior of the nest that it is doubtful whether the dupe would notice the difference.

Mr. R. S. Lamb has sent me details of finding a young cuckoo in a wren's nest beneath the eaves of a thatched cottage into which he believes the cuckoo could not have introduced her egg without using her bill, but definite evidence that the cuckoo ever behaves in this way is lacking. A bird which was watched from a very short distance while laying was seen to elongate the cloacal region of her body and move it from side to side as if feeling for the exact place in which to deposit the egg (Horne 1924). Undoubtedly the cuckoo can manœuvre her body in order to deposit the egg in awkwardly-placed or constructed nests, but sometimes she fails. A wren's nest was found with its entrance damaged, two eggs deserted and a cuckoo's egg on the ground one metre away (Hoertler 1934). Ware (1923) noticed that the portal of a wren's deserted nest containing a cuckoo's egg had been disturbed and Musselwhite (1923) remarked that another nest's entrance was slightly damaged and the cuckoo's egg was in the nest near the opening. Other instances of a similar nature have been cited by Jäckel (1891), Labitte (1948), Hellebrekers (1951) and Congreve (1951). They increase the probability that disarrangement of the nest rather than the appearance of the cuckoo's egg accounts for some instances of wrens deserting their nests.

Jourdain's inclusion of the wren among the species frequently victimised in this country (1911) is misleading. " Occasionally " would be more correct. The willow warbler is in the same category, yet one of these will attack a stuffed cuckoo while a wren will not (Edwards et al. 1949). Can it be that the contrast between the reactions of the willow warbler and the wren is due to the former having longer ancestral experience of the cuckoo than the latter? According to

Moffat (1911), in Ireland the cuckoo is mobbed only by the meadow pipit, the only Irish bird commonly victimised.

As the young cuckoo's eyes are shut and it cannot see clearly at which side of a wren's nest the aperture is situated it must be by repeated trial and error that each egg or chick is ejected. Thus getting rid of the clutch entails the expenditure of much energy, yet when Walter (1893) twice replaced four eggs which he found on the ground they were thrown out each time.

There is no definite evidence that a single wren is able to rear a cuckoo to independence, though this may be possible in spite of the parasite's relatively huge bulk (cf. photo in Kirkman 1911-13). Certainly a pair can do so. Probably a male wren who would not normally feed his own brood is sometimes induced to feed a young cuckoo by its importunity or, indirectly, by the sight of his mate's exertions. If, as Ashby noted (1932), a male wren will neglect his young to help hedge sparrows feed a cuckoo, we need not doubt the parasite's power to stimulate the male wren to feed him. At Panama a rufous-and-white wren (*Thryothorus rufalbus*) has been seen feeding a young striped cuckoo (Loetscher 1952), and in Surinam the shiny cowbird frequently parasitises the neotropical house wren (Haverschmidt 1952).

MAMMALIAN PREDATORS

That the European wren has evolved a more distinctive warning-call to signal the approach of ground predators than of airborne enemies confirms other evidence that its chief enemies are four-footed. When a wren becomes aware of the presence of a cat it hops and flits excitedly from twig to twig above or near where the animal is moving or lying in wait, at the same time reeling forth its regular *kreeee* alarm notes (p. 95). In spite of its apparently excited state a wren will sometimes look here and there for food as it dodges about uttering the series of alarm-calls. Very occasionally these calls are elicited by the approach of a human being or a dog, but in such circumstances the series is not long sustained. I have heard it now and then when rats were in the undergrowth, and also, after I placed a long-haired tippet near a nest, both male and female gave this type of alarm vigorously and continuously. As described later, it was uttered by a wren when an Irish stoat was near the fledglings. I have never known it called forth by the sight of a rabbit or hedgehog, though one would suppose that a glimpse of one of these animals partly concealed by the herbage might be mistaken occasionally for something more dangerous. Experiments with fur " models " of various kinds suggest that the

European wren is most alarmed by a fairly bulky and relatively long-haired object.

The *kreeee* alarm sometimes attracts other birds besides wrens, such as blackbirds or robins, to where a cat is concealed. Wrens, in their turn, will go where other species are mobbing a predator. I have seen two wrens leave their roost shortly after they had entered it, attracted to some bushes where blackbirds were making a commotion near to a cat. Earlier, mention was made of the wren which was diverted from entering her nest on hearing mobbing in progress a little distance away (p. 177). Dr. R. Hinde tells me that when he was conducting a series of experiments to ascertain the reactions of chaffinches to owl models a wren appeared, attracted by the " pink " alarm-note of the chaffinch. He also noted that young wrens in an aviary, reared by hand, reacted with sharp calls on hearing the alarm notes of chaffinches when these birds were shown a stuffed owl. Where two species live in close relationship and are liable to be attacked by the same predator it is not unusual for one species to react to the other's alarm notes. Bewick's wrens have been observed flying frantically for shelter when a bluebird uttered its warning call (Thomas 1946). In experiments during which I showed a stuffed owl and cat " models " to young wrens reared by hand to the age of two months, alarm calls were not uttered. Perhaps the reaction matures later, as it is rather unlikely that it is learned.

The behaviour I have described is not the invariable reaction of a wren to a cat. The bird may squat on a branch watching intently as the beast approaches, remaining immobile, or almost immobile, as it passes underneath. One bird remained practically motionless for 166 seconds and it is not unusual in such circumstances for a wren to " freeze " for about a minute. Prowling cats never seem to notice wrens which squat in this way. Such " freezing " is characteristic of wrens when disturbed by cats just before entering the roost and may be of importance in preventing the discovery of their sleeping places. On one occasion when a wren, coming to the roost, alighted a few feet away on his customary perch, he saw a cat pounce on a young blackbird fifteen yards distant. He flew off and did not return that night—but perhaps this was merely a coincidence.

A male wren with fledged young acts in an entirely different way. Highly excited, he will dart from perch to perch only three or four feet above the cat, swearing at it and sometimes so engrossing its attention that it follows the wren around. I have known a wren thus blindly lead the cat nearer the young but so tantalise it that the animal made no attempt to seize them. As a means of deflecting a predator this performance was much more crude than the distraction displays of some species (Armstrong 1949a, 1950d).

The same evening I witnessed another mixture of effective and ineffective behaviour. I found the cock wren chittering in a bush beneath which the cat was lying. After a while he desisted and went off to play erotically with the female, chasing and pouncing on her half a dozen times. On looking around for the youngsters I discovered two of them in a disused hedge sparrow's nest situated in the fork of a branch only two feet from the ground. When they fluttered out, on seeing me bending over them, one of the parents appeared, probably the female, and led them back to the same roost—very unobtrusively. Her undemonstrative methods were admirably adapted to avoid drawing attention to the dormitory, but the choice was inappropriate. It was perilously near the ground, the young had already been disturbed there, and the cat was still lying in wait only a dozen yards away. However, I have never known young wrens to be captured through being watched to their roost by a predator.

Particularly in suburban areas wrens are in jeopardy from cats. Of the 15 records of ringed wrens found dead 4 were killed by cats, whereas of the 101 ringed robins whose death has been recorded 44 fell victim to cats and only one was caught by a sparrowhawk (Lack 1946a). The 4 wrens were all between 4 and 7 months old— suggesting that young and inexperienced birds are most vulnerable. There is abundant evidence showing this to be true of other species. Twice in one summer Mr. J. H. Owen saw a wren in the clutches of a cat. On one of these occasions the cat was playing with the bird as with a mouse. Although cats find the flesh of robins distasteful they eat wrens; thus wrens conform to the general principle that cryptic species tend to be palatable (Cott 1946).

Several writers, apparently copying each other, have blamed cats for reducing the Iceland wren population, but it is improbable that they destroy an appreciable number. In the Faeroes, where wrens breed near houses more frequently than in Iceland, cats are said to destroy many of the young (Williamson 1947a). House wrens also are killed by them in North America, La Plata, Surinam and, no doubt, elsewhere (Bent 1948; Hudson 1920; Haverschmidt 1952).

English bird life would benefit if cats were less common and if fewer bird-lovers were not also cat-lovers. An unfinished wren's nest in Wren Wood at a height of 6 feet was torn in such a way as to suggest that the havoc was wrought by a cat. Elsewhere, another slightly lower nest in a yew was ripped open by one of these animals and the young devoured. Correspondents have told me of nests being cleared out by cats and of young wrens being seized as they emerged from the nest.

In North America foxes sometimes capture house wrens (Bent 1948), so wrens may occasionally be snapped up by these animals.

I was able to observe a wren's reactions to an Irish stoat (*Mustela erminea hibernica*) on hilly, whin-clad ground, sloping up from the shore in County Down. I heard the male uttering a *kreeee* alarm-call and, on approaching, noticed a blackbird and three linnets, as well as the wren, perched among the bushes in a state of noisy agitation. The wren continued his reeling note but soon flew some dozen yards up the declivity. The youngsters—there were at least three—followed one after another. Just after the last had flown the stoat began clucking insistently under the whin bush on which the fledgling had been perching. Meanwhile the family was being called farther up the hillside. By means of the gamekeeper's device of sucking the back of my hand to make a squealing call like a rabbit in distress, I coaxed the stoat out, but on seeing me the wary creature immediately skipped back into a crevice at the base of a stone wall. The wren had by now reached a thorn thicket at the top of the hill. After singing a few rather subdued and abbreviated songs he led the youngsters to roost in the thicket, for dusk was approaching. After chattering petulantly at me for five minutes the stoat disappeared. The wren's behaviour had been successful in warning the fledglings and leading them out of danger.

When I experimented with two stuffed stoats, one in summer pelage and the other in the white winter coat of the northern race, placing them in full view eighteen inches from a wren's nest, the bird was disquieted and suspicious, once or twice uttering short reeling notes, but after some tentative approaches she went in and out as before. Shetland wrens paid no more attention to the brown specimen than they might pay to any strange object. On the island of Fetlar, where I carried out the experiments, there are no stoats.

According to Montagu (1831) wrens will pursue a polecat " with loud manifestations of anger." Naumann (1822-53) refers to martens as enemies of the wren but gives no details. Hyde-Parker (1938) remarks that wrens make a loud outcry at a weasel and Mr. J. H. Owen tells me that he once saw one of these animals emerge from a wren's nest after devouring the young. Grey squirrels devour wren nestlings and Seigne (1930) believes that they tear open the nests of wrens and long-tailed tits from the top. When a squirrel appeared near a winter wren's nest the bird " ticked " repeatedly (C. Stanwood, *in litt.*). Chipmunks sometimes capture winter wrens (Forbush 1929).

I have never noticed a wren reacting to a rat, apart from brief utterances of the *kreeee* call. The rats in Wren Wood were never very numerous nor did they interfere with the wrens, so far as I could ascertain. Most of the occupied nests were situated where it would have been difficult or impossible for a rat to reach them. However, several B.T.O. observers record nests robbed in circumstances which suggested that rats were responsible.

A juvenile wren has been seen displaying at a water vole in a remarkable fashion. Squatting with wings spread horizontally so that they were within an inch of meeting in front of its wide-open beak the bird sometimes held its tail vertically upwards, at other times directly down, and occasionally oscillating between the two positions. It leaped about two inches into the air several times as the vole approached and passed but uttered no sound (Barrett 1947b). This strange behaviour may have been a displacement activity or one of those confused or mingled reactions which highly excited birds are apt to perform. There is some evidence that young birds with incompletely matured responses are particularly prone to exhibit distorted forms of behaviour. In Wren Wood a water vole once appeared near to where a wren was lining her nest, while the male was dancing attendance on her, but neither bird paid any attention to it.

Early one winter afternoon during a tour of inspection of old wrens' nests, when I was trying to ascertain which were being used as dormitories, I was puzzled to find the entrance to one of them blocked with moss. Thrusting in my finger, I was still more surprised to feel something soft and warm at the bottom of the nest. When I lifted the creature out, I found it was a very lively long-tailed field mouse. An artificial roosting-place for wrens, consisting of an inclined tin with a rough hole in the lid, was appropriated by a field mouse as a storehouse, and a nesting-box which had been partially packed with moss, probably by a tit, was used as a sleeping-place by one, and sometimes two, field mice.

Every time I visited a certain nest during April and May I found moss in the entrance and filling much of the cavity. I repeatedly tidied it up, hoping that it would be chosen by a female. It was. Some feathers were placed inside as lining, but no eggs were laid. One afternoon when I investigated it a field mouse ran out of a hole which it had made in the back of the nest. Next afternoon, and on several other occasions, in spite of the disturbance I made by poking it out with my finger, it was there again. This, the first nest of the season built by the wren, was not used for breeding. The female who had started to line it must have been deterred, either by the mouse or the material with which it choked the interior.

Occasionally field mice are reared in a wren's nest. Where such requisitioning of accommodation is frequent, by mice or other creatures (p. 268), those wrens building more than one nest early in the season would be most successful in obtaining mates and leaving descendants, and therefore multiple nest-building would be advantageous. Burkitt (1919-20), who noted moss-blocked nests in County Fermanagh, speculated as to the explanation. These observations resolve this minor mystery.

Long-tailed field mice sometimes destroy the eggs of small birds, nibbling neatly around the circumference and lapping up the contents, but I have never had reason to attribute the destruction of any eggs in Wren Wood to them. I placed a blue tit's and a great tit's egg together in an old nest within a foot of the mouse-occupied wren's nest, but they remained intact. However, small chicks disappeared from the wren's nest which I arranged for interior observation in circumstances which suggested the work of a field mouse. Youngsters which were found injured in another nest may have been attacked by a field mouse or, possibly, a shrew (p. 205).

Unoccupied wrens' nests which have not been used for breeding are occasionally appropriated by field voles and common shrews. Now and then a dormouse hibernates in an old wren's nest (J. H. Owen, *in litt.*).

In the United States snakes have been known to eat house wren nestlings and they probably sometimes devour the young of other species of wren (Alcorn 1931; Hunter 1935).

Parasites and Nidicoles

The parasites and nidicoles of the wren are discussed elsewhere (Armstrong 1953b). It serves as host for three species of feather-lice, *Penenirmus albiventris*, *Myrsidea troglodytis* and *Menacanthus tenuifrons* (T. Clay, *in litt.*), and two species of flea, *Ceratophyllus gallinae* and *Dasypsyllus gallinulae* (M. Rothschild, *in litt.*). Probably the latter was brought to Europe from the New World by the wren or, perhaps, the dipper. Various wasps, such as *Vespa sylvestris*, and bees may nest inside unoccupied wrens' nests. Tropical species, such as the white-bellied wren (*Uropsila leucogastra*), gain protection for their nests by placing them near the nests of hornets or ants (Sutton 1948). The chicks of the European wren are sometimes attacked by hippoboscid louse-flies. A variety of beetles, moths and other arthropods take refuge in wrens' nests.

The Taste of Wrens' Eggs

Cott (1949) rates the wren's eggs as the most distasteful of all those he tested[10]. In further experiments (1952) in which the eggs of 45 species were offered to rats the house wren's egg is assessed as the most unpalatable, next to the eggs of blue tit and whitethroat. His data show that, as a rule, small birds nesting in cavities lay unpalatable eggs. The nests of such species are much less frequently raided by predatory birds than those of comparable species breeding in more open situations. It would seem, therefore, that the unpalatability of the eggs of these species is an evolutionary adaptation tending to reduce predation by small mammals which have a keener sense of smell, and probably of taste, than birds, though it is a curious fact that martens, like snakes, will swallow porcelain eggs (Hediger 1950). The adaptation is the more advantageous as the incubation period of these birds tends to be longer than that of comparable open-nesting species; consequently the duration of their exposure to danger is longer. I have twice tasted wrens' eggs, involuntarily when an infertile egg which had been incubated for 25 days broke in my mouth as I climbed down from the nest, and voluntarily when I compared the taste of a fresh and fertile egg with eggs of great and blue tit. Both the latter tasted less pleasant than the wren's eggs, which seemed almost tasteless.

ESCAPE ADAPTATIONS

A contrast in escape adaptations between tits and wrens is apparent to the naturalist intent on ringing birds after dusk in winter. With great or blue tits his task is easy. He opens the nesting-box, lifts the tit out and fits the ring. Seldom or never does the bird attempt to escape by the entrance hole or the open lid. Its reactions are adapted to its traditional habits of nesting and roosting in a cavity impregnable except to one or two small species of mammal or a similarly-sized competitor for a nesting site or a roost. Such casual methods cannot be used for trapping wrens. When disturbed they commonly lie " doggo," and even when a finger is inserted there is no reaction, but the moment it is withdrawn they are apt to fly out. They bolt just when the predator is most likely to be off his guard. Not without reason did the Greeks call the wren δυσάλωτος, the elusive one. The Irish quote the proverb, " The fox is the cunningest beast in the world, barring the wren." If the birds' reactions were stereotyped it would be less difficult to trap them but individuals often do the unexpected. Sometimes all the birds roosting in a nest will explode from the exit, sometimes one or two remain within and fly out unexpectedly later. Occasionally a bird will remain quiescent in the nest despite great provocation. I spent ten minutes fixing a swing door of wire gauze at the entrance of a nest and after I had completed the job the wren flew out! At trapping stations the elusiveness of the wren is notorious.

Even in the dim light shortly after sunset wrens notice if there is a small space between the rim of a net and the entrance arch of the nest —and are out and away in an instant. Streamlining their bodies they torpedo their way through small interstices. When a wren escapes in a room it darts into corners and creeps under or behind articles of furniture in a mouse-like way.

A wren seldom flies straight out from the nest—indeed, the projecting eaves usually compel it to fly slightly downwards. This may well have survival value. Its short wings enable it to take flight very rapidly, in marked contrast to the house martin which has to make an appreciable pause as it extricates its long wings from the nest.

As is well known, many birds are apt to assume an inert state when handled, but I have never known a wren collapse in this way. It would seem that owing to its nimbleness in making its escape it has not evolved an adaptation of value to other species in enabling them to take advantage of the opportunity when a captor treats his motionless victim as dead.

DIVERSIONARY DISPLAY

Injury-simulation has not been recorded of the wren. The nearest approximation I have observed was when a bird which I disturbed while nest-building uttered a snatch of song and momentarily draggled his wings as he fluttered away over a mound of earth. A St. Kilda wren behaved somewhat similarly (Harrisson and Buchan 1934), and a male Shetland wren, alarmed at my presence near the nest, hopped up a rock with tail fanned and wings drooping after feeding the chicks. Such activities should be regarded as displacement display rather than diversionary display (Armstrong 1949a) though they might evolve into such display. Nice and Thomas (1948) report that when a fledgling Carolina wren was captured the male " showed a mild form of distraction display." Sometimes as I watched a wren fly off from where she had been incubating I have had the impression that the flight was retarded and more " fluttery " than normal flight. Perhaps from such simple beginnings the " impeded " flights of many species are evolved. It should be noted, however, that the crude approximations to distraction display reported of *T. troglodytes* refer to males performing what seems to be low-intensity epigamic display, whereas in most species the female performs the most vigorous distraction display. The wren's lack of an " injury-simulation " display may be due partly to such antics on the part of a very small bird being less conspicuous, and therefore less effective, than when performed by a larger species, and partly to the meagre variety and numbers of predatory mammals in those areas, mainly islands, where the wren most frequently breeds on or very near the ground. Thus selection has not operated in favour of the evolution of such forms of behaviour.

REACTIONS TO SOUNDS OUTSIDE THE NEST

A wren which has been several times disturbed from the nest becomes so sensitive to the slight noises made by an approaching person, such as the snap of a twig or a rustling among the leaves, that she slips off the nest before he can reach it. As we noted earlier, an incubating bird is often restless. At the nest which I arranged for interior observation I noticed that when branches creaked or twigs fell, due to the strong wind, the wren would start up and look out. If a twig broke beneath my feet she peeped forth nervously, but she was not disturbed by my head, covered with a black cloth as I peered through a gaping hole in the nest, nor by the slight noises I made an inch or two from her. Her responses were adapted to appreciate and react to sights and sounds indicative of an intruder outside the nest, not of one within. For a bird an object may have significance only in its accustomed setting. Thus a meadow pipit will disregard her own nestling, evicted by a young cuckoo, struggling outside the nest. I placed a mounted wren inside an observation nesting-box containing coal tit chicks, but the parent took no notice, though one might have supposed that the apparition of another bird inside the cavity would have aroused vigorous reactions. Similarly sounds have significance, or reaction-valence, for birds according to their setting. Birds frequently disturbed in nesting-boxes opening at the back persist in looking for the cause of alarm outside (Sherman 1910).

MORTALITY DUE TO MISADVENTURE

Of fifteen ringed wrens reported dead, two, ringed as nestlings, were found respectively six and eight months later in water tanks and the body of another was washed up on the shore at Baltasound, Unst (p. 21). Drowned birds are more likely to be noticed than those which perish in some other way, except, perhaps, those caught by cats, so these figures probably give an exaggerated idea of the proportion of wrens drowned.

Only one of my ringed wrens was recovered dead—in the autumn inside one of the nests built by the bird with which she had reared a brood in the spring. There was a long wound on the back which might have been caused by a cat's claw. The bodies of two unringed wrens were found not far from Wren Wood. My friend, Dr. W. H. Thorpe, discovered the carcass of a wren in an elder bush in the wood with a foot wedged in a crotch. It must be seldom that so nimble a bird meets so ignominious a death. The bodies of two newly-fledged birds of a brood I was watching were found in a garden-frame. As we noted earlier, adults are usually able to find their way out of an enclosed space to which they penetrate. During a stay of three weeks on St. Kilda Harrisson and Buchan (1936) found four wrens dead through misadventure, including one drowned in a tub.

MORTALITY DUE TO WEATHER

There are insufficient returns of ringed wrens on which to base estimates of the causes of mortality, apart from what has already been said. Nevertheless, it is a fair inference that neither the ravages of predators nor misadventures of various kinds are the principal factors in determining the size of the wren population. If disease or parasites were serious menaces to the species we would expect more indication that this is so. On the other hand, there is abundant evidence of wrens dying in hard weather. Therefore, we may reasonably assume that wren mortality is primarily due to unfavourable climatic and ecological conditions. This is probably true *a fortiori* of the Iceland wren. At no time during my study of the wren have I had the impression that the density of the population was so high as to introduce controlling factors limiting further increase.

All surveys of bird life in the British Isles and on the continent after severe winters, such as that by Drost and Schüz (1940), show a marked diminution in the numbers of wrens. Records abound of birds being found dead in their roosts during or after severe weather. Individuals roosting alone are sometimes found frozen (Ticehurst 1909). In January 1945 it was noticed that eight wrens were frequenting a house martin's nest in Breconshire. On the 25th, after a heavy snowfall, one was discovered dead in the snow, on the 29th two more were dead, and on the 30th the corpses of the remaining five were found (R. Gait, *in litt.*). Rivière (1927) noticed thirty wrens enter an old swallow's nest one January night during which there were 20° of frost. Next morning he found twelve dead underneath the nest. A correspondent of the Devon Bird Watching Society (Clark 1945) observed about sixteen coming to roost each night in two house martins' nests. On 27 January some seemed so feeble as to have difficulty in reaching the dormitory. Thereafter none visited it, but four were found dead in the garden. However, the prompt recrudescence of song and beginning of nest-building after prolonged severe weather suggest that, at least in favourable areas, wrens may survive hard weather in good condition. Iceland wrens, feeding by the seashore, shot in winter by Timmermann (1935), were fat. Kendeigh (1934), experimenting on the relationship between extremes of temperature and survival, has shown that at 32° F. the house sparrow survives nearly twice as long as the house wren. The latter being a migratory species one would not expect its hardiness to equal that of the sedentary sparrow. The European wren's communal roosting may be no less an indication that low temperatures are a menace to its survival. Gerstell (1939) found that quail in North America are better able to withstand low temperatures in the roosting covey than when isolated.

The British birds which have their numbers most severely depleted in hard winters are such small insectivorous species as the bearded tit, goldcrest and long-tailed tit. The green woodpecker, an insectivorous bird which feeds on the ground, may be seriously reduced in numbers but birds of the finch and crow families suffer comparatively little. After the 1946-47 winter the goldcrests which had bred regularly in Wren Wood for many years disappeared, but the long-tailed tits maintained themselves and no great diminution of the wren population was apparent in the wood and its neighbourhood. Strangely enough, no decrease was reported in the area between London and south Cambridgeshire although the species suffered heavily and generally in the country as a whole (Ticehurst and Hartley 1948). Although wrens seldom take advantage of food provided by bird lovers they seem to survive severe winters in greater numbers in localities with a fair number of human dwellings than in less inhabited areas. As Gilbert White noted, where there are outhouses and stockyards wrens can find food and shelter in hard times. In areas of meagre human habitation, such as the Norfolk Broads, wrens are practically exterminated in an inclement winter.

Some observers, arguing from what they see of birds in their own gardens or other limited areas, are prone to jump to conclusions in regard to the survival of wrens and some other birds after severe winters. The most favourable habitats are occupied both when the wren population is low and high. If naturalists unwittingly restrict their observations to these it may seem that numbers remain fairly normal, when, in fact, there has been a great decrease. After the hard winter of 1946-47 areas known to be comparatively uncongenial were untenanted. With wrens, and no doubt other birds, favourable areas become refuges from which neighbouring regions are restocked, and so, according as winters are mild or severe, the total area occupied by the species expands or contracts. In Iceland after the severe 1948-49 winter the only place

I found wrens was in a west coast fiord within a few miles of a whaling station where birds may have found scraps during the winter. Because the St. Kilda wren population in the village area on Hirta is usually about 10 pairs it has been assumed that the population remains constant, but this is fallacious as the numbers elsewhere vary. The number of wrens on Fair Isle also varies (Williamson 1951c). Strong winds reduce wren populations on islands by restricting feeding (Armstrong 1953e).

Censuses taken in autumn and again in February always show a diminution in numbers. On an Oxfordshire farm there was an average of five in October and two in February (Alexander 1932). In October 1945 and 1946 a Shetland wood held four, but in February 1946 there were two, and in 1947 only one. After the severe weather of February 1947 this bird disappeared and no wrens were recorded until July, when one appeared (Venables 1948). Dr. D. Lack tells me that in Wytham Great Wood where there were about 100 wrens in 1944 only one was observed at the end of the frost in 1945. Sluiters (1947) made a census of spring territories in a wood in Holland and obtained the following results:

TABLE XXVIII

CENSUS OF WREN TERRITORIES IN AMSTERDAM WOOD

Year	Number of territories	Area of wood investigated
1943	4	75ha. (187.5 acres)
1944	9	50ha. (125 acres)
1945	22	75ha. (187.5 acres)

The winter of 1942-43 was severe in Holland but the following three winters were mild. Thus it is apparent that the population in 1943 was depleted and that the succeeding mild winters enabled numbers to recover.

Kendeigh (1934) has correlated the population density of house wrens which breed in, and return from migration to, his observation area with temperature and humidity during spring, autumn and winter. His most recent analysis (1944) indicates that major fluctuations in population are correlated with temperatures below 56° F. in the wintering range (Fig. 37).

Out of the twenty-six nests studied by the Dutch observers in 1937 nine came to grief and about one-third of 450 nests noted with

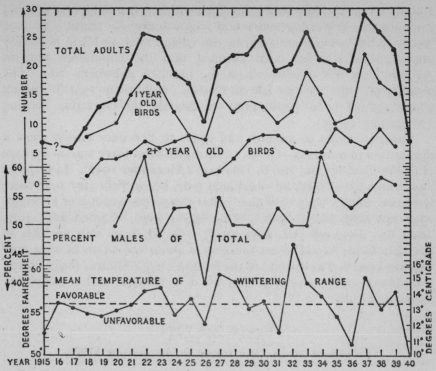

FIG. 37. Analysis of the population curve for house wrens in respect to age and sex and correlation with mean temperature of wintering range during December, January and February. The age of a few birds was not determined. It will be noted that immature birds appear to be more sensitive to environmental changes than birds of two years or older (*After Kendeigh 1944*)

eggs or young by B.T.O. recorders were robbed, destroyed or deserted. This proportion may not be quite representative as the observers may have found the most conspicuous nests, equally exposed to less innocent interference; they may even have unwittingly rendered some of the nests more liable to destruction. On the other hand, some of these nests were probably plundered after the last observation by the B.T.O. naturalists. Commonly the full complement of young emerges from nests which are not abandoned by the adults for one reason or another, although an unhatched egg or dead chick is sometimes found after the nest has been vacated. Kendeigh (1942) found that in 86 per cent of house wren nestings at least one chick was reared and that 79 per cent of the eggs developed into fledglings—considerably more successful nesting than was achieved by any of the other fifteen species studied. Three other observers, Kuerzi, McAtee and Walkinshaw, respectively found fledging success to be 55.2, 83.7 and 48.3 per cent (Allen and Nice 1952). Among passerines with open nests fledging success is normally between 40 and 48 per cent for species in north temperate regions, but among cavity-nesting birds the figure is higher—the average for fourteen species being 66.2 per cent (Allen and Nice 1952). Apparently the wren's nesting success is comparable with that of cavity-nesting rather than open-nesting passerines.

Age

Only one of my ringed wrens, Silver, was present for $2\frac{1}{2}$ years. Some males were known to have been driven out by usurpers and others may also have been expelled, or, perhaps, departed to seek territories elsewhere. However, as we have noted, male wrens do not lightly leave their domains. At Stein, the male No. 42 held the same territory for four breeding seasons, so he was at least five years old when the research came to an end. This is the greatest age to which a wren has been known to live. Kendeigh followed the fortunes of a male house wren until the bird's death at not less than six years and Laskey (1948) kept a female Carolina wren under observation for more than five years. A wild robin is known to have lived at least eleven years (Burkitt 1938) and a redstart six years (Buxton 1950). In captivity small passerines have survived as long as twenty-four years, but such an advanced age is quite exceptional. The average "expectation of life" for all passerine birds for which data are available is, of course, much below the maximum life-span. For the robin, at fledging, it is 10.8 months (Lack 1946a), and for the redstart only 9.3 months. Years must elapse before recoveries of ringed wrens are adequate for statistical analysis, but analogy suggests a mortality rate comparable to that of the house wren. As one wren of the very few whose ages are known reached five years of age it would seem that the survival rate is unlikely to be much below that of the house wren and may be slightly higher. Statistical theory shows that a species of which three out of 100 survive to five years has 50 per cent annual survival—that is, half of the birds of each age group survive each year, supposing the proportion surviving to be stable.

CHAPTER 15

ARISING AND ROOSTING

I wish you were a pleasant wren,
    And I your small accepted mate;
How we'd look down on toilsome men!
    We'd rise and go to bed at eight
    Or it may be not quite so late.
CHRISTINA ROSSETTI. *Child's Talk in April*

MY DATA with regard to the variations in the wren's working day would have been very inadequate had I not found a roost which was favoured by the ringed bird, Silver, for two winters, and also, though less constantly, in spring and summer. This bird's arising and roosting activities are shown in Fig. 38 and Tables XXXI and XXXII (pp. 283-84). In order to make the graphs more complete sound observations are included for those months when sight observations were unobtainable. In some instances they refer to Silver, but records of other birds are also given. It is improbable that the difference between the song and the arising time was ever more than a minute (p. 72). In most months sound observations were checked by sight records.

ARISING TIME

In considering the activities of organisms in relation to daylight the incidence of civil twilight is more significant than sunrise or sunset. Civil twilight is defined as beginning in the morning when the sun is 6° below the horizon. There is then just sufficient light for work to begin out of doors. Similarly at civil twilight in the evening outdoor occupations cease:

The ploughman homeward plods his weary way
And leaves the world to darkness and to me.

In the fields the working day used to be, according to the old phrase, " from star-setting to star-rising." The angle which the sun's path appears to make with the horizon alters according to the latitude and time of year so that the duration of twilight may vary greatly. At the spring and autumn equinoxes twilight is shortest owing to the angle

256

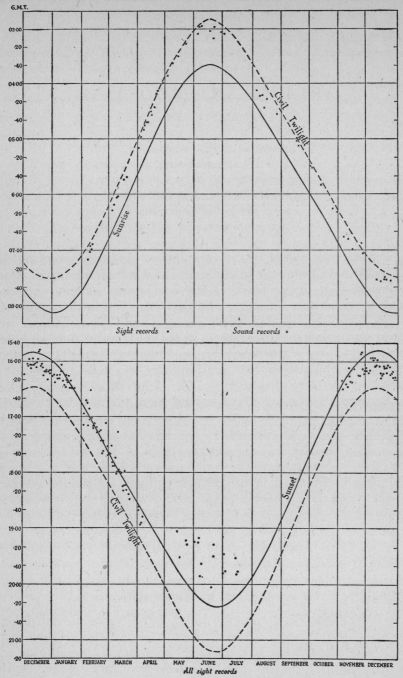

FIG. 38. Graphs showing the arising and roosting of wrens, mainly the male (Silver), from December 1943 to December 1944

at which the apparent path of the sun crosses the horizon being then
at a maximum. Towards the Arctic Circle the sun's path crosses the
horizon at an acute angle and twilight in summer is therefore prolonged.

The Table (p. 283) and graphs show that male wrens arise about
the same time in relation to twilight throughout the year. This is very
different from the situation in regard to roosting times. Moreover, it
differs from what is known of many other song birds.

Nice (1943) found that the awakening song of song sparrows on
clear mornings during January and February is heard about 25 minutes
before sunrise and 4 minutes after civil twilight. From 3 February to
4 March, when territories are being occupied, the song occurs close to
civil twilight, and in the succeeding period when the birds are established in their territories the awakening song averages 4 minutes before
civil twilight. The records for cloudy weather were from 3 to 6 minutes
later than the corresponding observations for clear weather. Many
other birds tend to sing earlier relative to sunrise as they come into
full song. During the first part of March American robins sing a few
minutes before the start of civil twilight and then suddenly alter to
singing long before civil twilight and as much as 73 minutes before
sunrise (Nice 1943). The dawn chorus of song thrushes in the North
of Ireland precedes sunrise by 40 minutes in February and gets earlier
until at the end of May it is 84 minutes before (Burkitt 1935). Great
tits emerge on the average 26 minutes before sunrise in winter but
start singing some 37 minutes before sunrise in April and May (Kluijver
1950), and caged robins become active earlier relative to sunrise in the
first week of January than in mid-December (Palmgren 1944).

As indicated by the order in which the various species begin to sing,
each has its own " threshold of arising brightness " to which it responds
(p. 71). This is correlated, no doubt, with powers of vision and
feeding habits. As these facts show, the " arising brightness " may vary
according to the time of year and the bird's physiological state.

Important as light is known to be in determining the arising time
of birds, it is not the only factor. Szymanski (1914) showed that if
birds are kept in cages with constant light-intensity day and night their
periods of rest and activity tend to remain unchanged for some time.
Whitman (1919) discovered that the young pigeon while still in the
egg was subject to a 24-hour cycle of rest and activity. Such observations show the importance of internal rhythms. Palmgren (1949)
remarks that sleep is " an autonomous periodical function, although
largely controlled by light conditions." Lutz (1931), who studied the
awakening songs of a house wren in the Panama Canal zone, came to

the conclusion that the bird behaved as a combination of chronometer and photometer. It was able to detect a light intensity of only .4 foot candle. In the same area a Panama house wren went to bed very close to the same time each evening (Chapman 1930). Many other observations in addition to the data given earlier (p. 197) might be cited indicating that birds and many other organisms, both vertebrate and invertebrate, are subject to an internal periodicity as well as an external control (Armstrong 1954). Probably the internal control tends to arouse the bird from sleep shortly before its " threshold of arising brightness " is reached so that it is ready to fly out. A very slight increase in brightness would not be sufficient to awaken a bird with eyes closed and head in its feathers within a dark roost.

It is improbable that the cock wren, hearing another sing, is stimulated to begin his day earlier than he would otherwise do; on several mornings when two males were roosting near to one another in an ivied roost the song of the first to emerge did not result in the other following him promptly. He flew out about ten minutes later. Much less is there reason to believe that any bird takes its arising cue from the song of any other species which precedes it though it is possible that earlier songs may help to awaken the later birds.

Arising and Retiring when Rearing Young

Female wrens, in common with most other female passerines usually leave the roost rather later than males. Incubating females are considerably later in emerging from the nest than males from the roost, as Table XXIX shows (p. 260).

It will be noted that in every instance the male rose before his mate, but there is no correlation between his first song and the female's emergence. The August 1945 observations, made in dull weather, show that the female rose later in relation to sunrise after the young hatched than before, but this was abnormal.

With a recording instrument, other data for the times of arising and retiring were obtained. In 1951 the incubating bird rose on the average 4.5 minutes after sunrise and retired 116.5 minutes before sunset. When there were young arising was, on the average, 15.9 minutes before sunrise and retiring 5.3 minutes before sunset. In 1952 the corresponding figures were 8.7 minutes before sunrise and 116.4 before sunset, then, during the nestling period, 21.9 minutes before sunrise and 4.6 minutes before sunset (Figs. 29 and 30). If one may generalise from a few instances, the male, when helping to feed the young, tends to cease earlier than his mate.

TABLE XXIX

RELATIONSHIP BETWEEN ARISING TIME OF MALE AND FEMALE WREN
DURING THE NESTING CYCLE

Date	Civil Twilight	Sunrise	Male's first song*	Male visits nest	Female's first appearance	Stage of nesting cycle
8/5/44	03.38	04.18	03.46		04.08 leaves nest	Beginning of incubation.
23/5/44	03.11	03.55	03.16	03.17	04.10 „	Hatched 25/5/44
17/6/44	02.49	03.39	03.03	03.43	03.27 arrived at nest†	Fledged 19/6/44
{ 21/6/44	02.50	03.39	03.10		03.23 leaves nest	One egg hatched in evening
{ 22/6/44	02.50	03.40	02.58		03.25 „	2 eggs hatched
29/6/44	02.54	03.43	03.03		03.11 leaves nest‡	Incubating
30/5/45	03.02	03.48	03.02		03.25 „	Brood fledged §
{ 1/8/45	03.39	04.20	03.53	05.28	04.19 leaves nest	Hatched 10/8/45
{ 11/8/45	03.58	04.36	04.27		05.08 „	
{ 26/5/47	03.07	03.53	03.22		03.43 leaves nest	Hatched 6/6/47
{ 4/6/47	02.57	03.44	03.08	05.50	03.18 „	

Bracketed observations concern the same pair of birds

*With the exception of the observations on 22 June 1944 the song was uttered by the bird's mate.
†The young being near to fledging the female did not sleep in the nest.
‡This bird, which left the nest exceptionally early, never returned.
§The female roosted with the family.

A pair of Shetland wrens discontinued their visits about twenty minutes before sunset.

The incubating house wren's activities begin about 2.3 minutes after sunrise and end, on the average, 6.4 minutes before sunset. When there are nestlings she rises 8 minutes earlier and retires 16 minutes later. The male's activity begins about 23 minutes before the female's during the incubation period and approximately 15 minutes earlier than the female during the nestling period (Kendeigh 1952).

The song of a male Carolina wren averaged 6 minutes before civil twilight on clear mornings but the female arrived about sunrise while building and feeding young (Nice and Thomas 1948). During the period of laying she left the nest 5 to 8 minutes after sunrise and returned to lay 23 to 26 minutes after sunrise, as compared with 10 to 12 minutes after sunrise in the earlier half of incubation, 22 to 23 minutes after during the later half, and 29 minutes after on a morning when she was brooding young. She evidently became increasingly drawn to the nest. Unfortunately, no later observations were made. They would probably have shown a cessation of this trend. The male's active day ended usually about sunset; so also did the female's until there were young to feed, when the return was always after sunset, once so late that she was unable to find the nest until a light was switched on in the porch where she was nesting. On the day incubation began the male's active day was 13 hours 41 minutes, the female's 12 hours 38 minutes, but four days before the young fledged the male's day had hardly altered; it was 13 hours 43 minutes, whereas the female's had been extended to 14 hours 6 minutes. During the final phase of the nesting cycle the male's day began and ended earlier than the female's. Among insectivorous passerines an extension of the female's day from the time when the nestlings are a few days old is usual. Thus during incubation a swallow went off her nest about 11 minutes after sunrise and retired 40 minutes before sunset, but when there were chicks she began before sunrise and ended after sunset (de Braey 1946).

In some situations very little light penetrates to the interior of the nest and the incubating female's arising time cannot be determined by the same light values as might arouse her were she roosting in a more open situation. Little or no light penetrated to the bird in the nest I altered (p. 27) yet the innate rhythm was apparently sufficient to arouse this wren to fulfil her duties normally.

RELATIONSHIP OF ARISING TO MOONLIGHT

It is difficult to determine precisely the influence of moonlight on the arising time of wrens because there are so many variables to assess, such as the phase of the moon, its height above the horizon, the effect of clouds or mist and the relationship between the positions of the sun and moon. None the less, data from two years' observations tend to show the effect of moonlight in augmenting the increasing daylight and arousing the wren earlier than would otherwise have occurred. These observations are based either on sight records of a bird leaving the roost or on the first utterance of call or song. Wrens go to roost at light intensities too bright for moonlight to have an appreciable effect.

TABLE XXX

EARLIEST RECORDED ARISING TIMES IN RELATION TO MOONLIGHT

Arising time	Minutes before civil twilight	Date	Days before or after full moon	Moonset	Moonrise
04.47	7	4/4/45	7 days after	08.56	
06.52	5	25/11/44*	5 days before	01.02	
07.18	5	20/12/45	1 day after	09.29	
03.59	3	27/4/44*	11 days before		08.01
06.25	3	6/11/44	6 days after	13.04	
05.36	3	18/3/45*	10 days before		08.36
06.15	2	27/2/45	Full moon	07.28	
04.24	2	16/4/45*	11 days before		07.41
07.11	1	6/12/44	6 days after	12.35	
06.18	1	26/2/45	1 day before	07.06	
04.45	0	8/4/44	Full moon	06.50	
03.38	0	8/5/44	Full moon	04.53	
03.02	0	30/5/45	3 days after	06.27	

On the dates marked with an asterisk the moon could have had no influence on the arising time of the wren. These anomalies are to be expected as various factors may operate to cause the emergence of a wren a few minutes early, such as individual idiosyncrasy, disturbance at the roost or the selection of a sleeping-place particularly exposed to light. Table XXX shows that of 119 observations 9 of the 13 earliest were on moonlit mornings, so probably moonlight accelerates the rising time.

The effect of moonlight on the activities of birds is most apparent with nocturnal or crepuscular species, such as the nightjar. Its ovulation is apparently controlled by the moon (Wynne-Edwards 1930). Ashmore (1935) noted that the first evening song was heard 51 minutes after sunset on moonlight evenings and 35 minutes after on moonless evenings. Its last morning song averages 78 minutes before sunset with moonlight and 40 without it. The principle of a later beginning of activity on moonlight evenings is of widespread application among nocturnal organisms, but these wren observations show that moonlight may affect the activities of diurnal species also.

Roosting Times throughout the Year

My records relating to the roosting times of wrens throughout the year are set out in Table XXXII (p. 284) and Fig. 38 (p. 257) (cf. Figs. 29 and 30). The sight records refer to Silver, except the roosting records from January 1944 to April of that year, when one other bird, and sometimes two, used the roost. One of these was a female. As this bird usually came earlier to the roost than either of the males and the data record the arrival of the first bird at the roost, the roosting times for the period of her presence may be regarded as averaging some minutes earlier than they would have done if Silver had been roosting alone. The earlier average roosting times between January and April in 1944 as compared with 1945 may thus be accounted for. After the first week of April 1944 until July Silver came to the roost only when the evening was unsettled, so that data are available only for overcast evenings, but in July a few observations were obtained on clear as well as overcast evenings. Silver did not roost between 17 July and 4 November 1944, but then continued throughout the winter and spring into May, when his roosting times became irregular and at last he went elsewhere again. No other bird shared the roost during the winter of 1944-45, though Silver was twice seen chasing a stranger. During January 1945 he spent some nights during inclement weather in a communal roost (p. 275). The roosting and rising records (based on sight observations) from November 1944 to May 1945 are thus uncomplicated by the presence of another bird. During the periods when the roost was unoccupied the data relate to various other wrens, those for the arising time to the first utterance of the birds, and those for roosting to the occasions when a bird was found in a roost or, in a few instances, to the last song or call when there was evidence that the bird was proceeding to roost.

The outstanding characteristic of the male wren's roosting behaviour, as shown in the graphs, is the comparatively abrupt transition from a roosting routine, which, although tending to become earlier in relation to sunset and civil twilight, did not diverge considerably from the curves for these until May, when the bird came to roost at much higher light values than in the winter or early spring. It is usual for passerine birds to settle in for the night earlier in relation to sunset than they arise in relation to sunrise. For example, male and female black phœbes leave the roost at dimmer and less varied light values than those in which they seek it in the evening (Oberlander 1939). This is true of wrens. The wood pewee's awakening song averages about 26 minutes before civil twilight while the last phrase in the evening is heard, on the average, 8½ minutes before civil twilight. Craig's theory which seeks to explain these facts by means of a concept of " anticipation " is inadequate. Haecker (1924) and others have suggested that fatigue renders the bird less sensitive to light and so in the evening it begins singing in brighter light than elicits its song in the morning.

The graphs show that the wren's roosting times vary less in mid-winter than in midsummer. This fact, in conjunction with roosting at higher light values in summer, suggests that in winter the bird stays until the dimness of the light makes foraging unprofitable. This is supported by observations of other species. Great tits go to roost an hour before sunset in August, but in December a few minutes after sunset, though during winter in the Arctic they may stay out even later. The relevance of hunger to the time of roosting has been demonstrated by Eygenraam (Kluijver 1950) for this species. He found that when a bird was fed on peanuts it retired earlier than if left to forage for itself. During the winter in Lapland most passerine species feed even in deep twilight as long as food is visible (Franz 1943) and Pynnönen (1939) found that the black woodpecker retires pro-gressively earlier in relation to sunset in spring and summer, but in autumn and winter at sunset or even later. In summer a male wren has no difficulty in obtaining adequate food for himself in spite of time occupied in singing, nest-building and courting. He retires to bed because there is no pressure to stay up. Similarly female wrens which roost on the eggs long before nightfall would not do so if they had any difficulty in finding sufficient food during their sorties (p. 183).

In summer a wren's attachment to the roost is tenuous. A bird, after entering, will fly out again with little or no provocation and go elsewhere. When preparing to roost he may be deterred by a person passing some distance away. In winter he is not so easily diverted elsewhere. Apparently a male Carolina wren may also readily desert a roosting place (Nice and Thomas 1948). It is unlikely that fatigue plays a significant part in causing wrens to seek the roost as males which actively feed nestlings will sometimes continue their efforts until fading light forces them to cease. A cock with no family cares may go to bed an hour earlier than another actively concerned with feeding young, though wrens engaged in nest-building roost at the usual times. As we have noted, females with a family of well-grown nestlings work indefatigably as long as sufficient light lasts. Their labours are probably more arduous than those of a male on days when he is nest-building. The extent to which the working day may be extended is shown by the prolonged labours of birds feeding young in the arctic and sub-arctic (Armstrong 1954).

Although Oberlander did not find that the state of the weather was sufficient to explain the roosting times of black phœbes his observations suggest a correlation with the availability of food. This is to be expected with birds which catch flying insects. It has been noticed that during periods of adverse weather young swifts do not increase normally in weight (Lack and Lack 1951b). Of course the activities of birds which catch prey on the wing are much more determined by weather than the foraging of birds such as the wren which can collect food successfully whatever the weather.

That the female wren, even when she has a family to feed, will begin her labours some twenty minutes after the male has started to sing suggests that the vocal defence of territory has a bearing on the earliness of the male's departure from the roost. It is, perhaps, rather precarious to correlate the male's tendency to leave the roost at a light intensity which varies little throughout the year with his practically continuous maintenance of territory, but it is of interest that the male song sparrow's arising time changes from that of the female to earlier when he takes up territory (Nice 1943). The buzzard, a bird without a territorial song as usually understood, arises later in relation to daylight than it goes to roost (Schuster 1949).

Influence of Clouds, Rain and Snow on Roosting Times

Palmgren (1949) justly remarks that in their rising and roosting birds are astonishingly sensitive to changing cloudiness. Thus, according to Nice (1943), the last songs of song sparrows average 10 minutes earlier in cloudy weather than in clear. It is a general rule, true of wrens and Bewick's wrens (Williams 1941), that birds roost earlier in relation to the light on cloudy days than on clear. Lutz (1931) found that the variation in the utterance of a Panama house wren's first song on 24 mornings, according as the weather was clear or cloudy, was within 15 minutes. The converse applies among nocturnal birds. Screech owls, for example, depart earlier and return later when it is cloudy than when it is clear (Allard 1937).

On evenings when there was a downpour Silver came particularly early. As he did so also on very overcast evenings before rain began to fall it was evident that reduced light intensity and not the discomfort of damp plumage brought him early to bed. On 11 March 1944 when he was accompanied at the roost by two companions, the first arrived 41 minutes before sunset and the last 13 minutes later. Apart from this occasion the earliest arrival that month was 16 minutes before sunset. Silver arrived 54 minutes before sunset on 11 May 1945. On both occasions there were dark clouds but no rain, apart from a few heavy drops on 11 March.

The effect of snow on the roosting behaviour of wrens is considered later (p. 276). Here it need only be mentioned that the increased brightness due to snow lying on the ground tended to retard the wren's arrival at the roost.

RELATIONSHIP OF WIND AND TEMPERATURE TO ROOSTING

As wrens frequent the undergrowth their activities are less affected by strong winds than those of many other species, so it is not surprising that I found no indication that wrens roosted earlier or later on a windy day.

The influence of temperature changes on roosting procedure is discussed later in connection with communal roosting as no correlation between temperature and roosting times was apparent except when inclement weather had aroused the impulse to roost communally.

SEX DIFFERENCES IN ROOSTING BEHAVIOUR

As we have already noted, it is usual among passerines for the female to go to bed earlier and leave the roost later than the male. This is true, in general, of wrens, but on several mornings a male and female who were apparently roosting in the same niche left the roost within some seconds of one another and about ten minutes after the male owning the territory in which they were roosting had emerged. Female Bewick's wrens depart 10 to 12 minutes after the male (Williams 1941). When pairs of starlings roost together the female goes in first and flies out 1 to 2 minutes later than the male (Morley 1939). The females of nocturnal birds also have shorter working hours than the males (Allard 1937). Among the few known exceptions to the rule that females rise later and retire earlier than males are various woodpeckers (Skutch 1948a, b). Perhaps the practice among these birds of the male incubating at night, in contrast to the procedure among passerines, may have some bearing on this behaviour. We have already noted that the rule of a shorter active day for the female does not always apply when the female is feeding nestlings, especially if she is without the help of the male.

Experimental evidence has shown that light is often one of the most important environmental factors influencing the date of migration (Armstrong 1947), so there may be, in some passerines, a correlation between the longer hours spent in the roost by the females and the earlier migration in spring of the males. Their longer daily exposure to light might accelerate the maturation of the physiological mechanisms responsible for the drive to migrate.

Individual Variation in Arising and Roosting

Individual birds vary in regard to the times at which they leave the roost and retire. This is attributable to their response being to slightly different light values. There may be six or more minutes between the utterances of their first songs by individual song sparrows (Nice 1943). Craig (1943) noted that of two neighbouring wood pewees one almost invariably began and ended his song earlier than the other. Certain identifiable buzzards frequenting a communal roost came almost to the minute at the same time relative to sunset again and again on comparable evenings (Schuster 1949). Such variation between individuals is recorded of house wrens, which, according to Allard (1930), are good " timekeepers." It is characteristic of wrens also. When two males were occupying a roost there were usually some minutes between the arrival of the birds and sometimes ten minutes' difference in their times of departure.

Memory of the Roosting Place

It is highly probable that a wren remembers a congenial roosting-place for some months even though the site be not visited. We have already noted that Silver, having deserted a roost in mid-July, did not use it again until 5 November. That the bird never visited the place is impossible to prove, but as the site was just outside my study window, and in full view of the much-frequented garden, its arrival at the roost would readily have been heard or seen. Even if he had come early in the morning I could hardly have failed to hear his song or calls as my bedroom was almost overhead.

When my friends Mr. and Mrs. R. E. Moreau were living at Madingley, near Cambridge, a wren came to the window of the room in which Mrs. Moreau was sitting on an exceptionally cold night at the end of January 1947, and tapped on the pane. It then went round to the window at the other side of the house and tapped again with its beak. The previous occupant informed Mrs. Moreau that wrens used to come into the house to roost. The most plausible explanation of this episode would seem to be that the bird remembered a roosting-place of the previous winter. In support of this it may be mentioned that a wren visited a greenhouse, generally twice daily, during the last three months of 1944, 1945 and 1946, to feed on aphides on a rose, ceasing its visits when the rose was pruned in January. Each year a wren reared young in a nesting-box a few yards from the greenhouse and once brought the family into it (Lafferty 1948).

There is no doubt that, at least in some respects, birds have retentive memories (Armstrong 1947; Thorpe 1951). Domestic fowl recognise an old home after several years (Schjelderup-Ebbe 1923) and many birds will return to an old nest site. Although squirrels apparently do not remember exactly where they have made caches of food (Hediger 1950) nutcrackers recollect where they have stored pine cones (Swanberg 1951)—a matter of vital importance to them during the winter. The ability to remember roosting places must similarly have survival value for wrens.

ROOSTING SITES

In winter I have found wrens roosting in nests where the brood had come to grief, but only once have I found several where young had been reared—and this nest had been refurbished after the young had left. No doubt soiled nests are occasionally used for roosting, but as they tend to disintegrate after the wear and tear of brood-rearing they are seldom in a suitable state to serve as dormitories by the winter. Dippers sometimes use the old nest as a sleeping-place (Rankin and Rankin 1940). Not infrequently the nests of house sparrows and house martins are chosen by wrens, also old swallows' nests, and occasionally even a blackbird's nest or other cup-shaped nest among vegetation. Wrens have been found roosting in a long-tailed tit's nest and long-tailed tits in a wren's (Turner 1929). Mr. N. Allen tells me of finding a goldcrest sleeping in a wren's nest and I have disturbed a blue tit sleeping in a dilapidated specimen. Many tropical birds appropriate the nests of other species for roosting and, in Britain, starlings and nuthatches sometimes sleep in disused woodpeckers' holes. Cavities in thatch, haystacks and trees or among aged ivy stems, crevices in old walls and nooks near the roof in cattle byres and sheds are used by wrens. To my knowledge one bird lodged nightly in an old coconut shell and another on a nail in a dark passage. Nesting-boxes containing a nest which has not been used for breeding are also chosen. Wrens have been found sleeping in nests of the greater spotted woodpecker and long-tailed tit under construction. Occasionally they cling vertically in a treecreeper's hollow in the fibrous bole of a Wellingtonia (Dunsheath and Doncaster 1941). Usually roosts are more than 5 and less than 15 feet from the ground, but I found a party resorting to an ivied tree-trunk 20 feet up, and house martin's nests used by wrens are sometimes even higher.

Naturally, in summer, wrens do not require such cosy roosting-places as in winter. An ample selection of safe and sheltered nooks is available for summer roosting in most wren habitats, so the birds are much less inclined to return night after night to the same recess. Sometimes females roost where they will afterwards lay, as Cabanis's wren (*Thryothorus m. modestus*) and various hole-nesting passerines do (Skutch 1940a). Male wrens occasionally sleep in nests of their own building in summer, but I have never known one repair for the night to his first nest of the season, although it might be expected to have attractions for him, especially when a cold spell occurs after its completion. European, winter and Korean wrens (*Troglodytes t. peninsulae*) and, no doubt, birds of other races take refuge from bad weather rather than from marauders by roosting in their nests. It is probably to their advantage during the summer to shelter in more open niches where they cannot readily be trapped by predators. However, I have known a Shetland wren roost for a few nights in August inside a nest which he built in June, and during the breeding season adult St. Kilda wrens sleep in nests in their territories (I. J. Ferguson-Lees, *in litt.*).

I barricaded the entrance to a nest which was being used by a male for sleeping in on summer nights and was surprised when I visited it some evenings later to flush him from it. On examining the nest I found a hole on the opposite side to that in which the entrance was situated. Presumably the bird on finding his entrance barred made a way in at the back. A Cabanis's wren, disturbed in his roosting nest, escaped by pushing through the flimsy wall, and Skutch (1940a) found an exceptional Chiapas cactus wren's breeding nest with an entrance back and front.

In summer I have come on male wrens roosting among ivy stems on a wall and noted birds of unknown sex sleeping in a cavity in a gnarled hawthorn stump, and in the hollow end of a log leaning over a pond. Independent juveniles are partial to unoccupied nests of their own species. Weeks after seeing families being led to nests which have not been used for breeding I have found a single bird roosting within —apparently one of the family who had become too attached to the dormitory to go elsewhere. It is quite exceptional to find juveniles roosting together after they have been fledged three or four weeks. Most of them disperse and go elsewhere; when two remain where they were reared they become intolerant of each other.

Just before breeding activity is about to begin birds which have roosted together, either from time to time or more regularly, may separate, the female seeking a sleeping-place of her own (p. 102). Adult neotropical house wrens also sleep singly in nests of all kinds, varying from a woodpecker's hole to the centre of a bunch of bananas

(Skutch 1940a).   Pairs of Bewick's wrens go to separate roosts even when the pair-bond is so thoroughly established that male and female copulate before doing so.   In the morning the male will seek out the female at her roost and call her off to tread her again (Williams 1941). Similarly I have known a male wren come at dawn to where the female he was courting had her sleeping quarters.   Carolina wrens also roost singly in all sorts of nooks, including the pocket of a shirt hanging on a clothes line and the fold of an old portière in a garage (Bent 1948).   Perhaps the tendency for male and female European wrens to seek individual roosts once milder temperatures prevail is of value to the species in reducing the risk of disaster to both birds just before breeding.   On a mud wasp's nest (*Sceliphron* sp.), out of reach of any small mammal, two rock wrens have been found asleep, clinging vertically side by side.   It was possible to pick them up by hand (Bond 1940).

THE NEST AS SLEEPING PLACE

Albertus Magnus refers to wrens assembling to roost together on winter nights in cavities in order to keep warm, but doubtless country folk had long been aware of this practice.   Indeed, the statement by Theophrastus (*De signis*) that when the wren hides in holes it is a portent of bad weather may be an *ex post facto* allusion to it.

Although the birds often choose sleeping-places other than their own nests they seem to prefer one of these if a sufficiently intact specimen is available.

> The very nest
> In which the child of Spring was reared
> Is warmed thro' winter by her feathery breast.

However, Wordsworth's fancy has to be qualified to the extent that, owing to the tendency for nests which have been used for breeding to disintegrate, unused nests are much more frequently resorted to as dormitories.   If for no other reason such a nest is preferable to many other cavities because of its small size.   In a larger enclosed space wrens cannot conserve their heat efficiently.   Moreover, when the nest is in a recess the fabric helps to keep the birds warm.   In discussing the roosting places chosen by birds Moore (1945) remarks: " If the wall of a tree cavity is hard unrotted wood, one small bird could do little towards raising the wall temperature.   But if the wall has an insulating layer of dry rot or other lining the wall itself would conduct heat outward less fast;   and if the bird fits the cavity wall (or if several birds crowd in to add their heating effects), the temperature of the wall may very well rise appreciably through the night and serve to reduce

the loss on critical nights to a rate permitting the birds to survive."
The variations in the temperature of the house wren's nest and eggs
during periods when the bird is on and off the nest have been ascertained
by Baldwin and Kendeigh (1932) (Fig. 27, p. 181). The temperature
at the bottom of the nest rises by several degrees when the bird has
been sitting some time. Obviously when two or more wrens roost
together in a nest within a cavity they can keep warmer than anywhere
else—except, perhaps, in a cow-byre, stable or henhouse.

Of our two other smallest birds the long-tailed tit roosts in communal winter dormitories, sometimes in a nest of its own species, or
other hollow niche, occasionally in a wren's nest (Turner 1911). Little
is known of the roosting habits of the goldcrest in winter, but a reference
by Lilford (1895) to the discovery of a cluster of these birds on a snow-
laden bough of yew suggests that they, too, may have a tendency to
huddle close to one another during severe weather. In spring pairs
may be found roosting together. As many as three house sparrows or
five tree sparrows will roost in company (Creutz 1949). I have noticed
that the nest-building and nest lining activities of house sparrows in
November are not, like the autumnal and winter nesting behaviour of
some other birds (Morley 1943), non-functional expressions of endocrine activity, but render the roosting nest cosier. The house sparrow
is related to the weavers. Some of these, such as the Cape weaver, use
the nest as a bedroom throughout the year (Skead 1947), but the male
masked weaver, having constructed the breeding nests, makes a small
crude sleeping nest for his own use (Enslin 1945).

In Britain the green, greater and lesser spotted woodpeckers
(Tutt 1951; Tracy 1943, 1950) and in America the downy and hairy
woodpeckers (Forbush 1927; Allen 1925; Skinner 1928) carve out
special roosts in autumn. Golden-naped woodpeckers excavate cavities
for sleeping in month by month (Skutch 1948a). Treecreepers, as
first pointed out by Foster (1923), scratch out roosting hollows in the
fibrous boles of Wellingtonias.

It is rather surprising that the fashioning of a nest specifically for
roosting is characteristic of the birds of warm regions rather than of
those of the arctic, sub-arctic or temperate regions. The red mountain
rails of New Guinea make small leaf shelters and roost in pairs within
them (Ripley 1947). The Mexican honeycreeper of Central America
and the verdin of the California deserts also make special sleeping nests
(Skutch 1940a; Jaeger 1933). Many tropical and sub-tropical species,
such as the white-throated munia (Whistler 1928) and Bahama honey-
creeper (Pough 1946), roost in old nests of their own species, and some
birds sleep in other birds' nests.

The high development of nest-roosting among the birds of tropical forests supports our earlier suggestion (p. 216) that predators are a greater menace to nesting birds in those regions than in northern latitudes. The roosting nest is, in origin, a hiding-place and refuge from nocturnal marauders rather than a snuggery enabling body temperature to be maintained. The roofed nest is a typical tropical type. No naturalist in equatorial forests can fail to be impressed by the numbers and variety of covered nests, many of them pendant. The wren, and probably also the house sparrow, brought their technique of constructing domed nests from the tropics. If the dipper is related to the wrens its nest may also be considered of southern origin.

ROOSTING NESTS OF TROPICAL WRENS

The nest-building and roosting habits of the wren can only be understood against the background of the bird's origin and the behaviour of its New World relatives. Of fourteen species of Central American wren which Skutch (1940a) traced to their sleeping-places only three do not roost in nests constructed by themselves; they are all species of *Troglodytes* (p. 232). He informs me that although most neotropical house wrens " put the young to bed " in covered nooks one local population favours cup-shaped nests or mossy crotches in calabash trees. However, at least one species of *Troglodytes* apparently not only roosts in a nest but constructs one which serves this function. Dr. H. O. Wagner writes that in Mexico he sometimes finds a crudely-built nest about a yard away from an occupied nest of *T. brunneicollis*. He thinks this may be a roosting-nest. The adults of some species, such as the neotropical house wren and Cabanis's wren, sleep singly, although the latter's pair-bond is maintained throughout the year and the birds go about together; others, such as the highland wood wren, roost in pairs, and yet others pass the night in family parties. Neotropical house wrens and banded cactus wrens lead the fledglings back to the nest in which they were reared, but Cabanis's wrens retire for the night, abandoning the youngsters to their own devices. The female may resort to the breeding nest to sleep.

Cabanis's wren and the lowland wood wren design their dormitory nests differently from their breeding nests. The sleeping nest of these species and also of the verdin (Jaeger 1933) is flimsier than the breeding nest. Palmer's thrashers use old or half-built nests for roosting (Bent 1948). Cabanis's wren makes a breeding nest which is nearly spherical, with the entrance facing obliquely downwards, but the dormitory nest is an unlined, crudely cylindrical pocket composed of grasses, tendrils and so forth, placed horizontally (Fig. 39). Apparently it is usually

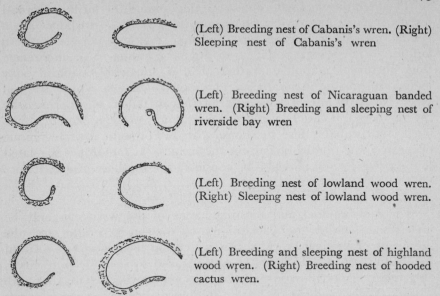

(Left) Breeding nest of Cabanis's wren. (Right) Sleeping nest of Cabanis's wren

(Left) Breeding nest of Nicaraguan banded wren. (Right) Breeding and sleeping nest of riverside bay wren

(Left) Breeding nest of lowland wood wren. (Right) Sleeping nest of lowland wood wren.

(Left) Breeding and sleeping nest of highland wood wren. (Right) Breeding nest of hooded cactus wren.

FIG. 39. Diagrams illustrating cross sections of nests of Central American wrens (*After Skutch 1940a*)

built not far from the breeding nest. This wren has been known to use the nest of the Mexican honeycreeper as a refuge for the night.

The lowland wood wren also makes a globular breeding nest with the entrance facing sideways and overshadowed by an extension of the roof. It may be situated only a few inches from the ground and is well concealed, but the dormitory nests are placed higher, in much more exposed and conspicuous situations in the forest undergrowth (Fig. 39). Apparently birds of these species usually sleep at the aperture of the nest, and are thus better able to perceive and escape from an advancing predator. Dr. Wagner informs me that *Thryothorus pleurostictus* makes many untidy nests, but the breeding nest is carefully constructed. He also remarks that, out of the breeding season, he saw five birds of a species of cactus wren building a nest—presumably as a dormitory. The Chiapas cactus wren makes a large breeding nest, some 14 in. by 11 in., often placed in the bull's horn acacia. The dormitory nest is somewhat smaller. Here the male spends his nights while his mate is brooding (Skutch 1940a).

Thanks to Skutch's investigations we know the functions of the two types of nest fashioned by these Central American species, but the significance of the differing structures built by male and female prairie

marsh wrens is uncertain. The male leaves a number of his nests unfinished, and it is exceptional for one of them to be used by the female
as a foundation for the breeding nest, though before she is ready to
build she may add a straw or two to one of her mate's nests. Her nest
is less capacious than that of the male and the chamber containing the
eggs is reached along a narrow passage inside the nest (Fig. 40).
Welter mentions the possibility that the males sleep in their nests, but
his observations suggest rather that they spend the night on reed-stems.
Oberholser (1938) says that the nests of the Louisiana marsh wren are
used for roosting. Bowles (1898) noticed that a nest of the closely
related tule wren, which he passed early in the day, later contained
three " nearly fledged young." He put forward the improbable
suggestion that if the family was numerous the youngsters eased the

situation by retiring to the auxiliary
nests at night. The most plausible
view is that the nests are used as
dormitories.

As short-billed sedge wrens move
about in parties until they migrate
it is highly probable that they roost
together, and, if so, that they use
auxiliary nests. If it be true, as it
appears to be, that after a short-billed
sedge wren deserts it may utilise one
of the auxiliary nests for breeding, we

FIG. 40. Diagrams illustrating cross
sections of the nests of the long-billed
marsh wren (*After photographs by Dr.
R. S. Palmer*)   (Left) Nest built by
female; (Right) Nest built by male

may assume with some confidence that these serve a somewhat similar
function to the supernumerary nests of the wren. Probably this species
is polygamous and the nests are available to accommodate additional
mates.

Before winter begins young northern cactus wrens build themselves
roosting places. Adults keep their nests in repair and reconstruct them
when necessary (Woods 1948). The entrances of old nests are
refurbished and feathers packed in so that the nest is warm in cold
weather (Bailey 1922). One observer found that a bird (or a pair)
rebuilt five or six nests situated within a range of fifty feet between
October and the beginning of December (Anthony 1891). Sometimes
six or seven nests are constructed in a single bush. These nests are
used for roosting, but when the breeding season arrives new nests are
always built. Some of the roosting nests are crude and without the
entrance tunnel characteristic of breeding nests.

In the light of these facts much of the nest-building and roosting
behaviour of the European wren is more easily interpreted. The

tendency to construct nests over a long period apparently is derived from the wren's neotropical ancestry and it is not surprising that occasionally the female wren should build almost the entire nest as nest-building by the female is strongly developed in some of the New World wrens. The leading of the young to roost and communal roosting are also characteristic of many American wrens. Adaptations evolved in the tropics have been modified to become advantageous in the very different environments of Europe, Asia and North America, serving different functions from those for which they were evolved. Multiple nest-building has become indispensably integrated with the European wren's polygamous habits, and the roofed nest, which evolved in the tropics as a protection from predators, now provides the wren in north temperate regions with a warm refuge from frost and snow.

Factors Determining Social Roosting

A number of passerine and other species show a tendency to roost together during severe weather. Even domestic fowl crowd together in a snow-drift if left outside on an inclement night. Swallows (Lorenz 1932) and sand martins (Keyserlingk 1937) cluster when overtaken by a snowstorm on migration. Although pairs of bluebirds do not normally tolerate other pairs as roosting companions they will do so after a heavy snowfall (Thomas 1946).

Until the onset of cold weather and wintry conditions wrens roost in isolation. Exceptions occasionally occur, as with most aspects of wren behaviour. Six wrens were found roosting together in a nesting-box whenever it was inspected on several occasions between mid-October and mid-February (S. Smith, in litt.). Such early and apparently regular social roosting is unusual. Williams (1947) noted four or five western winter wrens regularly roosting huddled close together like wren-tits on a branch at Carmel in California, for some weeks in December and January, except for two occasions when only one or two were present. In this region the weather is seldom or never as inclement as that which causes wrens to roost communally in Europe. It is remarkable that communal roosting has not been recorded of the Iceland wren nor of any of the races in the small island groups of the North Atlantic.

Changeable weather during January 1945 enabled me to make some observations on the crucial factors which determine whether wrens spend the night alone or in company. On Christmas Day, 1944, it turned frosty and on 26 and 28 December I found wrens roosting socially in Wren Wood. It became milder, until on the night of

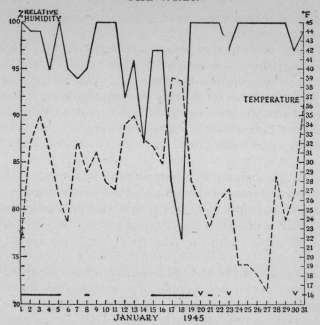

FIG. 41. Graph showing relationship between social roosting by wrens,
temperature and humidity. The horizontal lines at the base of the figure
indicate dates when the bird roosted alone; the gaps indicate that the bird
was absent, roosting socially. Occasions when the wren visited the roost but
departed to roost socially elsewhere are indicated by a V.

4 January there was a light snowfall which lingered next day. On
6 January it was sleeting at dusk and the wren, Silver, who had been
regular at his solitary roost, did not come to it. He was away, presumably at a communal dormitory, until 15 January, apart from the 8th,
after which night the snow lay 3 inches deep. He continued at his
isolated roost until the 20th when another fall of snow occurred. That
evening he came to inspect his roosting place and flew away again.
It was clear but cold on the 21st, and he spent the night alone at the
roost. After being absent on the 22nd he arrived on the evening of
the 23rd with two companions at the sleeping place, but after hopping
around they all went away. Not until 30 January did Silver appear
again—to find the ivy leaves dripping with moisture as the result of
a fall of snow in the night and a rapid thaw. He departed but returned
next evening to the roost and continued to frequent it regularly.

Analysing the meteorological data we find, in regard to humidity:
(a) Either the evening before or the morning of the day on which

the wren ceased consecutive solitary roosting relative humidity was 100 per cent.

(b) At some time the day before each vacillation (i.e. visit without roosting) there was nearly or quite 100 per cent humidity.

In regard to temperature the wren was alone at the roost on two occasions when the mean for the day was below freezing, on 1 January, perhaps influenced by the inertia of habit, and on 21 January—an anomalous visit difficult to explain, reminding us that other factors besides humidity and temperature play a part in determining communal roosting.

The graph of maximum humidity and minimum temperature shows that on the two occasions of vacillation after absence the data coincided —a decrease of humidity to 97 per cent and a minimum temperature of 27.2° F. after a period of lower temperature. As the difference in humidity is so slight it appears that the increase in temperature was more significant.

These data indicate that high humidity and low temperature in association are crucial in eliciting and maintaining social roosting. They suggest, however, that other environmental factors, such as the condition of the roosting place, have to be taken into consideration. The social and psychological factors are also important—the intensity of the bird's social impulses and whether he or she chances upon other individuals at roosting time or has already been roosting socially. When there are alterations from one procedure to the other the relative snugness of the solitary and social roosting places may also be relevant.

PROCEDURE OF ASSEMBLING AT THE ROOST

When wrens begin to associate for roosting, usually in December, two birds are sometimes found together. Dunsheath and Doncaster (1941) report frequently discovering wrens roosting in pairs from February onwards. Probably such partnerships depend more on weather than impulses aroused by the approach of the breeding season. The female of a roosting couple ringed by me mated later with another male (p. 90). A quotation from my field notes describes the behaviour of these birds as they sought the roost—a nest in a small yew:

21 January 1945
Two wrens answering one another, giving " chleep " calls for a minute of two, then a jumbled, soft, incomplete song was heard. I found one wren chevying the other in sexual chase through the bushes. Sub-song was uttered once or twice, louder than the typical soft court-ship song and rather like the jingly rallying song Then the male—

the female having disappeared, probably into the roost—perched on a twig two yards away and sang ever so soft a little warble for, perhaps, as long as ten seconds—a mere ghost of a song, only just audible. He then pecked the twig at his feet for about half a minute and flew off. . . .

One cold evening before I ringed these birds I put them out of their roosting nest and, after feeling in it to make sure there was not another wren inside, turned to go. I was surprised to see the two wrens perched almost overhead, only a few feet away. I waited for a minute or two close by and watched them return to the nest.

Dewar (1902) took thirty wrens out of a cavity in thatch. Many of them went back when he released them. Such behaviour only occurs in severe weather, and although it might be fraught with danger for the wrens if the disturber of their peace were a quadruped, some of the wrens would almost certainly perish if they were to attempt to find another roost in the darkness of a bitter night—even though a wren is able to find its way to a known roost after dusk. Six long-tailed tits flushed from a wren's nest one winter afternoon soon returned to it (Turner 1929). Sometimes when I have disturbed wrens from a roost at night they have gone away uttering short, sharp calls, as if trying to remain in touch with one another, but my impression was that they were not successful in doing so.

When the first cold snap comes wrens may be seen towards dusk going from place to place looking for a snug roost and seeking to establish contact with potential bedfellows. A bird which I watched on a December evening spent some time hopping here and there over a pollarded poplar, peering into crannies and singing occasionally. Apparently he was dissatisfied, for he now flew into an open garage and explored it. Not content with such accommodation as it offered he flew off some 25 yards and sang several times. After that I lost trace of him in the gathering darkness. Where several birds resort to a known roost they may arrive one after the other with little fuss or there may be a certain amount of activity such that it is difficult to decide which elements are sexual, aggressive or playful. On 18 December I visited a small wood on the County Down coast near which I had heard wrens singing and calling the previous evening. It was freezing. There were a few *kreeee* calls, then a rather faint song and suddenly a wren appeared chasing another. Both popped into a hole in a massive willow, then out they came in pursuit-flight once more. Another now appeared, hopping about near the cavity. Quite soon the two came back and went in quickly, one after the other. Almost immediately the third followed. Next evening there was a thaw and no birds entered the roost although I heard songs and a

variety of calls, including *kreeee* notes and an utterance resembling the
solicitation call of the female. In the very dim light on such occasions
it is exasperatingly difficult to ascertain what is happening in the
undergrowth. I have sometimes had the impression that sexual
impulses are aroused and that females warn off males who are too
importunate. Certainly some of the utterances are warning or defiance
calls.

Although birds may sometimes be seen hunting alone for a
suitable roost, as I have described, wrens seem to notice and
remember congenial-looking nooks as they wander about. In the
autumn one sees birds moving over ivy-covered walls and other such
potential roosting places as I have seldom noticed them do in spring.
They may be merely looking for prey, but such explorations would
lead to the discovery of roosting nooks.

The following observations give a picture of how a wren acquaints
itself with potential roosts and then guides others to them. On
29 November 1946 an unringed wren, which possibly might have been
one of those which followed Silver to the ivied roost on my house the
preceding January, inspected the place but did not stay. Next evening
this bird (as I presume) uttered a series of ticking calls while exploring
the north aspect of the house and then, after flying over the high roof
to Silver's sleeping place on the south wall, went away. No wrens
were seen near the roost until 09.30 on 1 December, when one perched
just outside it. However, late in the afternoon of 6 January, after two
days of bitter wind and hard frost five wrens appeared, all in constant
movement, peeping into the crannies and cavities of an old robinia
near the north wall and uttering sharp, pebbly calls, as such bands of
questing wrens always do—travel-talk rather similar to the sharp notes
characteristic of long-tailed tits. Light snow was falling, slowly deep-
ening the coverlet already on the ground. The busy little posse
fluttered over to the ivy on the north wall and investigated its possibilities. Then the leader flew to the gutter and the others soon
followed, straggling over the roof and down to the roost previously
occupied by Silver. They inspected it, darting about all the time in a
busy throng, more like insects than birds. Suddenly, after half a
minute, all the wrens streamed across the lawn to a chestnut tree, the
leader uttering sharp calls; but almost immediately they were off
again down the garden over the snowy lawn, grey in the gathering
gloom. It was as if a bunch of brown leaves had been torn off and
whisked away by a sudden gust. After spending some eight minutes
investigating gardens to the south, thirty yards away, they came
hurrying back to the chestnut tree, flying off almost at once in a

westerly direction. I lost them in the darkness. Four nights later I discovered three wrens roosting in a nest which a blackbird had built, but never used, on the north wall where the party had explored the ivy. Possibly it was here that the birds ended their peregrinations the previous night, though when I last saw them they were flying away from it. The three birds used this roost for several nights. It was inspected at dusk by one bird on 24 and 27 January, and by three on the 28th, but none of them stayed. On 6 February a fleeting visit was paid by a wren and thereafter it was no longer used as a dormitory.

It seems evident that wrens follow a leader to sites known to him. Probably among wrens, as among jackdaws, birds tend to follow a companion who is recognised as leader by his purposeful flight (Lorenz 1938). No doubt if search for a roost is protracted, different members of a party take turns at leading. Several observations indicate that males, as one would expect, normally take the lead, but females may sometimes do so. I have described how Silver returned to inspect his roost with two companions after being away for some time, presumably sleeping with them. Kluijver describes seeing a male go with a companion to his nest, singing softly. They left it and visited another nest, accompanied by three others, and eventually the party, which had become augmented to seven, was found in yet another nest. Mr. Boul tells me that a wren roosted for several weeks in a tit's nesting-box. One particularly cold night it was seen inspecting it and departing. After about three minutes a bird, presumed to be the same, returned with five others, and all entered and roosted in the box.

Wilson (1939) describes the procedure by which a large number of wrens congregate at a roost:

> Although I have known families of wrens roost together in some suitable place, often under hanging embankments of streams or behind slits of bark, I was never more surprised than when the different families of wrens around my garden forsook a nest-box where in the winter months they had been in the habit of retiring to sleep, in preference for a martin's nest under the eaves of my house; as many as 22 were nightly counted by different people as the birds entered the nest. When these wrens began to move bedwards the cock birds gave the command by short songs from different quarters and forthwith a steady advance began towards the house wall, on to which they flew, and then crept the last yard or two into the nest. For upwards of 15 minutes did the wrens continue to arrive at the nearby fence, along which they moved before flying across to the house. By the end of January when mild weather was being experienced, these wrens became quarrelsome and as many as four or five might be seen to fall from aloft in a bunch as they tried to evict each other from the martin's nest. A short while

before the party broke up one spring, having stayed throughout the depths of winter, another small aperture was made in the side of the nest, but for entering the original hole was always used, the other being an emergency exit or a ventilation shaft. During the last three winters the wrens were back in the same roost. This autumn there were over forty which appropriated seven martins' nests above my bedroom window.

Mr. Wilson kindly supplemented this description in response to my inquiries. The wrens began to frequent the roost in November. Some were seen making their way towards it from a mile away late in the afternoon. The first to arrive would sing loudly, and others would reply from the surrounding woods, but the singing was usually confined to within 100 yards of the house, and these little songs ceased about 50 yards from it. There was a good deal of chasing near the roost, but only one bird sang there. After the first few gatherings the singing was confined to the period immediately before the birds went to rest. In autumn the birds flew low into the undergrowth on leaving the roost, but in the early part of the year they flew high across the lawn. Towards the end of January when the fighting and chasing occurred—due to the recrudescence of impulses associated with breeding—there was very little singing. Similar squabbling has been noticed among roosting gatherings of prong-billed barbets as the nesting season approached (Skutch 1944).

This account suggests that when a suitable commodious roosting place is discovered in an area where wrens are plentiful, numbers increase through the songs, calls and movements of birds going towards it being noticed by others farther afield, and so forth, until after a few nights a large number converge on the roost, regardless of the territories they invade and cross. The songs play an important part in signalling the whereabouts of the roost.

The social roosting behaviour of the western winter wren does not seem to differ from that of the European wren. It has been described by Ehinger (1925):

> At the setting of the sun the wrens began to gather, and for half an hour they played about the bird-box in the most interesting manner. Singly and in groups they would dash up to the cabin wall, cling there a moment, then with a flying leap change their position to one a little nearer to the bird-box. This was continued until they could spring upon the roof of the box, from which they dropped to the little platform and entered. After a moment they would usually fly out again and circle around, only to repeat the manœuvre. Several times 10 to 15 wrens were counted clinging to the cabin wall at the same time, like so many great flies, when they would repeat the aforesaid manœuvre and

finally disappear through the tiny opening into their lodging house like little feathered mice. . . .

One evening 31 wrens managed to squeeze into this box, which was six inches square.

A surprisingly large number of wrens can get into a small space. Nine occupied an old song thrush's nest (Dunsheath and Doncaster 1941), ten squeezed into a coconut shell, seventeen were found in an old nest in a stable, but the record seems to be 46 in a nesting-box (Leybourne 1944).

Watson (1943) saw wrens gathering in little companies at dusk and flying up and down an old wall like bees in front of a hive, and then poising like humming-birds before entering crannies, inside which they huddled on top of each other, heads inwards. In the morning they left singly. Mr. Henry Barnes tells me that on 21 January 1947 he saw about 60 or 70 wrens darting about the hen-coops near his house at Wicken Fen. A little later they visited other hen-coops 20 yards on the other side of the house and probably roosted there. Such a large assemblage is remarkable in an area where the fen and flat fields around offer a rather uncongenial habitat for wrens in the breeding season. The older people in the neighbourhood regard such congregations of wrens as a sure portent of hard weather—though sceptical folk might suppose them to be consequent upon preceding severe conditions, as on this occasion. Mr. Barnes quoted a fragment of a jingle which he had heard years before from an old villager:

> When the tom-tits cluster
> Soon there'll be a bluster.

ARRANGEMENT IN THE ROOST

If there are only a few wrens in a nest or niche they crouch low, as well-grown nestlings do in the nest or roosting place when frightened. If larger numbers are present they squat on each other's backs, forming two or three layers or tiers. The birds rest with their heads inwards and tail towards the entrance or sides and the whole mass heaves gently as the wrens breathe (I. B. King, *in litt.*). A cluster of nine in a song thrush's nest did not wake until they were touched by hand (Dunsheath and Doncaster 1941). Even when a light is directed on them wrens may remain asleep. Bergman (1950) finds that as a general rule the more active a bird during the day the sounder it sleeps. I am all the more regretful that I have so often had to disturb these elfin creatures which have given me so much interest, anxiety and pleasure throughout these years.

TABLE XXXI
ARISING DATA

Month	Average number of minutes before sunrise of leaving roost	Average number of minutes after civil twilight of leaving roost	Number of observations
		1944	
January	—	—	—
February	28.2	8.4	5 Sight
March	26.2	9.3	6 Sight
April	31.4	3.3	1 Sight
			11 Sound
May	38.2	3.0	4 Sound
June	39.0	9.1	7 Sound
July	39.0	8.0	1 Sight
August	18.0	18.0	6 Sound
September	32.0	.5	2 Sound
October	25.6	8.0	5 Sound
November	33.2	9.0	4 Sound
			1 Sight
December	32.7	6.8	4 Sight
			3 Sound
		1945	
January	30.5	9.7	3 Sight
			1 Sound
February	32.6	2.8	3 Sight
			2 Sound
March	24.7	10.3	5 Sight
			11 Sound
April	32.8	3.6	2 Sight
			3 Sound
May	33.6	8.0	2 Sight
			4 Sound
June	37.0	11.7	4 Sound
July	35.0	9.5	2 Sound
August	29.2	12.8	5 Sound
September	19.6	13.6	3 Sound
October	26.5	6.7	4 Sound
November	30.3	6.3	3 Sound
December	35.5	6.5	2 Sound

As there is often a delay of some minutes between departure from the roost and the first utterance in August, September and October, the relatively late records for these months are not to be considered as indicating that the birds were later in arising than in other months. The sight records refer to the wren Silver (Fig. 38, p, 257).

TABLE XXXII

ROOSTING DATA

Month	Roosting times in minutes before (−) or after (+) sunset			Roosting times in minutes before civil twilight		
	Clear	Overcast	Average of all evenings	Clear	Overcast	Average of all evenings
1943						
December	+17.1	+10.1	+13.9	21.4	27.7	24.6
1944						
January	+ 8.8	+ 3.5	+ 6.0	29.9	35.2	32.7
February	+ 4.1	−12.2	− 2.9	30.3	46.7	37.4
March	+ 1.8	− 9.0	− 1.1	31.0	41.7	33.9
April		+ 8.4			25.2	
May		−36.5			79.0	
June		−48.0			95.0	
July	−29.3	−44.3	−36.8	76.3	92.3	84.3
August						
September						
October						
November	+12.3	+ .4	+ 7.1	26.0	38.4	31.4
December	+18.9	+13.4	+15.6	17.0	26.4	22.9
1945						
January	+16.0	+ 6.1	+10.4	22.7	32.8	28.4
February	+15.0	+ 9.7	+11.6	20.3	25.0	23.3
March	+11.8	+ 1.7	+ 7.1	21.3	31.7	26.1
April	+ 9.6	− 2.0	+ 4.7	23.0	37.4	29.8
May	−36.6	−40.2	−38.9	77.3	81.6	79.9

These data concern a single wren (Silver) except for some evenings in January, February and March 1944, when there were two, and occasionally three, wrens present. On such occasions the data show the time at which the first bird entered the roost. As this was usually the female, when she was present, the roosting times recorded were some minutes earlier than when Silver was roosting alone. This factor would contribute towards, or account for, the earlier records in the first months of 1944 as compared with 1945.

ADDENDA

1. Beecher (*Auk* (1953) 70: 270-333) suggests that wrens originated in the Old World. Even if this were true it would not render invalid the argument that they underwent extensive differentiation in the New World and extended their range northwards from the American tropics. His evidence in favour of the dippers being related to the thrushes is more cogent.

2. A male European wren, ardently feeding nestlings, perched repeatedly on my finger placed near the nest entrance. Boldness varies so much according to circumstances that comparisons between subspecies must be tentative.

3. The term " displacement activity," introduced by me (1947) to describe behaviour previously termed "substitute activity " (*Bird Display*, 1942), denotes types of incongruous behaviour due to conflicting drives. Wrens, and also bees, sometimes perform these activities with abnormal rapidity.

4. Later experience with a male wren which, having lost his mate, fed and roosted with the nestlings, introduces a doubt as to the sex of this bird, but the balance of probabilities is in favour of its being female.

5. A male wren, visiting a nest with eggs when the female is absent, may approach singing and displaying as if she were there.

6. A European wren with a nest in a yucca on an exposed bank flew to it while the female was near and displayed on a projecting leaf. In comparing the behaviour of subspecies it is difficult to determine when divergences are merely ecological.

7. Further data on the beginning of incubation, feeding tempo and the roles of the sexes will appear in a forthcoming paper in collaboration with Dr. H. L. K. Whitehouse.

8. The male southern house wren may bring food within half an hour of the hatch (Skutch 1953b.) There are many similarities between the behaviour of the southern house wren and the wren. Song continues except during the moult. Males arise earlier and retire later than females. The female sleeps in the nest-cavity before building. The male sometimes helps line. Eggs are laid before sunrise. Young may be fed five weeks after fledging. They are led to roosts but sometimes sleep in the nest-cavity until the hatching of the next brood. Song has been noted at 34 days. Nesting success is 57 per cent.

9. Uttendörfer (1952) shows that very occasionally the following raptors capture wrens: Lesser spotted eagle, peregrine, merlin and kestrel, eagle owl, tawny, long-eared, barn and pigmy owls.

10. C. F. Swynnerton (*Ibis*, 1916 pp. 529-606) noted that rats found wrens' eggs unpalatable.

ERRATA

In Fig. 3 *troylodytes* should read *troglodytes*. In Fig. 8, transcription II, W³ should read Wit³.

285

BIBLIOGRAPHY

*The place of publication of books is London unless listed otherwise. Titles of papers most important for the study of wrens are cited.

ALCORN, G. D. (1931). *Murrelet, 12:* 58.

ALDRICH, E. C. (1935). *In* Welter, 1935.

ALEXANDER, H. G. (1942). *Brit. Birds, 36:* 102-09.

ALEXANDER, W. B. (1932). *J. Anim. Ecol. 1:* 58-64. (1938) *Proc. VIII. Int. Orn. Congr. Oxford:* 560-67.

ALFORD, C. E. (1925). *Brit. Birds, 18:* 306-12.

ALI, S. A. (1930). *J. Bombay Nat. Hist. Soc., 34:* 947-64.

ALLARD, H. A. (1930). *Amer. Nat., 64:* 436-69. (1937) *Auk, 54:* 299-302.

ALLEN, A. A. (1914). *Abstr. Linn. Soc. N.Y.,* 1914: 43-128.

ALLEN, G. M. (1925). Birds and their Attributes.

ALLEN, J. A. (1887). *Bull. Nuttall orn. Cl., 2:* 82.

ALLEN, R. W. and NICE, M. M. (1952). *Amer. Midl. Nat., 47:* 606-65.

ANDERSON, A. (1948). *In* Nice and Thomas, 1948.

ANTEVS, A. (1947). Cactus wrens use " extra " nest. *Condor, 49:* 42.

ANTHONY, A. W. (1891). Notes on the cactus wren. *Zoe, 2:* 133-34.

ARMINGTON, S. (1951). *Vår Fågelvärld, 10:* 26-31.

ARMSTRONG, E. A. (1929). *Sci. Progr., 24:* 292-99; (1944) Some notes on the song of the wren. *Brit. Birds, 38:* 70-72; (1946a) Birds of the Grey Wind. 3rd edn; (1946b) Shakespeare's Imagination. 2nd edn; (1947) Bird Display and Behaviour; (1949a) *Ibis, 91:* 88-97, 179-88; (1949b) Bird Life; (1950a) The behaviour and breeding biology of the Iceland wren. *Ibis, 92:* 384-401; (1950b) *Symposia Soc. exp. Biol., 4:* 361-82; (1950c) Wrens of the far north. *Field, 196:* 931-32; (1950d) *Ill. Lond. News, 217:* 219; (1951) *Bull. Anim. Behav., 9:* 46-58; (1952) The behaviour and breeding biology of the Shetland wren. *Ibis, 94:* 220-42; (1953a) The behaviour and breeding biology of the Hebridean wren. *Brit. Birds, 46:* 37-50; (1953b) The history, behaviour and breeding biology of the St. Kilda wren. *Auk, 70:* 127-50; (1953c) *Discovery, 14:* 223-24; (1953d) Parasites and nidicoles of the wren. *Irish Nat. J.* 11: 57-64 (1953e) Island wrens. *Brit. Birds.* 46: 418-20; (1954) *Ibis.* 96: 1-30; (In preparation) The Folklore of British Birds. London, Collins; (In preparation) Bird Song.

ARMSTRONG, E. A. and PHILLIPS, G. W. (1925). *Brit. Birds, 18:* 226-30.

ARMSTRONG, E. A. and THORPE, W. H. (1952). " Casting " by young Shetland wrens. *Brit. Birds, 45:* 98-101.

ARNOLD, C. A. and M. A. (1952). *Brit. Birds, 45:* 175-80.

ASHBY, K. R. (1932). Young cuckoo fed by wren and hedge-sparrow. *Brit. Birds, 26:* 136.

ASHMORE, S. E. (1935). *Brit. Birds, 28:* 259-60.

ATKINSON, R. (1949). Island Going.

AYER, N. E. (1937). Difficulties of a cactus wren family. *News from Bird Banders, 12:* 31.

BAERENDS, G. P. and BAERENDS-VAN ROON (1950). *Behaviour*, Suppl. 1: 1-242.

BAILEY, F. M. (1922). Cactus wrens' nests in southern Arizona. *Condor, 24:* 163-68; (1928) Birds of New Mexico. *Publ. New Mexico Dept. Game and Fish.* Washington.

BAIRD, S. F., BREWER, T. M. and RIDGWAY, R. (1874). A History of North American Birds. I. Land Birds. Washington.

BALDWIN, S. P. (1921). The marriage relations of the house wren. *Auk, 38:* 232-44.

BALDWIN, S. P. and KENDEIGH, S. C. (1927). Attentiveness and inattentiveness in the nesting behaviour of the house wren. *Auk, 44:* 206-16; (1932) Physiology of the temperature of birds. *Sci. Publ. Cleveland Mus. nat. Hist., 3:* 1-196; (1937) *In* Nice, 1937: 125.

BARRAUD, E. M. (1948-49). *Birds Month by Month, 1:* 20-24.

BARRETT, J. H. (1947a). *Ibis, 89:* 439-50; (1947b) Unusual threat display of wren. *Brit. Birds, 40:* 150.

BARRETT-HAMILTON, G. E. H. (1900). *In* Ussher and Warren, 1900.

BATES, H. W. (1864). The Naturalist on the River Amazon. 2nd edn.

BATES, R. S. P. and LOWTHER, E. H. N. (1952). Breeding Birds of Kashmir. Oxford.

BAYLISS, C. K. (1917). A remarkable case of bird-feeding. *Auk, 34:* 90-91.

BECKMANN, K. O. (1926). Brütet der Zaunkönig zweimal? *Beitr. Fortpfl.-biol. Vög., 2:* 106.

BEEBE, C. W. (1917). Tropical Wild Life in British Guiana. New York; (1950) High Jungle.

BEEMER, E. G. (1947). Adaptability of Bewick wren to nest molestation. *Condor, 49:* 169.

BELCHER, C. F. and SMOOKER, G. D. (1936). *Ibis,* (13) 6: 792-813.

BENSON, F. M. (1945). *Ostrich, 16:* 61-71.

BENT, A. C. (1948). Life histories of North American nuthatches, wrens, thrashers and their allies. *Bull. U.S. nat. Mus. 195:* 1-475.

BENT, A. C. (1950). *Bull. U.S. nat. Mus. 197:* 1-411.

BENTHAM, H. (1925). *In* Allen, 1925.

BERGMAN, G. (1950). *Ornis Fenn., 27:* 109-24.

BEST, A. T. (1939). *Brit. Birds, 33:* 52-53.

BEST, M. G. S., TURNER, E. L. and HAVILAND, M. D. (1914). *Scot. Nat.* 1914: 31-34.

BIDWELL, E. (1896). *Bull. Brit. orn. Cl. 36. Ibis* (7) 2: 392-400.

BLACK J. G. (1920). Birdsnesting. Newcastle-upon-Tyne.

BLAIR, R. H. and TUCKER, B. W. (1941). *Brit. Birds, 34:* 206-15, 226-35, 250-55.

BLAKEMORE, A. (1946). Who sit and watch.

BLANCHARD, B. D. (1936). *Condor, 48:* 145-50; (1941) *Publ. Univ. Calif. Zool. 46:* 1-178.

BLETCHLY, J. D. (1938). *Brit. Birds, 32:* 8-12.

BLEZARD, E. *et al.* (1943). The Birds of Lakeland. Carlisle.

BLOMEFIELD, M. (1946). The Balleymung Pit.

BOLAM, G. (1912). The Birds of Northumberland and the Eastern Borders. Alnwick; (1932) *Trans. Nat. Hist. Soc. N'thumb., 8:* 1-165.

BOND, R. M. (1940). Sleeping posture of the rock wren. *Condor, 42:* 122.

BOORDE, A. (1562). Dyetary of Helth.

BOWLES, C. W. (1898). Duplicate nests. *Osprey, 3:* 46.

BOWLES, J. H. (1899). Decoy nests of the western winter wren. *Bull. Cooper orn. Cl. 1:* 72; (1909) *Condor, 11:* 56.

BOYD, A. W. (1936). *Brit. Birds, 29:* 3-21.

BRACKBILL, H. (1947a). *Wilson Bull.*, *59:* 116; (1947b) Another atypical house wren song. *Wilson Bull. 59:* 173; (1948) *In* Bent, 1948; (1950) *Bird-banding, 21:* 6-8.

BRAND, A. R. (1935). *Auk, 52:* 40-52; (1938) *Auk, 55:* 263-68.

BRAND, A. R. and KELLOGG, F. P. (1939). *Wilson Bull. 51:* 38-41.

BRANDT, H. (1943). Alaska Bird Trails. Cleveland.

BREAD, F. S. (1945). *Chicago Mag. 37:* 10-11.

BRECKENRIDGE, W. J. (1935). *Condor, 37:* 268-76.

BREHM, A. E. (1874). Bird Life.

BREWSTER, W. (1924). *Bull. Comp. Zool. Harvard, 66:* 1-209; (1938) *Bull. Comp. Zool. Harvard, 66:* 523-620.

BRIDGE, L. E. (1911). The story of the two house wrens. *Bird-Lore, 13:* 141-42.

BRODKORP, P. (1939). *Auk, 56:* 447-50.

BROOKS, E. (1932). *Indiana Aud. Soc. Year Book,* 1932: 29.

BROOKS, M. (1932). Carolina wrens roosting in abandoned hornets' nest. *Auk, 49:* 223-24.

BROWN, K. (1948a). *Brit. Birds, 41:* 214; (1948b) *Brit. Birds, 41:* 214.

BROWN, P. E. (1946). *Brit. Birds, 39:* 290-308; (1951) *In* Nethersole-Thompson, 1951.

BROWN, P. E. and DAVIES, M. G. (1949). Reed-warblers. Foy Publications, East Molesey, Surrey.

BROWN, R. H. (1927). *Brit. Birds, 21:* 188; (1937) *Brit. Birds, 31:* 156; (1943) *In* Morley, 1943.

BUCKNILL, J. A. (1900). Birds of Surrey.

BULLOUGH, W. S. (1942). *Philos. Trans. roy. Soc. Ser. B. 231:* 165-246.

BURCKHARDT, D. (1948). *Orn. Beob. 45:* 7-31.

BURKITT, J. P. (1919-20) The wren. *Irish Nat. 29:* 123-24; (1935) *Brit. Birds, 28:* 364-67; (1938) *Irish Nat. J. 7:* 85.

BURNS, F. L. (1937). *Oologist, 54:* 114-30.

BURROUGHS, J. (1895). Fresh Fields.

BUSSMANN, J. (1946). *Orn. Beob. 43:* 137-56.

BUXTON, A. (1946). Fisherman-Naturalist.

BUXTON, J. (1950). The Redstart.

CALHOUN, J. B. (1947). *Amer. Nat. 81:* 203-28.

CAMPBELL, A. G. (1941). *Emu, 40:* 357-64.

CAMPBELL, J. W. (1938). *In* Witherby *et al.* 1938: 219.

CARRICK, R. (1936). *Trans. roy. Ent. Soc. Lond. 85:* 131-39; (1949) Address to British Association. Newcastle; (1950) Address to B.O.U. Nov. 1950.

CARRIKER, M. A. (1944). *In* Wetmore, 1944.

CHAPMAN, F. M. (1928). *Bull. Amer. Mus. nat. Hist. 58:* 123-66; (1930) My Tropical Air Castle; (1935) *Bull. Amer. Mus. nat. Hist. 68:* 471-525.

CHAPMAN, F. M. and GRISCOM, L. (1924). The house wrens of the genus *Troglodytes. Bull. Amer. Mus. nat. Hist. 1:* 279-304.

CHAPPELL, B. (1948). *Ool. Rec. 22:* 1-8.

CHAVIGNY, J. DE (1934). *Alauda, 6:* 503-08.

CHERRIE, G. K. (1916). *Sci. Bull. Brooklyn Inst. 2:* 133-374.

CHISHOLM, A. H. (1944). *Ibis, 86:* 389-405; (1948a) *Vict. Nat. 65:* 30-32; (1948b) Bird Wonders of Australia. 3rd edn. Sydney and London.

CHRISTOLEIT, E. (1929a). *Beitr. Fortpfl.-biol Vög. 5:* 45; (1929b) *Beitr. Fortpfl.-biol Vög. 5:* 212.

CLAGUE, W. D. and GOODWIN, D. (1949). *Brit. Birds, 42:* 23.

CLANCEY, P. A. (1938). *Ibis*, (14) *2:* 746-54; (1943a) *Ibis, 85:* 87-92; (1943b) *Ibis, 85:* 95-97; (1947) *Bull. Brit. orn. Cl. 67:* 78-79.

CLARK, L. (1945). *Rep. Devon Bird Watching Soc.* 1945.

CLARK, R. B. (1949). Some statistical information about wren song. *Brit. Birds, 42:* 337-46.

CLARKE, W. E. (1915). The wren of St. Kilda: its status, plumages and habits. *Scot. Nat.* 1915: 291-96.

COLE, L. J. (1930). The laying cycle in the house wren. *Wilson Bull. 42:* 78.

COLES, C. (1937). *Proc. zool. Soc. Lond. 107:* 261-73.

COLLINGE, W. E. (1913). The Food of some British Wild Birds.

COLQUHOUN, M. K. (1942). *Brit. Birds, 35:* 234-40.

COLQUHOUN, M. K. and MORLEY, A. (1943). *J. Anim. Ecol. 12:* 75-78.

COMMON, M. A. (1948). Two days with a wren female. *Auk, 65:* 174-79.

CONDER, P. J. (1948). *Ibis, 90:* 493-524; (1950) *Brit. Birds, 43:* 299.

CONGREVE, W. M. (1951). *Ool. Rec. 25:* 1-8.

COOKE, M. T. (1950). *Bird-Banding, 21:* 145-48.

CORBET, A. S. (1923). *Brit. Birds, 16:* 217.

CORDEAUX, J. (1872). Birds of the Humber District.

CORDIER, A. A. (1927). *Auk, 44:* 169-78.

COTT, H. B. (1946). *Proc. zool. Soc. Lond. 116:* 371-524; (1949) *Ool. Rec. 23:* 1-9; (1952) *Proc. zool. Soc. Lond. 122:* 1-54.

COX, A. H. M. (1922). Some breeding-habits of the common wren. *Brit. Birds, 15:* 293-94.

COX, N. (1678). The Gentleman's Recreation.

COX, P. R. (1944). A statistical investigation into bird-song. *Brit. Birds, 38:* 3-9.

CRACKLES, E. (1948). *Brit. Birds, 41:* 351-52.

CRAIG, W. (1943). *Bull. N.Y. St. Mus. 334:* 1-186.

CRAMP, S. and TEAGLE, W. G. (1952). *Brit. Birds, 45:* 433-56.

CRANE, A. J. (1941). *Zoologica, N.Y. 26:* 145-208; (1949) *Zoologica, N.Y. 34:* 159-214.

CREUTZ, G. (1949). *Zool. Jahrb. 78:* 133-72.

CULLEN, J. M. (1947). *Brit. Birds, 40:* 374.

DAANJE, A. (1941). *Ardea, 30:* 1-42; (1950) *Behaviour, 3:* 48-98.

DALL, W. H. (1873). *Proc. Calif. Acad. Sci. 5:* 25-35.

DARWIN, C. (1845). Journal of . . . the Voyage of H.M.S. *Beagle* round the World. 2nd edn.

DAVID, A. and OUSTALET, M. E. (1877). Les oiseaux de la Chine. Paris.

DAVIS, D. E. (1941). *Wilson Bull. 53:* 157-68.

DAWSON, W. L. and BOWLES, J. H. (1909). The Birds of Washington. *1.* Seattle.

DE BRAEY, L. (1946). *Gerfaut, 36:* 133-38.

DE LA MARE, W. J. (1943). Love.

DENT, G. (1939). *Brit. Birds, 33:* 51-52.

DEWAR, D. (1928). Birds at the Nest.

DEWAR, G. (1902). The Birds in our Wood.

DEWAR, J. M. (1936). *Brit. Birds, 30:* 178-79.

DICKEY, D. R. and VAN ROSSEM, A. J. (1938). *Field Mus. nat. Hist. Zool. 23:* 1-609.

DIJK, O. VAN (1904). Winterkoning-winterbroeder. *De Levende Natuur, 9:* 252.

DIXON, C. (1885). *Ibis,* (5) *3:* 69-97; (1888) Our Rarer Birds.

DIXON, J. S. and BOND, R. M. (1937). *Condor, 39:* 97-102.

DOBSON, R. (1952). The Birds of the Channel Islands.

DOIDGE, B. (1946). *Western Counties Ill. Annual,* 1946: 109.

DROST, R. (1927). *Orn. Monatsb. 35:* 131-33; (1931) Der Zaunkönig, *Troglodytes t. troglodytes* (L.) als Zugvogel. *Vogelzug, 2:* 133.

DROST, R. and SCHÜZ, E. (1940). *Vogelzug, 11:* 161-91.

DUNSHEATH, M. H. and DONCASTER, C. C. (1941). *Brit. Birds, 35:* 138-48.

DUVAL, G. R. (1953). *Bird Notes, 25:* 219-20

DUVE, G. (1928). Goldammernest auf einem Zaunkönignest. *Beitr. Fortpfl.-biol Vög., 4:* 221.

EDWARDS, G., HOSKING, E. and SMITH, S. (1949). *Brit. Birds, 42:* 13-19.

EGGEBRECHT, E. (1937). *J. Orn. 85:* 636-76.

EHINGER, C. E. (1925). A winter wren's lodging house. *Murrelet, 6:* 37-39.

ELLIOTT, J. S. (1933). *Brit. Birds, 27:* 48.

ELLIS, J. C. S. (1936). *Brit. Birds, 30:* 232.

EMLEN, J. M. (1941). *Condor, 43:* 209-19.

ENGLAND, M. D. (1945). *Brit. Birds, 38:* 274.

ENSLIN, C. M. (1945). *Ostrich, 16:* 96-101.

ERICKSON, M. M. (1938). *Univ. Calif. Publ. Zool. 42:* 247-334.

ERRINGTON, P. L., HAMERSTROM, F. and HAMERSTROM, F. N. (1941). *Bull. Agr. Exp. Station Iowa State Coll. Agr. 277.*

EVANS, A. H. (1903). Turner on Birds. Cambridge.

EVETTS, K. E. (1932). *Brit. Birds, 25:* 332.

EWERS, D. (1942). *J. Comp. Psychol. 33:* 75-86.

FABER, F. (1822). Prodromus der islandischen Ornithologie. Copenhagen.

FATIO, V. and STUDER, T. (1907). Catalogue des oiseaux de la Suisse, *4:* 487-504.

FEILDEN, H. W. (1872). *Zool. 30:* 3210-25.

FINN, F. (1907). Ornithological Oddities.

FISHER, A. K. (1893). *Bull. U.S. Dept. Agr. Biol. Surv. 3.*

FITTER, R. S. R. (1945). London's Natural History.

FLETCHER, L. B. (1944). Unusual nesting of house wrens. *Bird-Banding, 15:* 160-61.

FORBUSH, E. H. (1916). Ninth annual report of the state ornithologist for the year 1916; *In* Bent, 1948; (1927) *Rep. Mass. Dept. Agr. 2 and 3;* (1929) *Rep. Mass. Dept. Agr. 3:* 350-52; (1935) *In* Skutch, 1935.

FORREST, H. E. (1924). Winter breeding of the wren. *Brit. Birds, 18:* 275.

FOSTER, N. (1923). *Irish Nat. 32:* 1-2.

FRANZ, J. (1943). *J. Orn. 91:* 154-65.

FREEMAN, C. P. and BATES, G. L. (1937). *Brit. Birds, 30:* 302-04.

FREITAG, F. (1936). *Vogelring, 9:* 43-49.

F. S. (1951). *Country Life, 109:* 471.

FUERTES, L. A. (1916). *Smithsonian Inst. Rep.* 1915: 299-323.

GAIT, R. (1946). The life cycle of a common wren. *Country Life, 99:* 112-14.

GARLING, M. (1928). Doppelnest von *Turdus merula* und *Troglodytes troglodytes. Beitr. Fortpfl.-biol. Vög. 4:* 25-26.

GÉROUDET, P. (1951). *Nos Oiseaux, 20:* 201-205.

GERSTELL, R. (1939). *N. Amer. Wildlife Conf. 4:* 462-67.

GIBB, J. (1947). *Brit. Birds, 40:* 172-74; (1950) *Ibis, 92:* 507-39.

GILBERT, H. A. (1929). *Brit. Birds, 22:* 188-89.

GILLESPIE, J. A. (1930). *Bird-Banding, 1:* 42.

GLADSTONE, H. S. (1910). The Birds of Dumfriesshire.

GLEGG, W. E. (1935). A History of the Birds of Middlesex; (1951) *Ool. Rev. 25:* 42-44.

GOODWIN, D. (1948). *Ibis, 90:* 280-84.

GOSNELL, H. T. (1949). *Brit. Birds, 42:* 87.

GRABHAM, O. (1895). *Zool. 19:* 307.

GRAHAM, H. D. (1890). The Birds of Iona and Mull, 1852-70. Edinburgh.

GRAY, R. (1871). Birds of the West of Scotland. Glasgow.

GREY, E. (1927). The Charm of Birds.

GRINNELL, J. and STORER, T. W. (1924). Animal life in the Yosemite. *Publ. Central Mus. Vert. Zool. Univ. Calif.*

GRISCOM, L. (1945). Modern Bird Study. Harvard and Oxford.

GROEBBELS, F. (1932). *Beitr. Fortpfl.-biol. Vög. 8:* 113-15.

GROSS, A. O. (1948). Eastern house wren. *In* Bent, 1948.

GRUNACK, A. (1879). Die Zucht des Zaunkönigs in Gefangenschaft. *Deutsche Acclimatisation, 1:* 37-39.

HAARTMAN, L. VON (1945). *Vår Fågelvärld, 4:* 27-32; (1949) *Acta zool. fenn. 56:* 1-104; (1951) *Behaviour, 3:* 256-74.

HAECKER, V. (1916). *Biol. Zbl. 36:* 403-31; (1924) *Pflügers Archiv. 204:* 718-25.

HAMERSTROM, F. (1947). House wren feeding cowbird. *Wilson Bull. 59:* 114.

HAMILTON, E. (1879). *Zool.* (3) *2:* 273-91.

HANN, H. W. (1937). *Wilson Bull. 49:* 145-237; (1950) *Condor, 52:* 49-62.

HARCOURT, E. V. (1851). *Proc. zool. Soc. Lond.* 1851: 141-46.

HARRISSON, T. H. and BUCHAN, J. N. S. (1934). A field study of the St. Kilda wren (*Troglodytes troglodytes hirtensis*), etc. *J. Anim. Ecol. 3:* 133-45; (1936) Further notes on a field study of the St. Kilda wren (*Troglodytes troglodytes* Seeb.), etc. *Scot. Nat.* 1936: 9-21.

HARTERT, E. (1910). Die Vögel der paläarktischen Fauna. Berlin. *1:* 776-84.

HARTHAN, A. J. (1947). Birds of Worcestershire. Worcester.

HARTING, J. E. (1920). *Field, 136:* 379-80.

HARTLEY, P. H. T. (1950). *Symposia Soc. exp. Biol. 4:* 313-36.

HARVIE-BROWN, J. A. and CORDEAUX, J. (1880). *Zool.* (3) *4:* 161-204.

HASLAM, S. H. (1844). *Zool. 2:* 564.

HAVERSCHMIDT, Fr. (1949). The Life of the White Stork. Leiden; (1950) *Wilson Bull. 62:* 39; (1952) Nesting behavior of the southern house wren in Surinam. *Condor, 54:* 292-95.

HAVILAND, M. D. (1926). Forest, Steppe and Tundra: Studies in Animal Environment. Cambridge.

HEATH, H. (1920). The nesting habits of the Alaska wren. *Condor, 22:* 49-55.

HEAVEN, J. W. G. (1948). Wrens feeding young flycatchers. *Country Life, 104:* 2687.

HEDIGER, H. (1950). Wild Animals in Captivity.

HEINROTH, O. (1909). *J. Orn. 57:* 56-83; (1930) *Naturwiss. 18:* 983-85.

HEINROTH, O. and HEINROTH, M. (1924-33). Die Vögel Mitteleuropas. Berlin.

HELLEBREKERS, A. W. (1949). *Ool. Rec. 23:* 52-54.

HELLEBREKERS, W. PH. J. (1951). *Ool. Rec. 25:* 14-16.

HELLMAYR, C. E. (1934). Catalogue of birds of the Americas. 7. *Publ. Field Mus. Nat. Hist. Chicago.*

HEMPEL, K. M. (1919). Notes on nesting bluebirds and house wrens. *Bird-Lore, 21:* 173-74.

HENDERSON, M. (1937). *Brit. Birds, 31:* 58.

HENRICI, P. (1926). *Beitr. Fortpfl.-biol. Vög. 2:* 165-69.

HERRICK, F. H. (1935). Wild Birds at Home. New York.

HEYDWEILER, A. M. (1935). *Bird-Banding, 6:* 1-11.

HILLS, V. G. (1924). *Auk. 41:* 615-16.

HINDE, R. (1952). *Behaviour.* Suppl. 2: 1-201.

HINDWOOD, K. A. (1948). *Emu, 48:* 53-56.

HOERTLER, F. (1934). Einige Beobachtungen über den Zaunkönig. *Beitr. Fortpfl.-biol. Vög. 10:* 226.

HOFFMANN, G. (1935). *Orn. Mber. 43:* 120-21.

HOHN, E. O. (1947). *Proc. zool. Soc. Lond. 117:* 281-304.

HOLM, B. (1950). *Norrbotens Natur, 2:* 27-103.

HOLMES, P. F. and KEITH, D. B. (1936). *Ibis,* (13) *6:* 322-30.

HOLZAPFEL, M. (1939). *J. Orn. 87:* 525-53.

HOOS, D. (1937). *Ardea, 26:* 173-202.

HORNE, E. (1924). *Brit. Birds, 17:* 215.

HORTLING, I. (1929). Ornitologisk Handbok. Helsingfors.

HOSKING, E. (1943). *Brit. Birds, 37:* 2-9.

HOSKING, E. and SMITH, S. (1949). *Brit. Birds, 42:* 358.

HOWARD, H. E. (1920). Territory in Bird Life; (1929) An Introduction to the Study of Bird Behaviour. Cambridge; (1935) The Nature of a Bird's World. Cambridge.

HOWELL, A. H. and OLDYS, H. (1907). The Bewick wren in the district of Columbia, with a description of its song. *Auk, 24:* 149-53.

HOYT, J. S. Y. (1948). *Auk, 65:* 188-96.

HUDSON, W. H. (1892). The Naturalist in La Plata; (1920) Birds of La Plata; (1930) South American Romances.

HUNT, L. M. (1904). The long-billed marsh wren. *Cassinia, 8:* 14-16.

HUNTER, L. E. (1935). *Wilson Bull. 47:* 74-75.

HUXLEY, J. (1942). Evolution: The Modern Synthesis; (1949) *Brit. Birds, 42:* 185-86.

HYDE-PARKER, T. (1938). *Bird Notes and News, 18:* 3-4.

INGRAM, G. C. S. and SALMON, H. M. (1934). Birds in Britain To-day.

IVOR, H. R. (1944). *Wilson Büll. 56:* 91-104.

JÄCKEL, A. J. (1891). Systematische Übersicht der Vögel Bayerns. Munich and Leipzig.

JACKMAN, R. J. (1947). *In* Gibb, 1947.

JAEGER, E. (1933). The California Deserts: A Visitor's Handbook. Stanford and Oxford; (1947) *Condor, 49:* 171; (1950) Our Desert Neighbors. Stanford and London.

JAHN, H. (1942). *J. Orn. 90:* 194-96.

JONES, C. (1939). Rock wrens at Wupatki. *Southwestern Natl. Monuments Mthly. Rep. Suppl.* July, 1939: 69-72.

JOURDAIN, F. C. R. (1911). *In* Kirkman, 1911-13; (1919) *Brit. Birds, 16:* 82; (1925) *Proc. zool. Soc. Lond.* 1925: 639-67; (1938a) *In* Witherby *et al. 2:* 138; (1938b) *In* Witherby *et al. 1:* 220; (1938c) *In* Witherby *et al. 1:* 294; (1939a) *In* Witherby *et al. 3:* 23; (1939b) *In* Witherby *et al. 3:* 158; (1940) *Brit. Birds, 33:* 303.

JOUY, P. L. (1883). *Proc. U.S. nat. Mus. 6:* 273-318.

KALLIBAY, P. (1906). Die Vögel der Preussischen Provinz Schlesien. Breslau.

KEARTON, R. (n.d.). The Adventures of Cock Robin.

KELSALL, J. E. and MUNN, P. W. (1905). Birds of Hampshire and the Isle of Wight.

KENDEIGH, S. C. (1934). The rôle of environment in the life of birds. *Ecol. Monogr. 4:* 299-417; (1940) *Auk, 57:* 499-513; (1941) Territorial and mating behaviour of the house wren. *Ill. Biol. Monogr. 18:* 1-120; (1942) *J. Wildlife Manag. 6:* 19-26; (1944) *Ecol. Monogr. 14:* 67-106; (1945) *Wilson Bull. 57:* 145-64; (1952) Parental care and its evolution in birds. *Ill. Biol. Monogr. 22:* 1-356.

KENDEIGH, S. C. and BALDWIN, S. P. (1928). Development of temperature control in nestling house-wrens. *Amer. Nat. 62:* 249-77; (1937) *Ecol. Monogr. 7:* 91-124.

KESSEL, B. (1950). *Bird-Banding, 21:* 112-14.

KEYSERLINGK, A. G. (1937). *Orn. Mber. 45:* 185-88.

KIRKMAN, F. B. (1911-13). The British Bird Book.

KLOCKARS, B. (1941). *Orn. Fenn. 18:* 73-110.

KLUIJVER, H. N. (1933). *Versl. Plziekt. Dienst. Wageningen, 69:* 1-146; (1935) *Ardea, 24:* 133-36; (1949) *In* In het Voetspoor van Thijsse. Wageningen; (1950) *Ardea, 38:* 99-135; (1951) *Ardea, 39:* 1-135.

KLUIJVER, H. N., LIGTVOET, J., VAN DEN OUWELANT, C. and ZEGWAARD, F. (1940). De levenswijze van den winterkoning *Troglodytes tr. troglodytes* (L.). *Limosa, 13:* 1-51.

KOCHS, W. (1935). *Beitr. Fortpfl.-biol. Vög. 11:* 31-32.

KOENIG, O. (1951). *Osterreichische Zool. Zschr. 3:* 1-82.

KORTLANDT, A. (1940). *Arch. néerl. Zool. 4:* 401-2.

KUHK, R. (1943). *In* Ornithologie als biologische Wissenschaft. Ed. E. Mayr and E. Schüz. Heidelberg; (1949) *J. Orn. 91:* 361-64.

KUMMERLOWE, H. and NIETHAMMER, G. (1934). *Alauda, 6:* 452-68.

KUUSISTO, P. (1941). *Acta zool. fenn. 31:* 1-120.

LABITTE, A. (1930). *Oiseau, 11:* 635-37; (1948) *Oiseau, 18:* 78-93.

LACK, D. (1932). *Ibis,* (13) 2: 266-84; (1939a) *Proc. zool. Soc. Lond. A. 109:* 169-78; (1939b) *J. Anim. Ecol. 8:* 277-85; (1941) *Ibis,* (14) 5: 407-41; (1945) *Occ. Papers Calif. Acad. Sci. 21:* 1-151; (1946a) The Life of the Robin. 2nd edn; (1946b) *Brit. Birds, 39:* 98-109, 130-35; (1947a) *Ibis, 89:* 302-52; (1947b) Darwin's Finches. Cambridge; (1948a) *Brit. Birds 41:* 98-104, 130-37; (1948b) *Ibis, 90:* 252-79; (1948c) *Ibis, 90:* 25-45; (1950) *Ibis, 92:* 288-316.

LACK, D. and LACK, E. (1951a) *J. Anim. Ecol. 20:* 173-79; (1951b) *Ibis, 93:* 503-46.

LACK, D. and LIGHT, W. (1941). *Brit. Birds, 35:* 47-53.

LACK, D. and VENABLES, L. S. V. (1937). *J. Anim. Ecol. 6:* 62-72.

LAFFERTY, H. A. (1948). An enterprising wren. *Irish Nat. J. 9:* 129-30.

LANCUM, H. (1953). *News Chron.* 20 June.

LANDT, J. (1810). A Description of the Feroe Islands.

LANE, F. W. (1948). Animal Wonderland.

LASKEY, A. R. (1944). *Wilson Bull. 56:* 27-44; (1946a) Some Bewick wren nesting data. *Migrant, 17:* 39-43; (1946b) Watching a Carolina wren's nest. *Chicago Nat. 9:* 59-62; (1948) Some nesting data on the Carolina wren at Nashville, Tennessee. *Bird-Banding, 19:* 101-21; (1950) A courting Carolina wren building over nestlings. *Bird-Banding, 21:* 1-6.

LATHAM, R. M. (1947). *J. Wildlife Manag. 11:* 139-49.

LA TOUCHE, J. D. (1925-30). A Handbook of Birds of Eastern China.

LAWRENCE, L. DE K. (1948). *Auk. 65:* 204-19.

LEES, J. (1946). *Brit. Birds, 39:* 136-41.

LEGUAT, F. (1708). Voyage et avantures de François Leguat, etc.

LEHTONEN, L. (1947). *Orn. Fenn. 24:* 32-47.

LEOPOLD, A. S. (1944). *Condor, 46:* 133-97.

LEYBOURNE, P. (1944). *In* Witherby *et al. 5:* 293.

LILFORD, LORD (1895). Notes on the Birds of Northamptonshire. *1:* 135.

LINK, J. A. (1903). Der Europäischer Kuckuck. Berlin.

LOCKLEY, R. M. (1946). *In* Lack, 1946a.

LOETSCHER, F. W. (1952). *Condor, 54:* 169.

LOFBERG, L. M. (1931). *Condor, 33:* 245-46.

Löhrl, H. (1949). *Vogelwarte, 2:* 24-99; (1951) *J. Orn. 93:* 41-60.

Lönnberg, G. (1935). Svenska fåglars flyttning. Stockholm.

Lorenz, K. (1932). *Vogelzug, 3:* 4-10; (1935) *J. Orn 83:* 137-213, 289-413; (1938) *Proc. VIII Int. orn. Congr.* Oxford, 1934; 207-18. Oxford; (1943) *In* Nice, 1943; (1950) *Symposia Soc. exp. Biol 4:* 221-68.

Lottinger, A. J. (1775). Le coucou. Nancy.

Løvenskiold, H. L. (1947). Hånbok over Norges fugler. Oslo.

Lowe, F. A. (1934). Days with Rarer Birds.

Ludlow, F. and Kinnear, N. B. (1937). *Ibis,* (14) *1:* 249-93; (1944) *Ibis, 86:* 176-208.

Lutz, F. E. (1931). *Amer. Mus. Nov. 468:* 176-208.

Lynes, H. (1912). *Ibis,* (9) *6:* 121-87.

McAtee, W. L. (1950). The Carolina wren *Thryothorus ludovicianus* as a mimic. *Wilson Bull. 62:* 136.

Macgillivray, W. (1837-52). A History of British Birds.

Mächler, G. (1947). Beobachtungen an Nestern der Zaunkönigs. *Die Vögel der Heimat, 17:* 85-87.

McIlwraith, T. (1894). The Birds of Ontario.

Macpherson, A. H. (1929). *Brit. Birds, 22:* 222-44.

Makatsch, W. (1935). Brutnachbarschaft zwischen Zaunkönig und Hecken-braunelle. *Beitr. Fortpfl.-biol. Vög. 11:* 73; (1937) Brutparasitismus. Leipzig.

Manson-Bahr, F. (1946). *Brit. Birds, 39:* 160.

Marples, G. (1933). *N.W. Nat. 8:* 199-201; (1935a) *Brit. Birds, 28:* 309-10; (1935b) *Brit. Birds, 29:* 22-35; (1939a) Unusual singing of wrens. *Brit. Birds, 32:* 397-98; (1939b) *Brit. Birds, 33:* 4-11; (1940) Observations on breeding and song of wren. *Brit. Birds, 33:* 294-303.

Marshall, A. J. (1949). *Proc. zool. Soc. Lond. 119:* 711-16.

May, D. J. (1947a). *Brit. Birds, 40:* 2-11; (1947b) *Brit. Birds, 40:* 326-27; (1947c) *Brit. Birds, 40:* 48; (1949) *Ibis, 91:* 24-54.

Mayr, E. (1946). *Wilson Bull. 58:* 3-41.

Mayr, E. and Amadon, D. (1951). *Novit. Amer. Mus. nat. Hist. 1496:* 1-42.

Mayr, E. and Schüz, E. (1949). Ornithologie als biologische Wissenschaft. Fest-schrift zum 60. Geburtstag von Erwin Stresemann. Heidelberg.

Mees, G. F. (1950). *Brit. Birds, 43:* 295-96.

Meinertzhagen, R. (1949). *Ibis, 91:* 465-82.

Menner, E. (1938). *Zool. Jahrb. Abt. allg. Zool. Physiol. Tiere, 58:* 481-538.

Merritt, M. (1916). *Wilson Bull. 28:* 92-94.

Miller, A. H. (1952). *Condor, 54:* 322.

Miller, E. V. (1941). Behavior of the Bewick wren. *Condor, 43:* 81-99.

Miller, L. (1952). *Condor, 54:* 89-92.

Mitchell, M. H. (1950). *Wilson Bull. 62:* 138.

Moffat, C. B. (1911). *Zool.* (4) *15:* 236.

Moir, M. (1951). *Brit. Birds, 44:* 201.

Montagu, G. (1831). Ornithological Dictionary. 2nd edn.

Moore, A. D. (1945). *Wilson Bull. 57:* 253-60.

Moreau, R. E. (1937). *Proc. Zool. Soc. Lond. A. 107:* 331-46; (1939) *Proc. zool. Soc. Lond. A. 109:* 109-25; (1940) *Ibis,* (14) *4:* 234-48; (1942) *Ibis,* (14) *6:* 27-49; (1944) *Ibis, 86:* 286-347; (1947) *J. Anim. Ecol. 16:* 205-209; (1949a) *Ibis, 91:* 256-79; (1949b) *In* Ornithologie als biologische Wissenschaft. Ed. E. Mayr and E. Schüz. Heidelberg.

Moreau, R. E. and Moreau, W. M. (1940). *Ibis,* (14) *4:* 639-56.

MORLEY, A. (1938). *In* Witherby *et al. 2:* 215; (1939) *Brit. Birds, 33:* 39-43; (1943) *Ibis, 85:* 132-58.

MOUILLARD, B. (1934). *Alauda, 6:* 196-211.

MOUNTFORT, G. R. (1935). *Brit. Birds, 28:* 368.

MOUSLEY, W. H. (1934). A study of the home life of the short-billed marsh wren (*Cistothorus stellaris*) *Auk, 51:* 439-45.

MUNN, P. W. (1931). *Novit. Zool. 37:* 53-132.

MURTON, J. (1869). Pugnacity of the wren. *Zool.* (2) *4:* 1644-45.

MUSSELWHITE, D. W. (1923). *Brit. Birds, 16:* 285; (1924) *Brit. Birds, 17:* 252.

MYLNE, C. K. (1952). Five wrens in succession at building of one nest. *Brit. Birds, 45:* 137.

NAUMANN, J. A. and NAUMANN, J. F. (1822-53). Naturgeschichte der Vögel Deutschlands. Leipzig.

NEAL, E. (1950). *Ill. Lond. News, 216:* 220.

NELDER, J. A. (1948). Display of wren. *Brit. Birds, 41:* 85.

NELSON, T. H. (1907). Birds of Yorkshire. London, Hull and York.

NERO, R. W. and EMLEN, J. T. (1951). *Condor, 53:* 105-15.

NETHERSOLE-THOMPSON, C. and NETHERSOLE-THOMPSON, D. (1942). *Brit. Birds, 35:* 162-69; (1943) *Brit. Birds. 37:* 88-94.

NETHERSOLE-THOMPSON, D. (1944a). *In* Witherby *et al. 5:* 230; (1944b) *In* Witherby *et al. 5:* 293; (1951) The Greenshank.

NICE, M. M. (1931). The birds of Oklahoma. *Univ. Oklahoma Biol. Survey, 1;* (1937) *Trans. Linn. Soc. N.Y. 4:* 1-247; (1943) *Trans. Linn. Soc. N.Y. 6:* 1-328; (1949) *In* Ornithologie als biologische Wissenschaft. Ed. E. Mayr and E. Schüz. Heidelberg.

NICE, M. M. and TER PELKWYK, J. (1941). *Auk, 58:* 195-214.

NICE, M. M. and THOMAS, R. H. (1948). A nesting of the Carolina wren. *Wilson Bull. 60:* 139-58.

NICHOLL, A. M. C. (1923). *Country Life, 54:* 178-79.

NICHOLS, J. T. (1921). *Auk, 38:* 461-62.

NICHOLSON, E. M. (1930). *Ibis,* (12) *6:* 280-314; (1951) Birds and Man.

NICHOLSON, E. M. and KOCH, L. (1936). Songs of Wild Birds.

NICOLS, A. (1883). Zoological Notes.

NIELSEN, E. K. (1945). *Spolia Zool. Mus. Hauniensis, 7.*

NIETHAMMER, G. (1937-38). Handbuch der Deutschen Vogelkunde. Leipzig.

NOBLE, G. K. and VOGT, W. (1935). *Auk, 58:* 195-214.

NOBLE, G. K. and WURM, M. (1940). *Endocrinology, 26:* 837-50.

NORTH, M. E. W. (1942). *Ibis,* (14) *6:* 499-508.

NORTON, D. D. (1929). *In* Forbush, 1929.

NUTTALL, T. (1932). A Manual of the Ornithology of the United States and of Canada. Cambridge, Mass. 2nd edn., 1840, with additions, The Land Birds. Boston.

OBERHOLSER, H. C. (1938). The Bird Life of Louisiana. New Orleans.

OBERLANDER, G. (1939). *Condor, 41:* 133-51.

ODUM, E. P. (1942a). *Auk, 59:* 499-531; (1942b) *Amer. J. Physiol. 136:* 618-22; (1944) *Wilson Bull. 56:* 48-49.

ODUM, E. P. and JOHNSTON, D. W. (1951). The house wren breeding in Georgia; an analysis of a range extension. *Auk. 68:* 357-66.

OLDHAM, C. (1937). *Trans. Herts. Nat. Hist. Soc. 20:* 105-20.

OLIVIER, G. (1949). *Brit. Birds, 42:* 183.

ORR, R. T. (1945). *Condor, 47:* 177-201.

OURY, E. (1932). *Alauda*, 1932: 718.

OWEN, J. H. (1915). *Brit. Birds*, *9:* 94; (1919a) *Brit. Birds*, *13:* 23; (1919b) Large clutch of wren's eggs. *Brit. Birds*, *13:* 82; (1940) *Brit. Birds*, *34:* 105-06; (1945) *Brit. Birds*, *38:* 271-73; (1948) *Brit. Birds*, *41:* 200-03.

OWEN, O. R. (1943). *Brit. Birds*, *36:* 245.

PAESSLER, R. (1928). *Beitr. Fortpfl.-biol. Vög. 4:* 30.

PALMER, R. S. (1949). Maine birds. *Bull. Mus. Comp. Zool. Harvard, 102:* 1-156.

PALMER, W. (1899). Extr. from The Fur Seals and Fur-Seal Islands of the North Pacific Ocean, *3:* 355-431.

PALMGREN, P. (1932). *Orn. Fenn. 9:* 68-74; (1944) *Z. Tierpsychol. 6:* 44-86; (1949) *Ibis, 91:* 561-75.

PARKER, H. W. (1946). *In* Cott, 1946.

PARKHURST, R. and LACK, D. (1946). *Brit. Birds, 39:* 358-64.

PAYN, W. H. (1948). *Ibis, 90:* 1-21.

PEARSE, T. (1933). Display of winter wren (*Nannus hiemalis pacificus*). *Murrelet, 14:* 45; (1948) *In* Bent, 1948.

PENNIE, I. D. (1948). *Scot. Nat. 60:* 157-63.

PERRY, R. (1948). In the High Grampians.

PHILLIPS, E. F. (1947). Bee-keeping. New York.

PICKWELL, G. (1948). *Auk, 65:* 359-73.

PICKWELL, G. B. (1931). *Trans. Acad. Sci. St. Louis, 27:* 1-153.

PIERS, H. (1898). *Auk, 15:* 195-96.

PIKE, O. G. (1930). Rambles in Britain's Bird-land; (1932) The Nightingale: its Story and Song.

PÖPPIG, —. (1874). *In* Brehm, 1874.

PORTIELJE, A. F. J. (1936). *J. Orn., 84:* 140-58.

POUGH, R. (1946). Audubon Bird Guide. Eastern Land Birds. New York.

POULTON, E. B. (1926). *Proc. R. ent. Soc. Lond.* 1926: 92-104.

PREBLE, E. A. and McATEE, W. L. (1923). *North Amer. Fauna, 46.*

PRENN, F. (1936). *J. Orn. 84:* 378-86.

PRING, C. J. (1927). *Brit. Birds, 21:* 156.

PROVOST, M. W. (1947). *Amer. Midl. Nat. 38:* 485-503.

PUTNAM, L. S. (1949). *Wilson Bull. 61:* 141-82.

PYNNÖNEN, A. (1939). *Ann. zool. Soc. Zool.-Bot. Fennicae Vanamo, 7:* 1-166.

RAINES, R. J. (1945). *Brit. Birds, 38:* 202-04.

RANKIN M. N. and RANKIN, D. H. (1940). *Irish Nat. J. 7:* 273-82.

RANKIN, N. (1947). Haunts of British Divers.

RAY, M. S. (1904). *Auk, 21:* 425-42.

RENDELL, L. (1946). *Rep. Cornwall Bird-watching and Pres. Soc. 16:* 17.

RENSCH, B. (1925). *Orn. Mber. 33:* 169-73.

REY, E. (1892). Altes und Neues aus dem Haushalte des Kuckucks. Leipzig.

RINGLEBEN, H. (1936). *Orn. Mber. 44:* 178-79.

RINKEL, G. L. (1940). *Ardea, 29:* 108-47.

RIPLEY, D. (1947). Trail of the Money Bird.

RIVIERE, B. B. (1927). *Brit. Birds, 20:* 258-66.

ROBERTS, B. B. (1940). *Sci. Rep. Brit. Graham Land Exped. 1934-37, 1:* 141-94.

ROBINSON, A. (1946-47). *Emu, 46:* 265-391; *47:* 11-28, 147-53.

ROLLIN, N. (1945). *Brit. Birds, 38:* 262-70; (1951) *Rep. Bird Research Stn. Glanton, 1:* 42.

ROMANES, G. J. (1883). Mental Evolution in Animals.

ROPE, G. T. (1889). *Zool.* (13) *3:* 184.

RUITER, C. G. S. (1941). *Ardea, 30:* 175-214.

RYDZEWSKI, W. (1949). *Acta. Orn. Musei. Zool. Polonici, Warsaw, 4:* 1-113.

RYVES, H. H. and RYVES, B. H. (1934a). *Brit. Birds, 28:* 2-26; (1934b). *Brit. Birds,* 28: 10-16

RYVES, B. H. (1938a). *In* Jourdain, 1938; (1938b) *Brit. Birds, 31:* 380-81; (1943) *Brit. Birds, 37:* 10-16; (1946) *Brit. Birds, 39:* 159.

SAEMUNDSSON, B. (1936). Islenzk dyr. 3. Fuglarnir (*Aves islandiae*). Reykjavik.

SALOMONSEN, F. (1933). *Troglodytes*-Studien. *J. Orn. 81:* 100-07; (1948) *Dansk. orn. foren. Tidsskr. 42:* 88; (1951) *Proc. X Int. orn. Congr. Uppsala, 1950:* 515-44.

SALVIN, B. and GODMAN, E. D. (1879-1904). *Biologia Centrali Americana. Aves. 1.*

SARGENT, G. T. (1940). *Condor, 42:* 49-60.

SAUNDERS, A. A. (1929). Bird Song. *N.Y. State Mus. Handb.* Albany; (1942) *Bird-Banding, 13:* 75-76; (1948a) *In* Bent, 1948; (1948b) *Auk, 65:* 373-83.

SAUNDERS, H. (1927). Manual of British Birds.

SAXBY, H. L. (1874). Birds of Shetland. Edinburgh.

SCHANTZ, W. E. (1927). *Auk, 54:* 189-91.

SCHEER, G. (1951). *Vogelwarte, 16:* 13-15.

SCHIFFERLI, A. and LANG, E. M. (1940). *J. Orn. 88:* 550-75.

SCHJELDERUP-EBBE, T. (1923). *Z. Psychol. 92:* 60-87.

SCHMAUS, M. (1928). *Beitr. Fortpfl.-Biol. Vög. 4:* 186.

SCHOLEY, G. J. (1933). *Ool. Rec. 13:* 92-93.

SCHREURS, T. (1941). *J. Orn. 89:* 182-203.

SCHUSTER, L. (1949). *In* Ornithologie als biologische Wissenschaft. Heidelberg. Ed. E. Mayr and E. Schüz.

SCHÜZ, E. (1931a). *Vogelzug, 2:* 19-28; (1931b) Der Zaunkönig, *Troglodytes t. troglodytes* (L.) als Zugvogel. *Vogelzug, 2:* 132; (1942) *Z. Tierpsychol. 5:* 1-37.

SCOTT, W. E. D. (1885). *Auk, 2:* 348-56.

SEEBOHM, H. (1882-95). A History of British Birds; (1884) *Zool. 43:* 333-35; (1890) Birds of the Japanese Empire.

SEIGNE, J. W. (1930). A Bird Watcher's Note Book.

SELOUS, E. (1905). Bird-Life Glimpses.

SERLE, W. and BRYSON, D. (1935). *Brit. Birds, 28:* 327-31.

SHAVER, J. M. and WALKER, G. (1930). *Auk, 47:* 385-96.

SHAW, W. T. (1944). *Condor, 46:* 90.

SHEPPERD, J. (1953). *Brit. Birds, 46:* 68.

SHERMAN, A. R. (1910). *Wilson Bull. 22:* 135-66; (1925) *Wilson Bull. 37:* 5-13; (1929) *In* Saunders, 1929.

SILVA, E. T. (1949). *Brit. Birds, 42:* 97-111.

SIMMONS, G. F. (1925). Birds of the Austin Region. Univ. of Texas Press.

SKAGGS, M. B. (1934). A study of the Bewick wren. *Bird-Lore, 36:* 365.

SKEAD, C. J. (1947). *Ostrich, 17:* 1-42.

SKINNER, M. P. (1928). A Guide to the Winter Birds of the North Carolina Sandhills. New York.

SKUTCH, A. F. (1935). Helpers at the nest. *Auk, 52:* 257-73; (1940a) Social and sleeping habits of Central American wrens. *Auk, 57:* 293-312; (1940b) *Sci. Monthly, 51:* 409-18; (1942) *Auk, 59:* 341-63; (1943) *Sci. Monthly, 56:* 358-64; (1944) *Auk, 61:* 61-88; (1945a) *Auk, 62:* 8-37; (1945b) *Condor, 47:* 85-94; (1946) *Sci. Monthly, 63:* 447-57; (1948a) *Auk, 65:* 225-60; (1948b) *Ibis, 90:* 433-49; (1951) *Condor, 53:* 3-15; (1952) *Ibis, 94:* 49-61; (1953a) *Ibis, 95:* 1-37; (1953b) Life history of the southern house wren. *Condor, 55:* 121-49.

SLUITERS, J. E. (1947). *Ardea, 35:* 183-221.

T.W.

SMITH, S. (1946). *Brit. Birds, 39:* 118.

SMYTHIES, B. E. (1949). *Ibis, 91:* 627-48.

SOUTHERN, H. N. and MORLEY, A. (1950). *Brit. Birds, 43:* 33-45.

SOUTHERN, J. (1949). *Brit. Birds, 42:* 118.

STALS, T. and KIGGEN, T. (1945). *Gerfaut, 35:* 107-08.

STATON, J. (1950). *Brit. Birds, 43:* 300.

STEGMANN, B. (1938). *Proc. VIII Int. orn. Congr.,* 1934: 476-500.

STEINFATT, O. (1938a). *Ber. Ver. schles. Ornith. 23:* 20-27; (1938b) *Orn. Monatsb. 46:* 65-76.

STEINGIER, F. (1950). *Natur u. Volk, 80:* 137-39.

STEVENSON, H. and GURNEY, J. H. (1872). *Zool. 30:* 3225-28.

STIMMELMAYR, A. (1930). *Verh. Orn. Ges. Bayern, 19:* 173.

STODDARD, H. L. (1948). *In* Bent, 1948.

STONER, D. (1930). *Proc. Iowa Acad. Sci. 35:* 337-39.

STURGIS, B. B. (1928). Field Book of Birds of the Panama Canal Zone. New York and London.

SUTTON, G. M. (1948). The nest and eggs of the white-bellied wren. *Condor, 50:* 101-02; (1949) *Misc. Publ. Mus. Zool. Univ. Michigan, 74:* 5-37.

SUTTON, G. M. and PETTINGILL, O. S. (1942). *Auk, 59:* 1-34.

SUTTON, G. M. and WILSON, R. S. (1946). *Condor, 48:* 83-91.

SWAINE, C. M. (1945). *Brit. Birds, 38:* 329-32.

SWANBERG, O. (1951). *Proc. X Int. orn. Congr. Uppsala, 1950:* 545-54.

SZYMANSKI, J. S. (1914). *Pflügers Archiv. 158:* 343-85.

TASHIAN, R. E. (1952). *Auk, 69:* 60-66.

TAVERNER, P. A. (1934). Birds of Canada. *Bull. Nat. Mus. Canada, 72.*

TAYLOR, J. S. (1946). *Ostrich, 17:* 145-55.

TAYLOR, J. W. (1905). *Bird-Lore, 7:* 209-10.

TEN KATE, C. G. B. (1926). *Ardea, 15:* 161.

THIENEMANN, J. (1909). VIII Jahrebericht (1908) des Vogelwarte Rossitten der *Troglodytes troglodytes* (L.) Zaunkönig. *J. Orn. 57:* 384-502.

THOMAS, E. S. (1943). A wren singing the songs of both Bewick's and the house wren. *Wilson Bull. 55:* 92-93.

THOMAS, R. H. (1946). *Bird-Banding, 17:* 61-67.

THOMPSON, W. (1849). Natural History of Ireland. *1.* Birds.

THOMSON, A. L. (1949). *Brit. Birds, 42:* 175-80; (1951) *Brit. Birds, 44:* 289-310.

THOMSON, G. M. (1922). The Naturalisation of Animals and Plants in New Zealand. Cambridge.

THORPE, W. H. (1926). *Ibis,* (12) *2:* 455-66; (1951) *Ibis, 93:* 1-52.

THORPE, W. H., COTTON, P. T. and HOLMES, P. F. (1936). *Ibis,* (13) *6:* 557-80.

TICEHURST, N. F. (1909). A History of the Birds of Kent; (1938) *In* Witherby *et al.* 1938, *2:* 115.

TICEHURST, N. F. and HARTLEY, P. H. T. (1948). *Brit. Birds, 41:* 322-24.

TIMMERMANN, G. (1931). *Beitr. Fortpfl.-biol. Vög. 7:* 28-29; (1932) *Beitr. Fortpfl.-biol. Vög. 8:* 214-17; (1935) Drei Aufsätze zur islandischen Zaunkönig (*Troglodytes t. islandicus* Hartert). *Greinar. Soc. Scient. Island, 1:* 37-47; (1949) Die Vögel Islands. *Soc. Sci. Islandica, 28:* Reykjavik.

TINBERGEN, L. (1946). Die Sperwer als roofvijand van Zangvogels. Leiden.

TINBERGEN, N. (1931). *Beitr. Fortpfl.-biol. Vög. 7:* 91-92; (1939) *Trans. Linn. Soc. N.Y.* 1939: 1-94; (1940) *Z. Tierpsycho . 4:* 1-40; (1942) *Biol. Biotheoret, 1:* 39-98.

TINBERGEN, N. and VAN IERSEL, J. J. A. (1947). *Behaviour, 1:* 57-63.

TODD, W. E. C. and CARRIKER, M. A. (1922). *Ann. Carnegie Mus. 14:* 1-611.

TOMES, R. F. (1901). Birds of Worcestershire. *In* Vict. County Hist. Worcs. *1.*

TOWNSEND, C. W. and ALLEN, G. M. (1907). *Proc. Boston Soc. nat. Hist. 33:* 277-428.

TRACY, N. (1943). *In* Nethersole-Thompson, 1943; (1950) *Country Life, 108:* 1492-93.

TRAUTMAN, M. B. (1940). *Misc. Publ. Univ. Michigan Mus. Zool. 44:* 1-466.

TRAYLOR, M. A. (1949). *Fieldiana, 31:* 269-75.

TREUENFELS, H. VON (1940). *J. Orn. 88:* 509-36.

TREVOR-BATTYE, A. (1913). Camping in Crete.

TRITTON, F. (1947). Wren swimming. *Brit. Birds, 40:* 179-80.

TRUMAN, F. (1947). *Country Life, 106:* 1220.

TUCKER, B. W. (1938). *In* Witherby *et al. 2:* 219; (1944) *Brit. Birds, 38:* 50-52.

TURCEK, F. J. (1948). *Amer. Midl. Nat. 40:* 391-94.

TURLE, —. (1900). *In* Ussher and Warren, 1900.

TURNER, E. L. (1911). *In* Kirkman, 1911-13; (1929) Stray Leaves from Nature's Notebook.

TURNER, W. (1544). *Avium praecipuarum.* Cf. Evans, 1903.

TUTT, H. R. (1947). *Brit. Birds, 40:* 86; (1951) *Proc. X Int. Orn. Congr. 1950:* 554-62.

TWINING, P. W. (1949). A mobile bird's nest. *Country Life, 106:* 690-91.

USSHER, R. J. (1912). Clare Island Survey. *Aves. Proc. Roy. Irish Acad. 31:* 1-54.

USSHER, R. J. and WARREN, R. (1900). The Birds of Ireland.

UTTENDÖRFER, O. (1930). *Ber. Ver. Schles. Orn., 16:* 29; (1952) Neue Ergebnisse über die Ernährung der Greifvögel und Eulen. Stuttgart.

VAN BENEDEN, A. (1935). *Gerfaut, 25:* 40.

VAN TYNE, J. (1950). *Occ. Pap. Mus. Zool. Univ. Michigan, 525:* 1-12.

VAN TYNE, J. and SUTTON, G. M. (1937). *Misc. Publ. Univ. Michigan Mus. Zool. 37:* 5-115.

VAURIE, C. (1951). Notes on the wrens and dippers of Western Asia and India. *Amer. Mus. Novit. 1485:* 1-19.

VENABLES, L. S. V. and VENABLES, U. M. (1948). *J. Anim. Ecol. 17:* 66-74.

VERWEY, J. (1930). *Zool. Jb. Abt. allg. Zool. Physiol. 48:* 1-120.

VINCENT, J. (1910). Diary (Unpublished).

VISICK, H. C. (1946). *Country Life, 99:* 812.

WALDECK, K. (1932). *Org. Cl. Ned. Vogelk. 5:* 155.

WALKINSHAW, L. H. (1935). Studies of the short-billed marsh-wren (*Cistothorus stellarit*) in Michigan. *Auk, 52:* 362-69.

WALLACE, J. G. (1948). *Tech. Bull. Mich. State Coll. 208.*

WALPOLE-BOND, J. A. (1909). *In* Ticehurst, 1909

WALTER, A. (1888). *Orn. Monatschr. 13:* 194-214; (1893) *Orn. Monatschr. 18:* 285.

WALTON, H. (1905). *Bull. Brit. orn. Cl. 15:* 93.

WALTON, —. (1925) *In* Allen, 1925.

WARE, R. (1923). *In* Musselwhite, 1923.

WATSON, E. G. (1943). Walking with Fancy.

WATSON, J. B. (1946). *Brit. Birds, 39:* 374-75.

WEIGOLD, H. (1926). Masse, Gewichte und Zug nach Alter und Geschlecht bei Helgolander Zugvögeln. Oldenburg i. O; (1930) Der Vogelzug auf Helgoland. Berlin.

WEIR, T. D. (1837-52). *In* Macgillivray, 1837-52.

WEISMAN, C. (1950). *Dansk. orn. foren. Tidskr. 44:* 19-22.

WELTER, W. A. (1935). The natural history of the long-billed marsh wren. *Wilson Bull. 47:* 3-34.

WETMORE, A. (1944). *Proc. U.S. Nat. Mus. 93:* 215-340.

WHEELER, H. E. (1931). The status, breeding range and habits of Marian's marsh wren. *Wilson Bull. 43:* 247-67.

WHEELOCK, I. G. (1904). Birds of California. Chicago.

WHISTLER, H. (1928). Popular handbook of Indian Birds. London and Edinburgh.

WHITAKER, A. (unpublished). MS. deposited in Edward Grey Inst. Oxford.

WHITAKER, J. (1907). Notes on the Birds of Nottinghamshire. Nottingham.

WHITAKER, H. E. (1945). Wren habitually entering house. *Brit. Birds, 38:* 237.

WHITE, G. (1789). The Natural History and Antiquities of Selborne, in the County of Southampton.

WHITEHOUSE, H. L. K. and ARMSTRONG, E. A. (1953). Rhythms in the breeding behaviour of the European wren. *Behaviour, 5:* 261-88.

WHITMAN, C. O. (1919). The Behavior of Pigeons. Posthumous works. Ed. O. Riddle.

WIGHT, E. M. (1934). *Migrant, 5:* 46.

WILKINSON, A. E. (1945). *Irish Nat. J. 7:* 261.

WILKINSON, E. S. (1929). Shanghai Birds. Shanghai.

WILLIAMS, L. (1941). Roosting habits of the chestnut-backed chickadee and the Bewick wren. *Condor, 43:* 274-85; (1943). *Wilson Bull. 54:* 238-49; (1947) A winter wren roost. *Condor, 49:* 124; (1952) *Condor, 54:* 3-47.

WILLIAMSON, K. (1947a). Three displays of the Faeroe wren. *Ibis, 89:* 514-15; (1947b) *Ibis, 89:* 435-39; (1951a) The wrens of Fair Isle. *Ibis, 93:* 599-601; (1951b) Geographical variation in the weight of the wren. *Bull. Fair I. Bird Observatory, 1:* 5-6; (1951c) *Annual Rep. Fair I. Bird Observatory,* 1951: 12.

WILLMORE, J. H. (1881). Wren's nest in January. *Zool.* (3) *5:* 108.

WILSON, J. O. (1939). Nature's Cavalcade.

WILSON, R. S. (1948). *Condor, 50:* 124-29.

WINGE, H. (1898). Grønlands Fugle, 21: 275.

WITHERBY, H. F., JOURDAIN, F. C. R., TICEHURST, N. F. and TUCKER, B. W. (1938-41). The Handbook of British Birds.

WOJTUSIAK, R. J. and FERENS, B. (1947). *Bull. Acad. Pol. Sci. Lettres.* B. 1946: 99-106.

WOLFE, L. R. (1950). *Auk, 67:* 433-35.

WOODS, R. S. (1948), Northern cactus wren. *In* Bent, 1948.

WYNNE-EDWARDS, V. C. (1930). *J. exp. Biol. 7:* 241-47.

YEATES, G. K. (1946). Bird Life in Two Deltas; (1948) Bird Haunts in Northern Britain.

ZIMMER, J. T. (1930). *Publ. Field Mus. nat. Hist. 17:* 233-480.

ACKNOWLEDGMENTS

So MANY have assisted me in studying wrens that it is impossible to mention them all by name. Their help has been highly appreciated. I am particularly grateful to the following:

Field work. In Cambridge, Miss Ursula Grigg, Miss Chrystabel Proctor, Christopher Smout and Hugh Dixon helped for short periods with observations. Mrs. W. H. Thorpe assisted with the ringing of some birds. Work in Iceland was greatly facilitated by the hospitality and transport provided by Dr. and Mrs. A. Löve. Mr. and Mrs. L. Lomas gave similar help in the Hebrides. Dr. and Mrs. H. L. K. Whitehouse co-operated with some of the work in Cambridge as well as in Iceland. Dr. P. Westall was my companion in the Hebrides, on St. Kilda, and later, in Lapland. In Shetland I had the assistance of Dr. W. H. Thorpe, who was also with me when I made the acquaintance of some of the wrens of Central and South America and the West Indies. To Professor E. Jaeger I owe my introduction to the deserts of the western United States and their wrens.

Travel. The scope of my observations would have been greatly limited but for the much-appreciated grant made by the committee of the Leverhulme Research Fellowships, which enabled me to visit Iceland, Shetland and the Hebrides. I am glad to express my thanks to Dr. G. Lucas of the Scottish Home Department, Captain Bruce and the ship's company of *Scotia* for transport to and from St. Kilda, and to Mr. J. Fisher for information prior to my visit.

Literature. My thanks are offered to Dr. H. N. Kluijver for lending me the field notes of his colleagues who studied the wren in Holland, and to Dr. D. Farner and Dr. H. Friedmann, through whom I received microfilms of the paper by Dr. Kluijver during the war. Dr. R. S. Palmer also sent me useful literature and a gramophone record of wren songs. I received the welcome gift of a winter wren song recording from Dr. P. Kellogg. Sir N. Kinnear checked the distribution of a subspecies. Mr. W. B. Alexander kindly lent me literature from the Alexander library in Oxford, verified references and commented on the manuscript.

MS. and proof readers. I am very grateful to those who read the MS., especially to Dr. J. S. Huxley, F.R.S., who made many helpful comments, also Dr. S. C. Kendeigh, Dr. H. N. Kluijver, Mr. R. E. Moreau and Dr. W. H. Thorpe, F.R.S. Dr. R. A. Hinde and Dr. H. L. K. Whitehouse kindly read the proofs.

Correspondents. The names of many who sent me information are mentioned in the text. Where a name appears without further reference the reader will understand that the information is based on a personal communication.

Photographs. To those photographers who have given illustrations I record my thanks, especially Prof. A. A. Allen, Mr. M. D. England, Dr. F. Gudmundsson, Mr. C. P. Newcomb, Mr. Job van Peppel, Dr. D. W. Snow and Mrs. G. Hearn, for the use of a photograph by her late husband.

Song recordings. My thanks are due to Miss Gladys Page-Wood for the transcripts of wren songs into musical notation, to Dr. W. R. Fish for the oscillograph recording and to Dr. Thorpe for the sound spectrograms.

Drawings. I am grateful to Miss Chloë Talbot-Kelly for her charming drawings and to Miss Alison Birch and Mr. J. F. Trotter for their work on the diagrams.

Production. I appreciate highly the care which Mr. James Fisher and Mr. Raleigh Trevelyan have devoted to the production of this book.

Without the easing of my task in many ways by my wife, Eunice, this work could not have been carried out.

EDWARD A. ARMSTRONG

INDEX

Part I—SUBSPECIES OF, *Troglodytes troglodytes*
(with distribution)

EUROPE AND NORTH AFRICA (13)

1. *T. t. troglodytes* (L.)
(British Is., continental Europe nearly to the Arctic Circle, east to the Urals, south to Orenburg, the Volga and the Mediterranean)

AGE 255; altitudinal range 13; appearance 22-23; arising 71-72, 256-262. BATHING 28-29; behaviour 22-30, 248-249; broods, overlapping 226-227; brooding 188-189. CALLS 73, 93-96, 243, 245; casting 204; clines 10-11; copulation 75, 130-131, 223; courtship feeding 128-130; courtship song 89-90. DESERTION 28; displacement activities 30, 48, 76, 116, 118, 158, 246, 248, 285; display, diversionary 249-250, greeting 117-118, nest-invitation 124-128, sexual 110-131, threat 47-49, 74-75, with nesting material 122-123; distribution 7-12; dominance 73-74, 111; 97-100, 102, 130-131, 174, 261; drinking 28. EGGS 165, 186; egg-shell disposal 187; experiments 90, 97-100, 102, 130-131, 174, 261. FEEDING 15, 23-25, 27, 106, 110, 116, 128-130, 183, 186, 190-201, 223-224; female, nest-building by 154-157, song of 90-91; fighting 30-31, 47-49, 75; fledging 221-223; flight 23, 110-114; folklore 1, 22-23; foraging 207-209; fostering 104-105, 227, 233-235. HABITAT 4, 12-16; hatching 186-187; homing 21-22. INCUBATION 129, 165-186; integration of activities 219-220. LINING 157-160. MALE, relation to incubating female 185-186; memory 267-268; migration 16-21, 87; mobbing 243; mortality 205-206, 250-255; movements 23, 25; moult 114. NEST-BUILDING 63, 123, 132-144; nestlings 186, 209-217, 221; nests, auxiliary 139-142, 230, contiguous 135-136; nest-sanitation 201. PAIR-BOND 100-102; palatability 247-248, 285; parasites 247; patrolling 44-45, 90, 185, 193; physiology 175; polygamy 33, 42, 49-51, 63, 67, 88, 102-110, 127, 156, 168, 193, 226, 274-275; pouncing 105, 110-111, 157; predation 20, 221, 235-250, 285; preening 30; probing 204; pursuits 110-114. QUILL RATTLING 121. RECOGNITION 97-100; refugia 80; rhythms 196-198; ringing 2, 5-6, 19; roosting 71-72, 85-87, 90, 104, 124, 171, 188, 203, 228-233, 235. SEX RATIO 108-109; song 12, 14, 22-23, 30, 36, 37, 45-46, 52-96, 99, 110, 123, 151, 193; speed of flight 23; spread of nesting 217-221; subsong 76, 88-90, 101; swimming 28. TAMENESS 25; taxonomy 11; temperature, reactions to, 175-181; territory 4, 19, 31-52, 66, 76-79, 103-106, 131, 225, 253; titivating nests 46, 125; transference activity 203, 240; trapping 5, 248-249; trespassing 46-47. VICTIMISATION BY CUCKOO 240-242. WEIGHT 10, 213. YOUNG, care of 186-235, song of 63, 85.

Another subspecies, *T. t. occidentalis* Verheyen, has been described in *Bull. Mus. roy. Hist. nat. de Belgique*, No. 33, p. 26, 1941, as breeding in Belgium, but its distinctiveness is questionable. Clancey (1943 a, b; 1947) has attempted to distinguish further subspecies in the British Isles, but they have been rejected by the B.O.U. List Committee. The Fair Isle wren was described by Williamson in 1951.

ASIA (24)

NORTH AMERICA (12)

Part II—WRENS OTHER THAN FORMS OF *Troglodytes troglodytes* MENTIONED IN THE TEXT

Part III—BIRDS OTHER THAN WRENS MENTIONED IN THE TEXT

Part IV

MAMMALS

FISHES

REPTILES AND AMPHIBIA

INVERTEBRATES

Part V—AUTHORITIES